D1267548

AFTER THE SEVENTH DAY

The World Man Created

RITCHIE CALDER

Simon and Schuster · New York · 1961

PUBLISHED BY SIMON AND SCHUSTER, INC., ROCKEFELLER CENTER, 630 FIFTH
AVENUE, NEW YORK 20, N. Y.

FIRST PRINTING   LIBRARY OF CONGRESS CATALOG CARD NUMBER: 60–12593

MANUFACTURED IN THE UNITED STATES OF AMERICA; PRINTED BY HERMER
LITHOGRAPHY, NEW YORK, N.Y.

*For the right to reproduce the illustrations or quotations on the pages indicated,
grateful acknowledgment is expressed to the following:*

P. 59: Routledge and Kegan Paul, Ltd. (based on *The Mentality of Apes* by W. Kohler)

Pp. 65, 67, 69, 73: Trustees of the British Museum

P. 70: Institut de Paléontologie Humaine, Paris (from *La Caverne* by E. Cartailhac and H. Breuil)

P. 93: Institute of Archaeology, Univ. of London

P. 106: Macmillan and Co., Ltd., London (after *The Pagan Tribes of Borneo* by C. Hose and W. McDougall)

P. 109: Die Abhandlungen der Preussischen Akademie der Wissenschaften zu Berlin (based on *Achter Vorläüfiger Bericht über die . . . Uruk-Warka Ausgrabungen* by Ernst Heinrich)

P. 112: The University Museum, Univ. of Penna.

P. 115: Martinus Nijhoff, The Hague (after *Assyrian Sculptures* by A. Paterson)

P. 126: Service des Antiquités Egyptiennes, Cairo (after *The Aswan Obelisk* by R. Engellbach)

P. 128: Robert Scott (based on *The Stones of Stonehenge* by E. H. Stone)

P. 149: Probsthain & Co. (after *Mohenjo-Daro and the Indus Civilization* by J. Marshall)

Pp. 181, 184, 188, 192: American Museum of Natural History (from *The Aztecs of Mexico* by G. C. Vaillant, Doubleday, Doran & Co.)

Pp. 189–190: Routledge and Kegan Paul, Ltd., and Farrar, Straus & Cudahy, N.Y. (from *The Discovery and Conquest of Mexico* by Bernal Diaz del Castillo)

Pp. 196, 199, 203, 206, 207: World Publishing Company (from *The Realm of the Incas* by Victor von Hagen)

Pp. 231: Alfred Kroner Verlag, Stuttgart, after *Schaffende Arbeit und Bildende Kunst im Altertum und Mittelalter* by P. Brandt)

P. 232: F. W. Robins, Esq. (after his book *The Story of the Lamp and Candle*, Oxford Univ. Press)

P. 234: Amalgamated Press (after *Universal History*, Vol. IV, by J. A. Hammerton)

P. 240: (from *Etruskische und Kampanische Vasenbilder* by E. Gerhard)

P. 246: Bruckmann Verlag, Munich (after *Griechische Vasenmalerei*, Vol. I, by A. Furtwängler and C. R. Reichold)

P. 277: Dreyer Forlag, Oslo (after *The Viking Ships* by A. W. Brøgger and H. Shetelig)

P. 282: Casa Hoepli, Milan (after *Storia Della Tecnica Dal Medio Evo Ai Nostri Giorni* by A. Uccelli)

P. 284: (from *A Treatise on the Steam Engine* by J. Farcy)

P. 286: Offices of Engineering, London (from *An Autobiography* by Sir Henry Bessemer)

P. 354: R. Voigtlander's Verlag, Leipzig (after *The Technical Arts of the Ancients* by A. Neuberger)

P. 376: Princeton Univ. Press (after *The Early Days of Oil* by P. H. Giddens)

P. 425: Indiana Univ. Press (from *Land for Tomorrow: Our Underdeveloped World*, by L. Dudley Stamp)

DEDICATION

TO

OUR PROGENY

[WITH APOLOGIES TO MALTHUS]

R. C. and Mabel McKail

BEGAT

Fiona	*Nigel*	*Angus*	*Allan*	*Isla*
[M. ERNEST RUDD]	[M. ELIZABETH PALMER]	?	?	?
BEGAT	BEGAT			
Alison	*Sarah*			
Judith	*Penelope*			
Lucy	*Simon*			
	Jonathan			

Acknowledgments

I would like to acknowledge my debt to all the authorities, past and present, whom I consulted. Particularly, I owe a debt to H. G. Wells, not only for his enduring writings but for his personal friendship and encouragement of ideas, which, fortified by experience, have fructified in this book.

I want to thank all those friends in the United Nations Specialized Agencies who have made my journeys possible and the many experts who have shared their experience with me in the field and in international conferences. And my Eskimo guides, Luke and Dave, whose intelligence and skills set me thinking about this book when holed up by a blizzard in the Arctic.

In the production of the book, my thanks are due to Imperial Chemical Industries, *The History of Technology* (O.U.P.) and my friend Dr. Trevor I. Williams for enabling me to use the excellent line drawings. And to Mr. Peter Collins for providing photographs which he took on our Sahara journey.

My special thanks are due to Lorna Lawrence for her help "beyond the call of duty" in the preparation and checking of this book.

And to my wife and family who endured the writing of it.

R.C.

Contents

Contents

PART
THREE *The Watershed* 89

PART FOUR *The Streams of Civilization* 139

Contents

PART
FIVE *The Bridge*   *163*

PART SIX *Hobnails of Chivalry* 227

Contents

PART
EIGHT *Flood Tide* *321*

Contents

"HOW MANY
OIL DRUMS, BOSS?"

THEY SAY of the Arctic Survival Course, "If you survive, you've passed." Well, I had passed. I had survived the rigors of the training which has to be endured by servicemen, or wise civilians, who are likely to be exposed to the hazards of the Frozen North. We had been landed by aircraft on an Arctic island, with Eskimo guides, to learn how "to live off the land," catch fish through seven feet of ice, hunt our food, sleep in snow houses, cope with blizzards and come to terms with temperatures of 50 degrees below zero and knife-edged winds. I had "passed," with gratitude for an experience which was to serve me in good stead on my further travels in the Polar regions, and with an unstinted admiration for the Eskimos.

We were back in base camp on Victoria Island, in the Beaufort Sea, and a U.S. Air Force aircraft had arrived from Edmonton to take me off. The crew had expected to spend the weekend in Florida and had been suddenly posted to the Arctic instead. It was their first experience of it, and they had not got mentally acclimatized. They had landed on sea ice and had neglected what others would have regarded as elementary precaution.

Overnight the engines had frozen up (that could be "cured" by using a giant blowtorch), but they had also been warned to filter their gasoline from the oil drums which had been stored in the open. The reason for filtering is that ice crystals form in the oil drums and can get sucked into the engine.

They did. Nuggets of ice lodged in the carburetor and nothing could shift them. There was only one thing to do: dismantle the engine. The crew brought the big carburetor into our hut and nursed it, like an orphan lamb, in front of our stove. For hours and hours they tried to find the block.

Dave, our Eskimo guide, ministered to their creature comforts with constant mugs of coffee, and as he did so he watched. The carburetor was quite unfamiliar to him, but presently he came to me and asked whether he could tell them where the blockage was. He did, and there it was. All he had done was to observe what they did and what they did not do.

This guide was a remarkable person. (Indeed, most Eskimos are remarkable people.) He was a natural mechanic and he could contrive anything out of a metal oil drum. Kitchen stoves were his specialty, but he had even made a refrigerator! He boasted his prowess with oil drums.

One night, in the base hut, Scott Alexander, a former Mountie who was the Commanding Officer of Arctic Survival, tried to tease him. He showed him a picture of the *Queen Elizabeth* ocean liner, told him how big it was, and said, "You couldn't make that, Dave, could you?"

The Eskimo studied it closely and said, "How many oil drums, boss?"

The point of the story is not that the Eskimos have a sense of humor but that they are ready to tackle anything in the modern world. As the Arctic has opened up, with construction camps, radar stations, air bases and mining centers, engineering contractors have discovered the surprising abilities of the Eskimos. They are intuitive engineers. With relatively little training an Eskimo can handle tractors and bulldozers as well as, or better than, *Kabloona*—the White Men—who are apt to forget that snow shifting is not muck shifting and that snow can be very tough indeed. They learn very quickly how to repair and maintain the machinery, mechanical or electrical. And, of course, they know more about Arctic conditions than visitors are likely to learn.

That is why they call the Eskimo *Innuit*, the Real Man. They know that *Kabloona* cannot exist in Eskimo country without a welter of civilized equipment such as heated houses, radios, aircraft, supply ships, and so on, while everything an Eskimo family needs to sustain life under the harshest conditions can be carried on a single dog sledge. When *Kabloona* goes traveling by land it is *Innuit* who must show him the way. So, since he can learn White Man's ways quicker than the White Man can learn his, the Eskimo, without arrogance, knows that he is the Real Man.

The mechanical aptitudes of the Eskimo are certainly amazing. I heard at firsthand the story of an Eskimo boy whom I met at a missionary school at Aklavik, on the Mackenzie Delta, 120 miles north of the Arctic Circle. He was given a present of a watch, and he did what every boy wants to do but what only an Eskimo boy would dare do. He immediately took the watch to pieces. The chapel bell rang. He put the pieces in his cap and stuffed it in his pocket, and after chapel he went to bed. The next day he put that watch together again. Which is one reason why the Canadian Government is now training Eskimos as highly proficient watchmakers, radio engineers, etc.

The explanation of the mechanical aptitudes of the Eskimos is fairly obvious, when you come to think of it. It is a high degree of Natural Selection. For 4,000 years the Eskimo has survived in the snow deserts, the Barrens. Only those with acute eyesight and a photographic memory could thus survive because, traveling over wide expanses of snow-covered landscape which drifts and changes, pin-pointing permanent landmarks becomes a natural and instinctive, subconscious faculty. They develop a blueprint mind. Combine that with fingers which have to be nimble and with the fact that, through all these thousands of years, they have had to improvise. They had no wood, because they lived beyond the tree line. They had no metal, except some native copper around Coppermine River, in the Central Arctic. They had the pelts and bones of the sea and land creatures which they hunted. They had slate and soapstone.

I have met Eskimos who, until thirty years ago, had never seen a white man and who had lived in the Stone Age. They made their bows—remarkable weapons—by laminating articulated caribou bone, baleen, springy whalebone, bound with caribou sinew. Their arrows and spears were tipped with slate. They hunted the caribou for hundreds of miles, by sledge or on foot. They fashioned their snow knives, to cut the firm snow for their igloos, from ivory or bone. They would sit for hours by the seal's breathing hole in the ice, waiting to harpoon it when it came up for air. In summer they would go to sea to chase the walrus and the seal in their skin canoes (*kayaks*) or in their skin boats (*umyaks*), which could hold a hunting crew.

Yet those same Eskimos would step unconcernedly into an aircraft, handle a radio set, or take a Geiger counter with them to find uranium on the way to their trap lines. But, still, in the Long Night, they carve their traditional soapstone and ivory figurines.

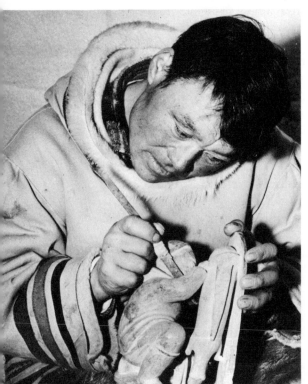

STONE AGE *Eskimo carving soapstone* [Peter Murdoch "The Beaver"]

Because I learned to like the Eskimo as a person and to respect him for his unusual intelligence and skills, I began to ponder. Sitting with Luke or Dave, my Eskimo guides, in the domed igloo which they could run up from virgin snow in thirty-five minutes—a remarkable feat of architecture and constructional engineering—I would ignore the blizzards outside and just concentrate on the problem of Man and his Environment.

How was it that a race as intelligent and as adept as the Eskimo had never expressed itself in what we would recognize as a culture? (There are Eskimo "cultures," but we will discuss them later.) The question, of course, is answered as soon as asked: they were the hostages of their environment. In the pattern of civilization, it was a case of "arrested development," not in terms of intelligence (they had to be clever to survive at all) but of cultural evolution.

They are a surviving example of how our primitive forefathers, once naked to the elements, discovered the ways to clothe themselves in the pelts of the animals which the toolmaking skills, justifying the description *Homo sapiens*, enabled them to kill. Thus they became masters of their climatic environment and were able to move from the warm regions, where furless, featherless Man had originated, into the Temperate Zone and then into

21

ARCTIC DOME [1] *An Eskimo igloo—4,000 years of snow architecture embodied* [Richard Harrington]

regions of rigorous cold. No modern scientific ingenuity, except as finesse, can improve on the *artiggi*, the *parka*, and the *mukluks* —the fur shirt, the fur overcoat, the sealskin boots—of the Eskimo. Perhaps it was the success of their "clothing technology" which kept them an Arctic people and, because the pelts were indispensable, kept them a hunting people. Nature had provided them with the "caribou runs," those regular migrations of the northern deer. It had also deprived them of any possibility of growing crops and becoming settled tillers, the essential prerequisites for elaborating a social and material culture.

They came to terms with an environment which was climatically rigorous, without the accessible metals which turned the Stone Age into the Bronze Age and into the Iron Age, without the fibers which could be woven to replace the need for skins, without the grains which might lead to agriculture, and without the sun-baked clays which would suggest ceramics. They were a people frozen into the matrix of a proto-civilization, a living anachronism, withal an innately intelligent one. They were a people waiting for oil drums. "How many oil drums, boss?"

For me, my experience of the Arctic was an experiment in space and time—a stepping back into history and forward into the future. It reminded me of what it has become the purpose of this book to show: that Man has mastered his environment by his own ingenuity; that his progress at every stage has been governed by the circumstances of his natural world, or of that part of it in which he found himself; that history, which we think of as wars and battle-won empires, was more truly dictated by what we would now call "technology," the applied knowledge which flourished, corrupted and failed; and that, in terms of our present knowledge, the limits which were reached, or imposed on successive civilizations, which grew in relative isolation, can be extended by modern science. The frontiers are no longer physical or climatic but those of knowledge or intention.

ARCTIC DOME   [2] *Radar station, polar sentinel in the atom-rocket age* [National Defense Photo, Canada]

Introduction

Once an hour a piece of man-made hardware can encircle this planet. A television camera in it would see neither frontiers, nor nations, nor races, nor ideologies but only, in terms of the universe, a tiny planet on which 2,900,000,000 (and, by 1980, 4,000,000,000) human beings have somehow contrived to live together, to feed each other, and, for survival, to help each other. Our knowledge can encompass this planet, like that artificial satellite, and liberate mankind from the circumstances which have dictated the limitations of past civilizations.

But it is in that past that we, in the present, can realize the challenge and opportunities of the future.

PART ONE

The Writing in the Sands

"They say the Lion and the Lizard keep
The Courts where Jamshyd gloried and drank
*   deep:*
And Bahram, that great Hunter—the Wild Ass
Stamps o'er his head, and he lies fast asleep."
                                    —OMAR KHAYYAM

Like the "trailers" of next week's films which highlight episodes without disclosing the plot, a long series of personal experiences, all over the world, have imprinted themselves on my mind and in my imagination—incidents which have made vivid for me the meaning of Man's achievements and follies. They illustrated (for me, at least) the slowly evolving drama of Man's struggle with nature throughout the ages.

For history is not just written in books; it is written in the sands of time. One can read it in a landscape, such as the dusty wastes of Mesopotamia, the graveyard of successive civilizations.

1 The Cock Which Crowed in Mosul

BENEATH THE BALCONY on which I was talking with the Director of Antiquities, in twentieth-century Baghdad, lay the river Tigris. Its waters were so heavy with silt that it did not ripple; it pleated. The lunch we had just eaten had been gritty with the wind-scourings of the Garden of Eden. The dust-laden winds from the desert were stifling.

"Once upon a time," he said, "the cock which crowed in Mosul could be heard in Basra."

It would be a shrill cock which could be heard over a distance of 700 miles. But he was quoting an old saying, fraught with ancient meaning and mocking at modern circumstances. It recalls a time when the valleys of the Tigris and the Euphrates were so closely settled that a cock in the north could start a relay of crowing which would reach the sea.

We had been discussing the fate of Mesopotamia, the Land of the Two Rivers, the cradle of the civilizations of Eridu, Ur, Erech, Lagash, Umma, Nippur, Kish, Nineveh, Asshur and Babylon itself. Ancient cities are now stranded in the desert sands like flotsam left by a receding tide.

History, as we are usually taught it, would suggest that wars and conquests were the cause of their decline and fall, but the Director and I were discussing reasons more profound than military ones. Geography, as we are usually taught it, might suggest that in the span of 5,000 years the climate of Mesopotamia had changed and had reduced the granary of the ancient world to an arid region, but the facts which we were considering were different.

27

The evidence shows plainly that those lost cities were sustained by human ingenuity, in the form of irrigation, and by methods quite consistent with rainfall and conditions no different from those which exist now. The circumstances which forced the abandonment of cities were the outcome of human intervention and not of any change in climate. Wars were only incidents in that human intervention—significant in the history books but still only incidents, spectacular but not conclusive.

From aerial photographs it is easy to see that the Tigris and the Euphrates, and the lesser rivers in the area, changed their courses and left cities high and dry. Even this was the work of mortal man. For example, the Euphrates once flowed past Ur, reaching the Persian Gulf near Eridu, but the warrior Rim-Sin straightened the course of the river so that it bypassed Ur. The people of Erech, to the north, dammed the river to irrigate their region, and Eridu and Lagash were both separated from the water and perished for lack of it. Erech later suffered the same fate; interference with its canals left it in a waterless desert. The Euphrates silted up and built up the soil which now separates Ur and Eridu from the sea and makes the Tigris and the Euphrates merely tributaries of the Shatt-al-Arab. This gives point to the Sumerian legend of the Creation which says, "The land was still sea when Eridu was made." In Sumerian times Ur was on the coast of the Persian Gulf instead of being, as it is now, 150 miles from the sea. Archeologists excavate quays and wharfage in the middle of the desert.

In modern Iraq the riddle of the sands is not difficult to decipher. As one travels across, or flies over, the Land of the Two Rivers, the past speaks eloquently. Aerial surveys show quite clearly the old watercourses, both natural and man-made. Across the wastelands run bunds. The meaning of these parallel dikes was explained to me by the Director of Antiquities.

The dikes mark the courses of the ancient canals and tell of the limits of ancient technology. When the canals silted, or were choked with drifting sand, they had to be dredged by muscle labor, by scooping and tilting the mud onto the banks. When, however, the bank became too high, the human effort of dredging became uneconomic. The lift was too great and it became easier to dig new canals than to dredge the old ones. So they were abandoned. Nevertheless, the irrigation systems thus revealed are a remarkable tribute to the skill and ingenuity of the Mesopotamians. They exploited different levels between the Euphrates and the Tigris and were able to produce canals by gravitational flow.

The profound lesson of all this is that when you start interfering with natural systems you must maintain your artificial systems. Once the efforts are relaxed for any reason, or once men become frivolously vainglorious, like Rim-Sin diverting the water from Eridu, or Sennacherib, the Assyrian, drowning Babylon at the beginning of the seventh century B.C., nature reasserts itself and takes its revenge.

"That," said an archeologist, as we stood upon the mound of a buried city and as he pointed to the reproachful landscape, "is proof of the ingenuity and the folly of mankind."

2 *"Mene, Mene, Tekel, Upharsin"*

ANOTHER IMPRESSION which endures with me is of standing in the reeds by the ruins of Babylon, at a spot where Alexander the Great, master of the known world, died in 320 B.C., in his thirty-third year.

Here the Euphrates and the Hillah Canal meet after enclosing the ancient city. This recalls the story of the Feast of Belshazzar. Belshazzar was the Babylonian general of the sixth century B.C. who was defending the city against Cyrus and the Persians. The garrison laughed when Cyrus began to dig a deep trench around the city in order, as they thought, to starve them out, whereas there were twenty years' provisions within the walls. Cyrus

29

AERIAL VIEW—SEVENTH CENTURY
B.C. *A reconstruction of Babylon seen over the Ishtar Gate
with the Tower of Babel in the
background* [The Oriental Institute, University of Chicago]

chose the night of the feast when the mysterious finger wrote on
the walls of the banqueting hall *"Mene, mene, tekel, upharsin"*
(God has numbered thy kingdom and found it wanting) and
diverted the Euphrates into the trench. The Persians invaded
the city across the dry river bed.

In the embrace of the waters stand the ravished ruins of Babylon, as tragic in their condition as in their meaning, because to
the attrition of time have been added the scars of the spoilers. In
intervening centuries it had been "quarried" for its masoned stone,
but in the past century, in the name of archeology, it has been
pillaged so thoroughly that it is now little more than a ground
plan of the city that was.

The glory that was the Babylon of Nebuchadnezzar has certainly departed. Apart from his wars and his subjugation and
carrying off of the Jews into capitivity, the chief work of Nebuchadnezzar was the aggrandizement and beautifying of Babylon
to surpass the vaunted claims of Nineveh. He repaired the great

Temple of Marduk and erected the vast Imperial Palace on top of which, rising terrace upon terrace, were the Hanging Gardens, one of the Seven Wonders of the World. He reconstructed the Tower of Babel. The "tower" was a ziggurat, a pyramid structure on the topmost tower of which was a spacious temple.

Nature has added a sardonic footnote to the aspirations and spoliations of Man. There is no doubt that the Hillah Canal was constructed, but I heard eminent experts on the spot arguing as to which of the two arms of the watercourse was man-made and which was the natural. Nature has blurred men's efforts and claimed them as her own.

The Euphrates, tired of being disturbed in its bed, got its revenge. At one time it reduced the neighborhood of Babylon to waterlogged marshes. Here the malarial mosquitoes bred. They produced death and disease and crippled the population so that they were not able to maintain the irrigation systems or till the fields. And so the process of collapse was speeded up and, with some justification, it can be claimed that it was the mosquito,

AERIAL VIEW—TWENTIETH CENTURY A.D. *The Pentagon, Washington, D.C.*
[Wide World]

and not the Mongols, which in the end destroyed Babylon. Long before the Asian hordes became the pagan "besom of destruction" which swept Babylon, in the fulfillment of the prophecy of Isaiah, the mosquitoes had become the commandos of the Lord of Hosts.

Alexander, the irresistible, conquered Babylon, swept through Persia and into India to become the master of civilizations older than his own. At the head of his armies, he returned by land to Babylon. There he sickened and died. "Here died Alexander the Great," said an Iraqui expert, as we stood among the marsh grasses of the waters of Babylon. "He died of malaria. The mosquito was the King of Babylon. Remember that the Babylonians' chief god, Nergal, had as his symbol the insect."

3 *Ping, the Jungle King*

ON THE INDIAN JUNGLE TRACK which we were traversing, a man-eating tiger had mauled and killed a tribesman just the day before. A jackal snarled in our path and then bounded into the undergrowth—a reminder that the tiger, for which it scavenged, would not be far away. Wild elephants trumpeted. This was the Kipling jungle of the Mowgli stories and Jim Corbetts' jungle of the *Man-eaters of Kumaon*.

We came upon some vine-smothered ruins and, out of the niches and the broken pediments, monkeys jibbered and mocked at us.

Here, in the Himalayan terai, on the borders of India, Tibet and Nepal, was another unforgettable reminder of Man's lost battle with nature.

Terai is not the name of a locality; it is a term applied to land which slopes gradually from the Himalayan foothills to the

Ganges plain and which stretches along the northern frontiers of India. This particular Terai lies south of Naini Tal and Almora, in the crutch formed by Tibet and Nepal. It is a land of many rivers, the snow-fed tributaries flowing south and west to the Ganges.

To grasp the significance of this jungle it is necessary to go back a thousand years to the time when there was a prosperous civilization cultivating the fertile alluvial soil washed down from the mountains. There came a time when the industrious peasants tried to extend their cultivation, in area and in season, by cutting irrigation canals from, and between, the Ganges's tributaries. Their very ingenuity destroyed them, because they cut the canals across the natural drainage of the region and the ground gradually turned to swamp. It became the breeding place of the malarial mosquito.

In the upshot the mosquitoes won and malaria either killed

WINGED DAGGER *The anopheles mosquito, spreader of malaria* [World Health Organization]

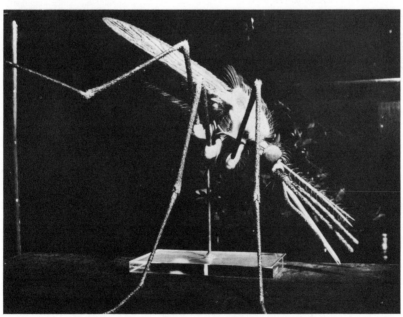

off or drove out most of the peasantry. The jungle marched in, smothered their canals, overgrew their villages and towns, and, where farms had prospered, there ranged the tigers, the wild elephants, the blue oxen, the jackals, the leopards, the cobras, the chitals and the wolves. The monkeys held ribald court in the halls of princes. Of that jungle (as of Babylon) Ping, the mosquito, was king.

Of course, in the legends which pass as the history of this region, the collapse is ascribed to wars, because men, in perverted conceit, always insist on being the instruments of their self-destruction and would never admit to anything so unheroic as being conquered by an insect.

Even the legendary story of the Tharus and the Bhuksas is, in truth, only a marginal note to the clinical pathology of the jungle. There are two tribes, sparse in number, but reputed, because of their survival in this malarial region, to have a natural immunity to the disease. They are certainly hardy breeds, who have persisted in this locality since time so remote that they are probably the aboriginals. They themselves claim, and perpetuate in their customs, a more glamorous account of their origins. According to them, they are descended from a royal family of Rajputs, the warrior caste of the Hindu socio-religious system.

After a battle in which the king and princes of this royal family were defeated and wiped out, the Rajput princesses fled into the jungle with the servants. From the intermarriage of the royal women with the men of the two servant subcastes, the Saises and the Chamars, came the Tharus and the Bhuksas respectively. A fact which might lend plausible confirmation to this is the relative status of men and women in present-day tribes. Unlike most women in India, the female sex here is not subservient. They are at least equal and, indeed, from accounts of fifty years ago, although I did not find them to be true today, the women refused to eat with the men, whom they treated as social inferiors. There is, traditionally, polyandry, that form of polygamy in which a woman has several husbands. In *Kim*, Kipling presents The Woman of Shamlegh, with her

OPERATION MOSQUITO *Malarial eradication organized like a military campaign in Iran* [Philip Boucas, World Health Organization]

many husbands whom she despised. Shamlegh is in the hills on the edge of this jungle.

However princely their origins, the two jungle tribes were reduced to truculent squalor; they were clannish and resented intruders from the world outside the jungle. They resisted the Indian Government's attempts to reclaim the 1,700,000 acres of this lost land with its arable soil and turn it into settlements for army veterans. The tribes had the mosquito as their ally in this resistance, because the reputation of the region as a malarial graveyard was sufficient to discourage any prospective settler.

So the Government called in the World Health Organization to deal with the malaria in advance of the bulldozers and tree dozers which would rip up the jungle and clear it for farming. The tribes' reception of the malaria teams was just as hostile. And with some justification, for what the Tharus and the Bhuksas

35

saw was convoys of trucks and jeeps and spray guns moving in. All this could not be directed against a tiny little insect. They refused to let the sprayers into their villages, much less their homes.

"Babujee, why do you come to kill us?" the Tharus demanded of the leader of the teams.

"Tharus," replied Dr. Peter Issaris, the Greek, "I come to give you life, not death. I come to kill the mosquitoes, not you. I come to save you from the fever."

It was true. A year later the mosquitoes had been conquered and thousands of acres of the jungle had been cleared. Dr. Issaris went back into the villages.

"Tharus," he said, "did I come to kill you?"

"No, Babujee. You came to kill the mosquitoes. And the lice!"

4 *The Locust Men*

ONE NIGHT, during the London blitz, with the antiaircraft guns pounding outside and enemy aircraft overhead, H. G. Wells, J. G. Winant, the American Ambassador, Ivan Maisky, the Russian Ambassador, and I were dining together at Wells's home in Regent's Park.

The conversation was not about bombs, or about the war, but about the ways in which the world could be altered for the better if the resources, the effort and the ingenuity which went into total war could be applied for peaceful purposes. We were quoting examples.

Maisky reminded us that in his pre-Revolutionary days he had been a science student and that in 1919–20 he had been sent by the Soviet Government to carry out an exploratory survey of

Outer Mongolia, that landlocked country which lies between the Gobi Desert and Lake Baikal. For eighteen months he had traveled backward and forward, on horse and camel, living in the yurts, the Mongol tents, and sharing the life of the nomads.

His constant companion on these journeys had been a thirteenth-century monk—not as a ghost, but in the form of a remarkable journal. This monk had been sent to Mongolia by Louis IX to try to convert the Khan to Christianity. St. Louis's intentions were not entirely religious. He was planning another crusade and had conceived a grand design in strategy. If Western Christendom were to attack the Saracens from the front and the Tartars would come out of the steppes of Asia and assail them from the rear, then victory would be assured. But Louis could not make an alliance with a heathen, so the monk's job was to convert him.

He did not succeed, but he kept a journal which, as Maisky testified, was a remarkable piece of shrewd and detailed observation. His account gave a pretty complete picture of the country, its people and its way of life. It was a "historical control" for Maisky's own survey.

As he said, the conditions had not changed in the intervening centuries. The Mongols of 1919 (circumstances have improved since then) were living exactly the same life as their forefathers, down to the details of their food, their tents and their nomadic economy, which still depended on five animals—the horse, the cow, the sheep, the goat and the camel.

One of the observations which Maisky had made and which he repeated to us was the explanation of the great Mongol migrations which we identify with Attila the Hun, Genghis Khan and Tamerlane. On his reckoning, the population of the steppes, human and animal, doubled every hundred years. Their tribal tracts could no longer support them and they would burst the bounds. The impetus would carry them into China, into India, into the Middle East and into Europe. They became, as H. G. Wells put it, "locust men."

Maisky made another observation during his survey. His conclusion surprised us. He said he knew why Mongolia had remained unchanged throughout the centuries. It was the climate. And he had decided how the climate could be changed. Outer Mongolia was shut off from the rain-bearing and tempering winds of the Pacific by a ring of mountains. He had suggested that by moving mountains great ventilating shafts could be driven through the range.

"And why didn't you?" asked Wells.

"Because the Soviet Union had to build tanks and battleships," said Maisky. "In a peaceful world it could have been done."

5 *"Delenda Est Carthago"*

WE STOOD on the hill above Carthage as the sun was approaching its setting. As it dropped toward the horizon and its rays came almost horizontally across the naked landscape, a strange thing happened: we saw the ground plan of Roman fields, 2,000 years ago. The shallow light had brought up, as shadowgraphs, the concealed contours. If I had been an experienced surveyor, I could have measured those fields. It would not have been difficult because they conformed to a regular pattern and to a geometrical precision.

This was really a culmination of an experience. I had already traveled out into the deserts to see the fortified farmhouses, those farm-forts the peasant garrisons of which had tilled the land and manned the ramparts against the desert marauders. Those fortified farmhouses had marked the perimeter of the settled area of North Africa, which had been one of the great Roman granaries. So, contemporarily, from the evidence of the extent of the province and the size and nature of those fields, it is possible to estimate how many people the area which we now call Tunisia was able to sustain. Merely to cultivate the area by the practices of the time (i.e., without tractors or combine harvesters) would have needed a peasant population three times the present population. They not only fed themselves but supplied food for Carthage itself, which had an estimated population of 600,000, for the trading ports of Oea, Leptis Magna and Sabratha, and for the bread and circuses of imperial Rome.

From that hilltop we could look two ways—down on the ruins of a city which had suffered the plunder of 2,000 years, and down on the ruins of a soil which had been plundered also.

With me was Charles Saumagne, a really remarkable Frenchman, then the (civilian) Inspector-General of Tunisia, a man who had dedicated his life to the genuine understanding of North Africa, its people and its land. He knew its past.

Like a stage producer setting a drama, he could shift the scenery of present and raise the curtain on what-had-been. With a sweep of his hand he could abolish modern Carthage, which might be any Mediterranean seaside resort, and conjure up a proud but grim history.

In place of streetcars there would be the city of Virgil's Dido, of that fugitive Elissa who fled from Tyre in, or around, 850 B.C. with other refugees from her brother's tyranny to re-establish what had been a Sidonian trading port, way back in the sixteenth century B.C.

This outpost of the Levantine Phoenicians was to become the great mercantile empire of Carthage and to be confronted by the rivalry of Rome. They clashed in the First and Second Punic Wars which destroyed the Carthaginian supremacy as a merchant people.

When the sea mastery of Carthage was broken and it was deprived of its means of trading, the Phoenician merchants, as inexperienced in the ways of the soil as the Jewish merchants, fashion models, doctors, typists and trinket makers who in the twentieth century became the farmers of modern Israel, turned their attention to their hinterland. The energies and enterprise which they had exercised in merchandising went into farming, and they became such efficient agronomists that their system of cultivation was the basis of all Roman and Greek farming in Africa for centuries thereafter. Their success was their undoing.

When a trivial, local quarrel developed between Carthage and Numidia, Rome, suspicious and uneasy about the people it had vanquished, seized the pretext. It offered what today would be called a "Good Offices Commission" to intervene in the quarrel. Cato, the Elder, was a member of that mission. He was that celebrated Roman who, having reached high office, retired to his Sabine farm to cultivate it with his own hands—the quoted example for all disinterested public men. But that was no comfort to Carthage. He was a farmer and, like his kind, was chary of competition. What he saw in North Africa confirmed his worst suspicions. Its prosperity was so offensive to him that he returned to Rome and proclaimed *"Delenda est Carthago"*— "Carthage must be destroyed." And it is noteworthy that in the Senate he waved, not the traditional sword, but a bunch of figs; the threat of Carthage was not military but economic. Carthage must be destroyed because it had learned the arts of peace too well. They who lived by the plow must perish by the plow. Militarily helpless, the Carthaginians were crushed in the Third Punic War, that ancient piece of Hitlerism. The Romans razed the proud city to the ground and symbolically drove a plow through the ruins.

With dramatic vividness, Saumagne reconstructed the last days of Phoenician Carthage to the tragic climax when the mothers, besieged in the Temple of Eshmun, flung their children over the parapets into the blazing ruins of their city before they perished themselves.

The Carthaginians who had mastered the Mediterranean Sea had mastered also the wilderness, and the granary they had created became the Roman spoils of war. When Julius Caesar, pursuing the last supporters of Pompey, reached Carthage, he found its ruins still sheltering the few survivors of the Punic population. He decided to rebuild it as a Roman city and, under the Caesars, Carthage was restored to pomp and circumstance, to be destroyed in turn by the Vandals, restored by Belisarius, and ravaged again by Hassan, the Arab, in A.D. 697.

In the night which followed that day when those ghost fields emerged from the past, Charles Saumagne and I were standing in the desert. The moonlight was glinting in the lantern eyes of the jerboas. A few fires were burning where the Bedouins had set light to the growing camel's-thorns to get warmth in the cold which had succeeded the blistering heat.

"Tell me," said Charles Saumagne earnestly, as we surveyed the silvered desolation, "that there are in the world ten men who believe that the desert can be made to blossom, ten men who believe that we can redeem the stupidities of mankind, and I shall die happy."

6 *The Living Pyramids*

HUNDREDS OF IMAGES of the Buddha look down from their niches and stupas to the great pyramid temple of Borobudur. This Buddhist temple is situated near where the rivers Ello and Progo meet in the heart of Java. I was taken there to be impressed by this marvel of Hindu architecture, at least 1,300 years old. I was duly enthusiastic. This great stone structure stands on a base 600 feet square, and one climbs through galleries of images, a tremendous testimony to the devoutness and the craftsmanship of an earlier civilization. It belongs to that age when the Hindu Empire stretched from India, through the Indonesian Islands, to Bali.

But I was more enthusiastic about the living pyramids, which belong to an even older civilization. Those terraces of inanimate stone did not move me half as much as the pyramids of growing rice—the terraces which climb the mountains. Every foot of soil—and sometimes the ledges are no more than a foot wide—on the side of the erstwhile volcanoes is made to yield rice, with ingenious water management to flood each terrace for the wet paddy. Often they yield more than rice, because these thrifty peasants, following the craft of their ancestry, have the knack of fish farming. The fingerlings which they put in when they flood the terraces and which "graze" in the underwater pastures of the growing rice, are about the size of sardines or pilchards when they are gathered three months later. This is a vital source of protein for the peasants, supplementing their rice diet. This living architecture of terraces is something which they inherited from ancient China where, through the mil-

STONE PYRAMID *The Hindu temple of Borobudur, Java* [Indonesian Information Office]

LIVING PYRAMID *The rice terraces of Borobudur, Java* [World Health Organization]

lenniums, the peasants had husbanded every foot of soil and every drop of water.

In those same hills of Kulumprogo I saw a sight which will remain forever unforgettable. Like gnomes in some weird fairy tale, copper-red bodies were digging and delving in the mud at the bottom of a pit and scurrying like ants up a swaying bamboo ladder as long as a fire escape, with baskets of mud on their heads.

It was all part of the incredible scene which I watched under the blistering sun until I became giddy and my muscles ached in sympathy with the backbreaking efforts of those toilers. I felt as though I had stepped back out of the twentieth century and was watching the Babylonian slaves digging the Hillah Canal. In this way and with such primitive tools they must have diverted the Euphrates.

Those peasants were cutting a forty-mile-long canal with nothing but their own muscles, pickaxes, mattocks, hammers and chisels. When they encountered rocks, they just chiseled their way through. They did not use gelignite because they did not have any and because, for them, man power was cheaper than explosives. So they used hammers and chisels and wedges to chip and split the rock into pieces small enough for the bearers to carry in their head baskets. Work which a mechanical shovel or a bulldozer and a few sticks of dynamite could accomplish in a few days took hundreds of peasants months of strenuous effort. In a year they had advanced two and a half miles through the volcanic mountains.

Those were not Babylonian slaves. They were free farmers working for a greater freedom on an enterprise which they themselves had started. Those were the Hungry Hills, where throughout the generations life was even more desperate than in the plains. To those peasants looking down from the hills, the valleys with their paddy fields were a sort of Promised Land. In the mountains there were only coconuts, bananas and cassava, from which comes tapioca. One thing which is common throughout the world is that at the lowest levels of human survival, short of eating slugs, like the Australian aborigines, people turn to such things as cassava to give them starch for energy but for little else. To such people even a handful of rice is a luxury.

Those hill peoples wanted rice, but rice needs water and the Progo River bypassed their slopes. So as a result of the clearing of the region of the crippling disease yaws, the peasants turned their new-found energy to a purpose—to cut a canal, to bring the water from the Progo River along the ridges of their mountains, so that they, too, could have steep-tiered terraces flushed with cascades of water from above. This tremendous effort was an act of dedication as profound as the building of that temple of Borobudur. But it was a dedication to life for themselves, their children and for their children's children.

The first effect on me was to provoke a feeling of indignation and resentment. After all, this was the twentieth century. I was there for the United Nations, and surely something could be done to give them bulldozers and dynamite, for example. When I voiced my indignation, however, I received a very salutary reproach from a wise United Nations expert who knew the country and the people.

"Try to understand," he said, "that this is their canal. For the first time they will have something which they will not owe to the moneylenders. Always they have been in debt for the means of their own existence. If anyone were to offer them material help, they could not believe that it was, in fact, disinterested. They would think that this was again some device of the moneylenders. No, let them fulfill themselves and their purpose. Then when they believe in themselves they may believe in the help that we can give them."

7 *Blood and Soil*

WITH A TWENTIETH-CENTURY SHUDDER at the dark stains of six-teenth-century blood which discolored the runnels of the altars of Monte Alban, I decided that nothing had so disfigured Mexican history as that episode of human sacrifice.

This was the holy city of the Zapotecs, built on a man-made

plateau leveled by the sawing off of two mountaintops. Massive temple buildings testified to the power and the arrogance of the priestly cult which left an aura of brutality around the stones themselves. There was something gladiatorial in the architecture and a sense of the inhuman in the stylized friezes. It was not pure imagination which produced this feeling; rather it was the contrast with the softer and kindlier architecture and figurings of the temples at Mitla, just a few miles away in an adjoining valley—the relics of a civilization which had had no human sacrifice.

The sense of arrogance was emphasized in the archeological diggings which had cut through the temple terraces and had revealed how succeeding orders of priesthood had obliterated the carvings and craftwork of their predecessors by piling masoned stones, so that the step work rose higher and higher and more and more portentously. Each succession had built on the foundations of its past but had buried that past in the process.

In the pelota courts, within the temple confines, the finest youth had exercised to the acme of athletic perfection. Only the perfect was good enough for the gods. Male and female, the young people were bred for sacrifice.

On the ceremonial occasions they were thrown upon the altars; their living bosoms were cut open and their beating hearts torn out by the priests. Their blood flowed down these runnels.

But those priests did not only tear the hearts out of their victims; they tore the heart out of the country. From the summit of a temple we looked down upon a ravaged countryside. The Valley of Oaxaca once had a fertility as legendary as the Garden of Eden. Now there was desolation, bald hills, and valleys gashed with gulley erosion. To build their temples the priests had had the massive blocks of masonry carried up the steep hillside and had fired the forests to produce charcoal to make lime for the temples. The rains had scoured off the unprotected soil and left a landscape in ruins, more ominous even than the stone ruins of those departed priesthoods.

"This," said M. Paul Rivet, the French archeologist, with a sweep of his arm over the temple city, "produced that."

8 *Night at Noon*

AT HIGH NOON we flew into night. The flight stewards switched on the lights in the cabin of the Trans-Canada airliner as we approached Winnipeg. There was consternation among the passengers at this apocalyptic blotting out of the May sun. Then the aircraft began to climb and escaped from the darkness into sunshine again. Below, however, was a dark pall. Instead of the usual skyscape of white plains and mountains of cloud, the sunshine made sinister the billows of what looked like dark brown smoke.

Indeed, I thought we must be flying over a vast forest fire with smoke so dense that it hid the fires themselves. But the pilot came back to explain that this was a dust storm, which was hanging over the city of Winnipeg and was so thick at ground level that it was impossible to land at the airport. To the passengers' dismay, he said he might have to fly on to Toronto. This was bad news for those passengers who had been booked to land hours earlier at Saskatoon but who had been unable to do so because of the floods. It was also bad news for me, because I had timed my arrival at Winnipeg to catch a flight which was to link up with my expedition to the North Pole.

For over an hour we circled over the city, and then a hole appeared in the dust clouds. The pilot dived through and we landed in a rainstorm, which was sheets of mud. Everything in Winnipeg was covered with a layer of khaki—like a gigantic camouflage.

The weathermen had taken samples of that dust, right up to its ceiling. At 8,000 feet the dust had been that of Texas —1,500 miles away. At various levels the samples were from Oklahoma, Nebraska and the Dakotas. The heavy particles of dust nearer the ground were those of Manitoba. The explanation given me at the time was that there had been a sharp thaw in the frost-bound northern states, followed by an unseasonable heat which had dried out the soil. The winds from the south had whipped the topsoil into the sky, all the way from the Gulf of Mexico to the prairies of Canada.

It was just an incident, but an ominous one—a reminder of the Dust Bowl of 1934–35, when the soil of Oklahoma blotted out the sun over New York. For weeks and months the farmers in the Dust Bowl states of the West had stood helplessly in their fields watching the wind rob them of the topsoil which was the foundation of their livelihood. The lesson, then, was plain enough. This was the punishment of nature's lawbreakers. Once the Midwest had had a natural cover of tough, thickly matted grass over which the winds could roar harmlessly because it kept the soil intact. When Man applied his methods of agriculture to the endless pastures, he had broken this natural cover, cropped and harvested the plains, with rich reward, until he had taken from it most of its nourishment and its natural coherence and had left it as dust. He had cut down the forests which had tempered the winds and had left the land naked to their mercy.

That was a salutary warning which the United States heeded. The soil-conservation programs and the replanting of forest areas, windbreaks and shelter belts were put in hand. In eight years the Forest Service planted 220,000,000 trees. They had set up the "nets to catch the wind."

"Man cannot change all the forces of nature," said President Roosevelt, in endorsing the plan to check wind erosion, "but he can modify his own surroundings."

PART TWO

The Toolmaking Animal

Boswell: *"I think Benjamin Franklin's definition of* Man *is a good one—'a toolmaking animal.'"* Johnson: *"But many a man never made a tool; and suppose a man without arms—he could not make a tool."*

1 In the Beginning

THE DEBATE still continues as to where, in the world, the human race, *Homo sapiens*, originated. The strong presumption, however, suggests Africa. As Père Pierre Teilhard de Chardin, one of the world's greatest experts on early man, said:

It is apparently in the depths of Africa, not on the shores of the Mediterranean or on the Asiatic plateau, that the primeval centre of human expansion and dispersion must have been located, long before this centre shifted in much later times, towards (or even split between) Eurasia and America. (International Symposium on Anthropology in New York in 1952.)

There is a plausible reason why this should be so. While most of the great land masses underwent the grinding of ice and the convulsions of mountain making, the southern part of the African continent was exempt. From millions of years ago, even from the time when our evolutionary ancestors were still fish in the Paleozoic seas and when forest vegetation had still to appear on earth, the continent south of the Great Rift has remained intact—a laboratory bench for experiments in evolution.

The evolution in which this book is interested is that which gave Man the faculties and capacities which made him able to come to terms with his environment instead of being merely subject to it. In other words, it is interested in Man as what Benjamin Franklin called him, "a toolmaking animal."

The elements of Man's skills existed in creatures which lived about 50,000,000 years ago. Their modern survivors are the tree shrews, lemurs and tarsiers. They had five movable digits on each limb, which were well adapted to climbing trees and swinging on branches. Unlike four-footed animals, with paws and claws, the first digit—the thumb—was flexible so that the creature had the ability to grasp the small insects which it ate and to pluck fruit with its front limbs. Thus these limbs (which could not yet answer to the description of arms and hands) began to acquire the functions which in four-footed animals are usually performed by jaws and teeth.

These creatures, called prosimians, had eyes on each side of the head, but in course of time the eyes shifted to the front of the head so that they could be focused on an object which the brain then resolved as a stereoscopic picture—three-dimensional. The tarsier, still surviving in the East Indies, is a living survival of this stage of evolution. It has eyes like enormous spectacle lenses, and they are forward-looking.

These primitive creatures were the ancestors of monkeys, apes and men. It was probably because, small and inoffensive, they had to take to the trees to escape from their enemies that they evolved differently from the ground-dwelling mammals. On the ground animals can rely largely, both in seeking their food and avoiding their enemies, on their sense of smell, but in the trees they have to depend on alertness of the other senses of sight and touch and hearing. So they acquired brains in which the senses other than smell had to be more developed. The brain increased in size, until within the restrictions of the skull the tissue of nerve cells had to fold itself over and become the convolutions and lobes. Today in Man the 10,000,000,000 brain cells, weighing three pounds, are packed into the casket of the skull eight inches long and four inches deep.

The prehensile digits of those early forelimbs created a new sense. A dog, observing a suspicious object, will sniff it, but a monkey, confronted with something unusual, will look at it and finger it. If what the dog sniffs is a hedgehog, it may feel it as well. The sense of feel magnified into pain will develop into an instinct, what to avoid.

In the monkey, however, as in Man, the hand became not only a grasping organ but a sensitive instrument of touch. Combined with sight, touch was to become the factor in manual skills.

The faculties which were developed to meet the needs of our tree-living ancestry were also limited by the conditions prescribed by their environment. Those who continued to live in the treetops, like the wild monkeys of today, developed special auxiliaries, like the prehensile tail which gives the New World monkeys what amounts to a fifth arm. But there is no reason to suppose that they are, today, any more intelligent than their ancestors of 40,000,000 years ago. Other forest dwellers, like the baboons, might become ground dwellers, but they developed feet which were like hands.

2 *Proconsul*

MUCH CLOSER to us in the descent from our common ancestry are the apes. After monkeys and apes had come into existence there was a time of immense importance to subsequent evolution when the apes became diversified. This was about 25,000,000 years ago, and the best evidence for it comes from tropical Africa and from the island of Rusinga in the northeast corner of Lake Victoria. Among the many fossil apes found there is Proconsul, which is not very far off the direct line of human ancestry. Proconsul was still monkeylike. It was capable of tree life and of swinging by its arms from branch to branch, but it was also capable of rearing up and walking on two legs.

From this group two lines emerged. One line of descent persisted as the forest ape, developing longer and longer arms and bough-grasping hands. The other led to Man, through apelike creatures which became accustomed to more open country, away sometimes from the forests.

Those grassland creatures developed the habit of walking on two legs. This left the hands free to carry the young and to collect food. These early *Hominidae* were probably already quite different from the apes or *Pongidae* as long ago as 10,000,000 years. What differentiated them was that *Hominidae* walked erect. The apes like the orangutan and the chimpanzees walked either on all fours or in a crouching position. Incidentally, they walked by using the knuckles of the forelimbs as paws. But the type which was to be developed into Man changed its skeleton through the modification of the pelvic girdle, which enabled it to move in a more upright manner. The rear "hands" became feet. They lost the power of clutching and became the pedestals on which Man could stand straight. The legs also outgrew the arms in length. The hand remained as it had been, with its power to grip, but, since it was no longer required for walking on, it became progressively more sensitive and skilled as the organ of manipulation.

3 *Australopithecus*

SKIPPING MILLIONS of years—because this was a slow process—we find in the Pliocene and early Pleistocene periods (roughly a million to 750,000 years ago) a type which was recognizably more ape than man. These creatures, *Australopithecus*, existed in southern Africa. They were small, less than four feet high, and walked erect. Their remains have been found in Bechuanaland and in the Transvaal. They lived in limestone caves and there is evidence that they may have used fire. Unlike forest monkeys, they appear to have been carnivorous, because in the caves there are fragments of animal bones, egg shells, crab shells and antelope-limb bones. These antelope bones are interesting because they had been smashed to extract the marrow.

It is, of course, the habit of baboons occasionally to prey on lambs and other animals of similar size, using their powerful canine teeth as offensive weapons. To deal with larger animals such as an antelope, they have to herd together, close in on it and tear it to pieces. In the case of the *Australopithecus*, the South African ape man or man ape, the canine teeth are small and level with the other teeth so that they could not have been used as tearing fangs. They must have had to use weapons to fell their victims. It is not yet certain that they made weapons, but stones from distant streams have been found in conjunction with the fossils, indicating that they utilized, as arms, such items as nature had already provided; stones for missiles, or sticks or animal long bones as clubs. By Benjamin Franklin's definition, therefore, the South African creatures were not "men," that is, "toolmaking animals," although they were "tool-using."

There is an argument, however, that they may have existed contemporaneously with toolmaking creatures. And very significant finds were made in Tanganyika in 1959.

The earliest "tools" can be dated by their geological setting as existing over half a million years ago. At first human artifacts were crudely shaped pebbles. Plenty of evidence of these have been found in river and lake terraces in Uganda and Tanganyika. This pebble culture was followed by more advanced forms of shaping rough tools, showing a slow but steady progress up to about 100,000 years ago.

4 *Peking Man*

TOOLMAKING and meat eating seem to have gone together. Large quantities of meat bones were found in association with the remains of the Peking Man (*Sinanthropus*), and it is not difficult to understand why toolmaking arose out of carnivorous habits. Although with their natural weapons—stones and cudgels— these proto-men might easily kill game, they would have obvious difficulty in removing the skin and the fur and finding the flesh. Without strong fangs, like the animals, they would find it difficult to tear the animal apart. They would find "fangs" in the shape of sharp pieces of stone, and when they could not find such sharp pieces they would break stones to get the edges. Here was one origin of toolmaking.

The change-over from being a vegetarian to being a meat eater also affected the character of the way of life of the early Man himself. A meat-eating creature needs a smaller quantity of food—in bulk—than the vegetarian. Instead of having to eat almost continuously like their fruit-eating cousins, the earliest Men then had to spend most of their daytime in hunting. Instead of continuously replenishing their energy by nibbling plant food, they could eat meals of concentrated protein in the shape of flesh and store their energy against the efforts of the next stage.

5 *Thinking Man*

IF THE ARGUMENTS of apparent facts are accepted and Africa is acknowledged as the cradle at least of the *Hominidae,* the creatures who were either our grand-to-the-nth-fathers or our great-to-the-nth-uncles, then Man strayed a long, long way from home. But, of course, he took a long, long time about it: *Australopithecus,* the South African mannish ape, existed about 1,000,000 years ago; 500,000 years later Peking Man and Java Man had emerged as far away as Asia; in Europe we find the Heidelberg Man (about 400,000 years ago), the Swanscombe Man (about 300,000 years ago), the Fontechevade Man (about 200,000 years ago), and the Neanderthal Man (about 100,000 years ago). On that time scale, eventual beings, whom we would be prepared to recognize in the portrait gallery of our ancestors as *Homo,* rate a mere 50,000 years—just the blink of an eye.

During those aeons the physical characteristics were changing. The knuckle-walking creature had ceased to go on all fours or even to slouch (like a gorilla). His legs had lengthened in proportion to his arms. His teeth had ceased to be fangs for tearing—in any defensive way—and had become useful only for bite-slicing and chewing. His jaw had shrunk; his physiognomy had changed; his snout was becoming a nose (more suitable for wearing spectacles later on), and his skull was gradually giving him a higher brow. He had lost the last outward vestige of a tail and he had shed most of his hair—at least he was no longer a furred animal. Peculiarly, among all the creatures, he

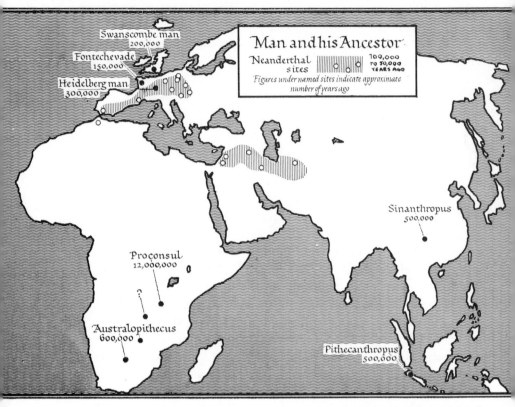

Man and his Ancestor

Neanderthal sites ▓▓▓ 100,000 TO 50,000 YEARS AGO

Figures under named sites indicate approximate number of years ago

Swanscombe man 200,000

Fontechevade 150,000

Heidelberg man 300,000

Sinanthropus 500,000

Proconsul 12,000,000

Australopithecus 600,000

Pithecanthropus 500,000

had become the one least equipped to cope naturally with the elements. He had neither fur, feather, shell nor scale. At best he had a skin which would pigment as a protection from the rays of the sun. That, however, implied that there was sun and warmth, and yet presently we find him contending with conditions for which he was ill-equipped by nature.

6 The Fire-making Man

THE REASON for his mobility over the surface of the earth and for the survival of his evolutionary species was that he became a toolmaking and fire-making animal. It is clever of a baboon to pick up a stone and fling it at an enemy or a prey, but it is quite a step to put that stone on a stick and use it as a club. For one thing, it implies a shrewdness of observation. We can see that, in principle, the club is the extension of the forearm and the clenched fist. To outreach his enemy, primitive Man found that by clutching a bone or a branch of a tree he could

Chimpanzee making a tool

hit it out of range of fangs or claws. The clenched fist, the "packed punch," was useful in dealing with his own kind; turn that clenched fist into stone, extend the forearm with a shaft, and you had a club. The sharp-edged flint or broken pebble with which he could cut open the skins of the animals which provided his food became, for offensive purposes, a "fist fang," a crude knife or dagger. This, again, as the spear, at the end of stick could give primitive Man an advantage over his enemies.

The distinction between tool-using and toolmaking is important. Chimpanzees are the only apes reliably reported to make tools. A chimpanzee will try to reach an object with a stick. It knows it can extend its arm in this way. If the stick is not long enough, a tame chimpanzee has been known to fit a piece of wood into a bamboo cane to get a further extension. One might call this "toolmaking," but the term would be more appropriate if, instead of the second piece of wood, the chimpanzee inserted a broken flint as a spearhead. In other words, toolmaking really means a combination of ideas. It is not only observation—imitating or "aping" something which already exists; it is also an association of ideas and manipulative skills to transform these ideas into practice. Toolmaking depends on the flexible digits.

Once primitive Man was able to kill his food prey or a bestial enemy and he could strip off the skin, he found that wrapping himself in such a skin would keep his body warm. But this led to an even more important discovery—that in these furs he had the means of adapting himself to climatic temperatures. He could dress himself not only according to the season but according to the heat or cold of the day. If he wanted to be warmer, he wrapped himself in more furs, and if he wanted to be cooler, he shed them.

Thus he was no longer hostage to the tropical heat of his origins or limited by his nakedness. He could move into the Temperate Zone or ultimately into the Frozen Zone. Indeed, as a species he was able to survive the Ice Ages.

This climatic survival by *Homo sapiens* and his immediate precursors depended on something else as well. Toolmaking was one thing. Fire tending was another. It is a characteristic of wild animals (as distinct from the domesticated cat purring on the hearth rug) that they fear fire. In the primitive world fire could only be associated with destruction—the lightning flash and the forest fire which it would start, or the scorching destruction inflamed by the white heat of volcanic lava flow, or the mysterious fires sprouting from the ground which we now know as the flames of natural gas or oil seepage. Fire was frightening. The deep instinct of all animals was to avoid it. Yet somehow, somewhere, our primitive ancestors came to terms with it.

Leaving aside the Greek legends of Prometheus stealing the fire from the gods (a legend which in varied forms is reflected in the mythologies of many peoples), the rational but still remarkable explanation probably lies with lightning striking a tree. "Remarkable" because the creature who was to become the fire tender must have had imagination, which is something more than the instincts of the animals. Imagination exaggerates the instincts of fear. No form of fire is more frightening than the cosmic force of lightning. Yet someone, somewhere, observed the chain reaction that lightning created fire and that a spark or a firebrand could convey that fire. Here was observation and a courage which transcended the beasts'. To take fire and tame it—to confront nature in its most terrifying form of lightning and to see its fire not as a threat but as a promise—that was primitive Man's first epic victory over nature.

Fire tending must have come first—keeping alive a flame borrowed from nature. Fire making—creating flame at will by flint sparks or wood friction—came much later. What fire meant was that our primitive ancestors were now able to defend themselves against wild animals, keep warm and roast their food.

Animals have their shelters, the nest, the lair or the den. Our ancestral creatures had their caves. With fire they were able to add to their shelter the amenity of controllable heat.

Taming of fire as imagined by Vitruvius (1547)

7 Memory Man

WITH FIRE, with weatherproof shelters and skins at his command, primitive Man became free to spread into every climatic zone.

One might say that the manumission which set him free was written in his own hand, for it was his toolmaking which made it possible in the first instance. But that is only partly true. Combined with the skill which his hand acquired was his power to see things in relation to each other, to classify them and to see ways of changing them. Nor would that have been enough. He had to have some means of passing on, and sharing, inventive ideas, within his contemporary group and from generation to generation.

This is what we call "tradition" as distinct from "instinct," which is a built-in memory to be passed on in the genes of any species. Tradition is experiment which becomes experience, and it has to be consciously passed on in the same way as the craftsman training his apprentice. To observe, to note and to do something as an individual is not enough, but to communicate observations and skills to others so that they can add further experiments to the sum of experience is to create a culture. Where tradition is limited, culture ceases to grow and will wither away. Or when tradition becomes fossilized in conventions—"what was good enough for my father is good enough for me"—it becomes a relic of interest only to archeologists, a dead end in human development.

Passing on information presumes some form of language. The use of tools presupposes intelligent behavior. A toolmaker, it has been said, is also a wordmaker. The slow cultural evolution which is evident in the Lower Paleolithic was almost certainly related to the rudimentary form of their language. The hand-ax peoples were still communicating by gesture and crude noises. Moreover, they were scattered sparsely, and it needs a large group both to improve on skills by sharing experience and to create a language. Improvement also depends on an element of competition; the individual may be satisfied with a crude implement, but if his neighbor has a better one, more stylish or more efficient, he will be encouraged to refine his own. That is the beginning of art. A flint hand ax may be either a ragged piece of stone—as crude as the broken bottle of the saloon fights today—or it can be as carefully worked as the Acheulean (before the Third Ice Age) specimen found at Wolvercote in Oxfordshire or equally skillful specimens in South Africa, Kenya or Madras. Pride in workmanship is not the quality of the hermit but the shared appraisal of the group.

Craftsmanship, therefore, was the product, as well as the stimulus, of the early social group. It also helped the process of social differentiation. The fleetest hunter, or the shrewdest spear thrower, might not be the best flint flaker. So that even in the simple hunting group an element of specialization developed. And certainly of standardization. Tools became recognizably functional—the spearhead, triangular with sharpened edges, was classifiably different from the D-shaped scrapers with which the pelts were prepared. The Neanderthalers were already using flint spokeshaves to sharpen wooden spears which they hardened by fire. They were no longer improvising; they were making tools of a standard type; they had a purpose for a particular tool in their minds.

8 New Man

ABOUT 40,000 YEARS AGO rapid cultural advances, accelerating the processes of the previous million years, began with the emergence of highly successful types of *Homo sapiens*, notably

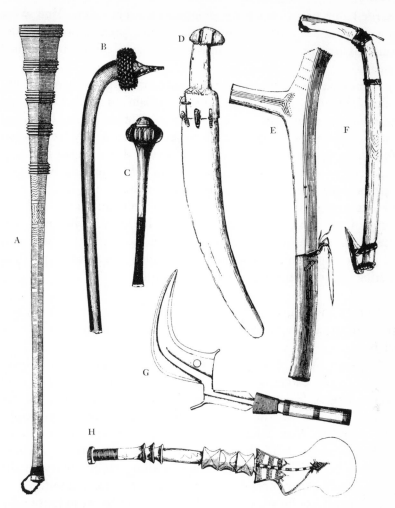

[A, B, C] *Wooden clubs from the Pacific islands.* [D, E, F] *Eskimo bone snow knife, antler club and blubber hook.* [G, H] *Iron knives from the Congo.*

the Cro-Magnons. They spread from southwest Asia during the second half of the last Ice Age. They replaced the Neander-thalers, who disappeared—apparently suffering the fate which has overtaken recent aboriginals in contact with European culture; they were either killed off by superior weapons or starved out of existence by competition. The New Men were not only much more inventive than their predecessors but developed artistic skills which, in many respects, cannot be excelled today.

Almost certainly this was the result of the growth of an oral vocabulary by which they could explain to each other and teach their apprentices. They not only made tools, but they made toolmaking tools. For example, flint chisels were devised for working bone, antler, ivory and wood. They began to apply mechanical methods to the movement of tools and weapons. Spears were launched with throwers which, on the lever principle, increased the propelling power of a man's arm and the range from which he could strike at his prey. The bow was invented, probably in North Africa. It not only was a means of propelling an arrow, but it also provided a method of twirling a stick and thus produced the rotary drill.

Rotary motion, of which the bow drill is an example, was a point of departure in some ways more significant than the taming of fire.

Consider the ingenuity which was involved: previous advances had been the extension of the properties of the limbs; the club was a longer forearm and a heavier fist. It was true that the ball-and-socket of the human joints was a rotary principle, but primitive Man could only observe it in the disarticulated skeletons of his kind. In those bony relics the principle could scarcely be self-evident. There was nothing really rotary in the New Man's experience; he had to discover it for himself.

A smooth, round stick with a flint point can be set in motion by a different set of muscular movements. The stirring movement can enlarge a dibble hole in the ground, but if one wants to bore a hole in hard material, the hard-pointed stick has to be clamped vertically. This can be done by rolling it between the palms of the hand—transforming a horizontal movement into a rotary one. The ancients discovered that by a spinning friction they could drill a hole in the toughest bone or ivory. They also found that friction produced heat and could thus provide a manageable source of fire—like modern Boy Scouts rubbing sticks together. They then found that by fixing the drill in a sleeve or socket, by holding it rigid in the hole and by twisting a sinew or thong around it, they could cause it to spin. This led on to the bow drill, in which the ends of the cord or sinew were attached to the extremities of a bow and kept in tension so that the rotation could be maintained by a sawing movement. The bow drill is still used efficiently by the Eskimos today. The drill is held in an ivory socket which the Eskimo grips in his powerful jaws, and he pushes it, as it must be pushed, into the material to be worked by the powerful thrust of his neck; he then "saws" with the bow. In various forms this type of drill has existed in prehistory, also in historical times and in present-day primitive societies. Geographically it is spread all over the world and raises big questions about "diffusion" (the transfer of skills by migration) or whether in each area it was independently discovered.

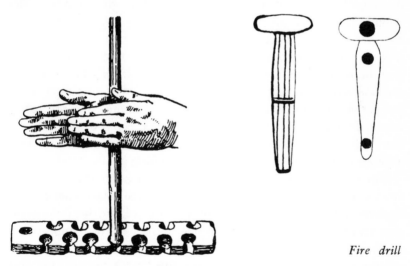

Fire drill

From the rotary principle came the fire drill, also the rotary quern, which ground seeds between revolving stones, and the spindle, by which fibers could be spun into threads. Related to this was the potter's wheel and the wheel for vehicles.

9 *Man on Wheels*

THE WHEEL was truly revolutionary—in both senses of the term. Mechanically it provided continuous rotary motion, and culturally it was so significant that some anthropologists and historians tend to judge the abilities of a race or people by the existence among them of the wheel. The gibe against the black African is that he has been perennially backward because "he never developed the wheeled vehicle." (With the evidence of the wheel in the Saharan rock pictures, this gibe becomes disputable.) Neither did the Eskimo, the Mayans, the Incas nor the Aztecs have wheeled vehicles, but no one would suggest that any of these were deficient in innate intelligence. There is a more obvious explanation for the lack of the wheel in certain geographic areas: tropical forests, with close-set trees and undergrowth, would certainly discourage the use of a wheeled vehicle, just as they would defeat a jeep today; a sledge is obviously more efficient in the snow deserts, and carts have positive disadvantages in mountainous country.

Nevertheless, the wheeled vehicle was one of Man's greatest discoveries. It is easy to see how primitive Man might have discovered how to move heavy objects by rolling them along on tree trunks and shuffling them from one set of trunks onto another. It was, however, a big step in imagination, and in technology, to advance from that to the fixed axletree, the hub, and the disc wheel.

The earliest evidence we have of the use of wheeled vehicles is the tablet picture of a sledge on four solid wheels. This shows that it existed in Lower Mesopotamia, at Erech, in Sumeria,

Limestone relief from Ur, before 2500 B.C.

about 3500 B.C. A thousand years later the kings of Ur were being buried complete with their hearses. Several royal tombs at Kish, Susa and Ur, dating between 3000 and 2000 B.C., contain the vestiges of such vehicles. The wood, however, has virtually vanished, and the vehicles are no more than molds— imprints in the soil. It is not convincingly apparent from these whether the axletree and the wheels were all of a piece (like a dumbbell), with the axle rotating in a fixed socket in the sledge (which was what the carriage basically was), or whether the axle was fixed and the disc-wheel rotated on a hub. Sumerian pictures usually show a circular hole in the wheel, suggesting a hub, and a peg through the axle, suggesting a lynch pin, holding on the wheel. There is comprehensive evidence of wheeled vehicles before 2000 B.C. in China, the Sind, the Balkans, Sardinia, Spain, Scandinavia, and the British Isles. Man, on wheels, was certainly getting around! Even before 3000 B.C. he was already using the wheel as a military engine (which, in its origins, must have been as demoralizing as the Pyrrhic elephants or the First World War tanks). Chariots were a decisive arm of Sumerian warfare.

10 Man and His Group

THE EARLIEST and simplest form of society was the hunting group. Our early progenitor, naked to the elements, fangless and clawless and not as fleet as most of the beasts that might prey on him, would fare ill as the lone hunter. Only in combination with his fellows, pooling their resources of ingenuity and prowess, could he really hope to survive. The group could be small, but it had to be large enough to be viable.

They had to follow their prey, so they ranged far afield and in the course of time spread across the land surface. They could do this, as has already been pointed out, only when they were the masters of their personal environment, when they could clothe themselves, or unclothe themselves, to meet the climatic variations.

By the time New Man appeared, Cro-Magnon and his like, he was no longer merely wrapping the skins around himself but shaping them and seaming them, stitching with awl and sinew, into costumes which could clothe his entire body—costumes which were not unlike those of latter-day Eskimos.

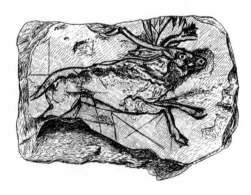

Galloping reindeer engraved on plaque of schist, Indre, France

He had mastered fire—first, no doubt, as the common campfire of the group, but then as the domestic hearth in his family cave. It gave him warmth at night and a cooking fire. As an important factor in his cultural development, he discovered fire also as a source of illumination. When he needed portable light, he could use a brand taken from the fire (the brand was also a weapon against his enemies). He discovered that certain woods burned well and not too quickly. He found that lumps of tree resin could provide a bright and lasting flame. He also discovered that fats could burn and provide him with his primitive candles. Oil, with some sort of wick, could give him a continuing flame, and saucer lamps were known to the Paleolithic cave dweller.

Illumination became another factor in the mastery of his environment. His movements were no longer limited by the sun hours or by daylight. He could go underground, with miners' lamps, to get the buried flint stones for his tools and weapons— and, incidentally, to discover that fire could be used to rend rocks. When night put an end to his hunting, he could extend his day in lighted leisure. Like the modern Eskimo carving his soapstone or ivory during the long Arctic night, he discovered interests which became arts. The cave drawings at Altamira, Spain, the work of artists 15,000 years ago, and the rock drawings throughout Europe and Africa show that Man, in those days as now, was not only a shrewd observer (down to anatomical detail) but had the irresistible urge to record his observations.

11 *Man Tames His Food*

VERY EARLY in Man's history he discovered another means of reducing the exigencies of his environment. Unlike the beasts which must gorge themselves on food when it is available and starve when it is not, Man learned how to preserve food, by hanging it in the smoke of his cave, by drying it in the heat of the sun, by pickling it in brine, or by rubbing it in coarse salt. In colder climates he discovered elemental refrigeration—storing food in the frozen ground or covering it with stones, which would not only keep it safe from foraging beasts but would keep it cold and delay putrefaction. None of these were inventions. They were discoveries through observation of natural processes, which he turned to his own advantage.

The primitive hunters began to domesticate animals as well as to pursue them. Almost certainly the first animal to be domesticated was the dog, which was to become Man's partner in the hunt. What the jackal is to the tiger, the wild dog was to Man. The jackal eats the remains of the tiger's prey. The dog ate the offal which the human hunter left. The jackal, however, is an inferior breed because he is almost incapable of hunting for himself. The wild dog, while he might be an occasional hanger-on, was also a natural hunter. Moreover, he hunted in packs, with an acknowledged leader.

Creatures which follow a leader can be led; they will transfer their loyalty if the leader, in this case Man, is superior in strength and cunning. There is also the instinct in humans which makes them pet creatures of which they are not afraid. The wild dogs that hung around the hunting group, to scavenge or to rob, not only lost their fear-smell of Man but Man began to pet them, to throw them scraps of food, so that they would come back for more. A stray pup would become a natural plaything. And gradually the wild dog, or certain varieties of it, would become dependent on the human group, with an allegiance to it, and would hunt with the group and become a valuable ally.

Another factor in early domestication of animals was the use of the decoy. Deer hunters, for example, would breed deer in captivity and use the female or the rutting stag to attract the wild herds, to distract their attention or allay their fears and allow the hunter to get within striking distance. Deer tamed for this kind of usefulness would naturally be tended and cared

Hunting scenes from Abydos, Egypt (before 3000 B.C.) showing lasso, throwing stick, spear, bow and clubs

for by the group and, sharing nomadic habits, would develop an affinity—like the reindeer of the Old World Arctic.

The strange thing is that the reindeer's cousin, the caribou of the New World, although a gregarious, innocent creature, which in all the millenniums has never learned in its migrations to avoid the predations of Man, has never been domesticated by him. Although there is evidence in Eskimo ivory carvings of the use of deer decoys, the American deer have never been herded. So much so that, when the Canadian Government, anxious about the depletion of the wild herds of caribou and the consequent threat of starvation to the hunting Eskimos, decided to do something about it, they had to import reindeer. In Alaska this step had already been taken. Lapland deer were already being herded there, and the Canadians, in 1929, made arrangements for the delivery of 3,000 reindeer from Alaska to a range near the mouth of the Mackenzie.

This was the beginning of an epic trek in contemporary history. The drive from Alaska started in December 1929 under the direction of a veteran Lapp, assisted by other Lapps and several Eskimos. The herd migration was beset by privations and hazards during the crossing of the mountains of northern Alaska and the desolate coastal plain of the Mackenzie Delta. Some of the reindeer broke away and found their way back to the range from which they had come. Many were killed by the blizzards or massacred by the wolves which followed the trek. The losses were heavy, but nature was persistent and the births of fawns each year made up the deficit. The reindeer arrived in Canadian territory three years after they had started, but it still took them another year and a half to reach the range east of the Mackenzie. To cover a distance of about 500 miles had taken four and a half years!

Decoy domestication was probably the origin of tame cattle. It is known that cattle, such as aurochs and bison, were used as decoys by the hunters, but it is more likely that they were in a similar category to the present-day elephant, caught and tamed for a particular purpose, but not really ."farmed." Sheep and goats were among the creatures early domesticated. Fowl, in the beginning, were probably regarded more as pets—game-cocks for fighting, for example—rather than as an economic proposition. The horse, the ass, the camel and the llama appear to have been relatively late-comers in the process of domestication. They belong to the bigger social groups which needed beasts of burden to carry themselves and their chattels, rather than to the smaller hunting groups which needed domesticated animals as supplementary food.

With the progressive domestication of animals the way was prepared for the evolution from a hunting society to a pastoral society, still nomadic, but with the source of food under human direction and control. Man was becoming a manager.

12 *The Neolithic Revolution*

AT ONE STAGE of the evolution of Man his progenitors were vegetarians, and at every stage there has been an ambivalence— part herbivore, part carnivore. The flesh-eating hunters had their salad days as well. Even the Eskimo, who from necessity ate more animal and fish protein than probably any race on earth, had his natural greengroceries—summer plants, which he treated as delicacies.

In a cave on Mount Carmel, in the Holy Land, Dr. Dorothy Garrod unearthed flint sickles, set in carved bone handles— proof that 8,000 years ago men harvested grain. On Mount Hermon, to the north, the botanical explorer Aaron Aaronsohn found the coarse grasses, the seeds of which those early men had recognized as food and which became the ancestors of wheat and barley.

All those thousands of years ago, long before Abraham left Chaldean Ur to become the Hebrew patriarch, father of a pastoral people, those ancestral men had realized the virtues of grain. They nibbled the seeds in the ears and found them good. They discovered that from those seeds more grasses with more seeds grew, that if they scratched the ground the seeds grew better, and that if they chose well-watered soil, as in the river valleys, the grains grew still more plentifully.

That, not the domestication of animals for pastoral herding, was the beginning of what we like to call "civilization" but which really means the growth of city cultures.

When men began to till the ground, they became settlers. Their primitive homesteads grew into villages, villages into towns, towns into cities, cities into empires. They found that they could grow crops, sufficient not only for themselves and their families but for others—the potters, the weavers, the metal smiths, the priests and the doctors. With surpluses they could exchange food and goods with other settlements. Trade began but barter was cumbrous, so they invented tokens. Money was exchanged for goods.

Cultivation means the deliberate sowing or planting on a prescribed area to produce a predictable crop. This was inconsistent with a nomadic life, although it can be safely assumed that the hunters and the herders had some knowledge of potential crop growing. Nuts, seeds and the pips of fruits brought in by the fruit gatherers of a wandering tribe must have germinated near the campsites. Similarly the root plants which they ate must have been observed to sprout. The observation must have been there for countless thousands of years, but some group—like the sickle users of Mount Carmel—must have had the initiative to abandon a way of life. They must have abjured the chase and the herd wanderings over the steppes to await the seasonal recurrence of the crops they planted. This has been called the "Neolithic Revolution." And a revolution it certainly was.

13 *The Allegory of Cain and Abel*

THE BIBLICAL STORY of Cain and Abel can be read as the powerful allegory of this revolution. Abel was the shepherd. He drove his flocks and herds over the wide pastures of the Middle East. Cain was the New Man, the cultivator who applied knowledge to the problems of livelihood. The herdsman could get enough forage for his animals during the seasons of the rains which brought up the herbage of desert and steppe, but in the dry season the custom of necessity had made him retreat to the river lands. Then came the time when Cain, the settler, had occupied those river lands and was cultivating his plants, domesticating his animals and nurturing his soil. He displaced Abel; he "killed" the nomad.

(The story was repeated in the United States in the last century, when aeons of time were telescoped into decades. The Indian hunters were replaced by the cattlemen, the cattlemen by the sheep farmers, and the herdsmen by the homesteaders. Each resisted the other.)

The first cultivators were by no means restricted to cereals. Their food-gathering predecessors had known the value of green vegetables—cabbage, lettuce, spinach, nettles, cress and peas. They knew roots, like carrots, onions and radishes, and fruits and nuts and oil seeds. Particularly they valued the pulses, the seeds of leguminous plants, such as wild beans, peas, lentils and vetches.

At Merimde, the early settlement in the Nile Delta, peas have been discovered dating back to 4400 B.C. They were also found, with the lentil, in the ruins of Troy and those of Minoan Crete. The black lentils are indigenous in southeast Russia and in countries of the Far East. In the Orient the high protein content of pulses made them a valued source of food of the early peoples, as soya is today in China and Japan and gram in India.

14 *From Food Gatherer to Food Grower*

GRAINS, however, were the crops which determined the character of the Neolithic Revolution.

In the foothills of northeastern Iraq, at Jarmo, studies have been made of one of the oldest agricultural settlements yet discovered. It has been possible to date, with some scientific accuracy, the remains of this Neolithic deposit. This has been done by the radiocarbon method. Carbon which emits rays is present in natural carbon and can be detected and measured by laboratory techniques. This carbon, C^{14}, has a half life of 5,360 years—that is to say, half the ray-emitting atoms which would be present in any quantity of carbon will have "expired" in that period and, at any time, the proportion present will be a measure of the age of any sample. This dating puts the age of Jarmo at about 5000 B.C. (Jericho ante dates this by about 2,500 years).

(i) Wheat and Barley

Cultivated emmer wheat has been found at Jarmo in association with two-row barley (with six grains of two opposed spikelets) with einkorn wheat present as a weed.

Emmer is what botanists call "tetraploid." This means that it consists of four sets of seven chromosomes (the packages of genes which carry the hereditary traits from one generation to the next), and these, in the reproductive cells of the plants, divide into two equal series of fourteen chromosomes. *Einkorn* is a "diploid," that is, with two sets of seven chromosomes. A third dynasty of wheat is the *bread-wheat* group, which is "hexaploid," that is, with six sets of seven chromosomes which in the reproductive cells divide into two equal groups of twenty-one chromosomes.

From archeological evidence it would seem that the first wheat taken into cultivation was emmer. Wild emmer occurs in Palestine, Jordan, Syria, Mesopotamia, Armenia and Persia. Wild einkorn occurs in the Balkans and western Asia Minor and on the shores of the Caspian and throughout Mesopotamia and western Persia. No wild bread-wheat has been found, so that it can only be assumed that it is a natural hybrid—between emmer and einkorn.

Barley in the wild state has been traced to Palestine, Arabia, Asia Minor, Transcaucasia, Persia, Afghanistan and Tibet.

Grain husbandry, both of wheat and barley, spread up the Danube into central and western Europe. From Troy, north-westward, einkorn was more successful and persistent than emmer, a plant of hotter environment, although the latter became adapted to colder conditions and, presumptively, played the Eve to einkorn's Adam in the development of Europe's bread-wheat.

(ii) Rye and Oats

Rye and oats began their careers as the weeds of the wheat and barley fields. Experiments in Brandenburg have proved that, if an equal number of wheat and rye seeds are planted to-gether, the crop changes to pure rye within three years and have showed that, where climatic conditions become difficult for wheat, the rye takes over—a dispensation of nature which made it possible for cereal cultivation in the cold Baltic region. Oats had a similar history—a farsightedness of nature to provide the northerly Scots with their porridge!

(iii) Rice

For two thirds of the world's population today the staple grain is rice. The nearest wild plant to cultivated rice is *Oryza fatua*, which is found wild throughout southeastern Asia as far south as Java. About a dozen different species of *Oryza* are found in Asia, Africa and South America. It is possible, however, that some of these wild species are degenerates from cultivated rice which at some time or other had been imported into various regions.

Even today we can learn from the peasants in southeast Asia how our early ancestors obtained this rice for cultivation; they tie the awns or beards together before maturity so that they do not scatter and can be saved as seed.

Rice was not the crop of the Egyptians or Chaldeans in very ancient times. It is, therefore, improbable that its culture origi-nated in Africa and followed an eastern route into Asia. Another fact which reinforces the theory of the Asian origin of rice is that, in the most ancient languages of the Orient, agriculture and rice are synonymous. Although in the earliest recorded history of China there are references to rice, its prehistory more probably belongs to the area of southeast Asia, whence it must have spread northward into China and into India and been carried westward by the Aryan dispersal. It was introduced into Indonesia by the Malays in their migration there about 1500 B.C.

It was a dry-land crop in its first forms of cultivation. The wet paddy fields were a much later development. The first authentic record of irrigation for rice cultivation is to be found in the *Book of Poetry*, supposed to have been written during the Chou dynasty in the eighth century B.C. There are references in other old writings to "land tilled with fire and hoed with water," which refers to the burning off of the trees and undergrowth, the flooding of the land and the puddling of the soil. The practice, however, is probably older than this recorded history, because the wonderful system of terraces on the mountainsides of the Philippines was constructed by settlers from South China about 2000 B.C., and they presumably brought their practice from long-past experience.

(iv) Maize

Although the plants of the American continents were ultimately to double the food supply of the older continents, no plant cultivated by the American Indians was known to Asia, Europe or Africa prior to the White settlement of America.

In the absence of any archeological evidence to contradict it, the presumption is that *Homo sapiens* reached the New World somewhere between fifteen and twenty-five thousand years ago (see pages 171–172).

Along the shores of dried-up lakes in California and Texas mortars and grinding stones have been found which show that the early American crushed nuts and seeds into flour. These desert cultures are very important because they show a way of life which leads eventually to the growth of agriculture. Hunting, fishing and food gathering seem always to have been combined. No hunting group in the Americas appears to be entirely carnivorous. Each took advantage of the vegetable products, of which, in North America, four hundred species are known to have been used.

In early Brazil the staple diet was cassava, alias manioc, alias tapioca. The use of this as a source of food shows a surprising degree of expert intelligence. The starch, which is the food, comes from the soft root of the plant. This has to be stripped of its rind and grated down to a pulp which has to be pressed to remove the poisonous juice. The flour thus left was formed into cakes and baked.

The highlands of Peru yielded the white potato, which, at a later stage, was to be such an enormous factor in the food economy of the Old World. But in America, as in Asia and in Europe, the development of cereal culture was the ultimate basis of agriculture and settlement.

Maize, or corn, is one of the most remarkable of all cultivated plants. It is one of the dozen or so crops which stand between mankind and starvation.

To the scientists it still has the quality of a mystery—literally of a "whodunit"—because, as it exists today, it must be the result of human intervention. It is unique among cereal grasses.

The terminal inflorescence, commonly called the "tassel," usually bears only male flowers, each of which contains three pollen sacks packed tightly with 2,500 pollen grains. They are light in weight and are easily carried by the wind. The inflorescences on the side, which become the familiar cobs of corn, have only female flowers. These have pollen-receptive organs, called "silks," covered with fine hairs to capture the wind-blown pollen. Maize, therefore, unlike other cereals, is a naturally cross-pollinated plant. That is why it has been possible to produce hybrid corn, one of the most spectacular applications of applied biology in modern history.

Cultivated corn, however, has no mechanism for the dispersal of its seeds because, unlike other grains, which are individually protected by chaff, the corncob is entirely encased in a husk.

This is very convenient for human requirements, but it renders it incapable of existing in nature. Corn could not survive without man's protection. How, then, did it grow before man came along to help it?

Professor Paul C. Mangelsdorf, in a paper presented to the American Philosophical Society in Philadelphia in 1958, offered a fascinating reconstruction of corn's past:

From two hundred feet below the present site of Mexico City fossil evidence, comprising a number of pollen grains, was extracted during a drilling. The pollen was identified as that of corn, and, although it was at least 80,000 years old, it was scarcely distinguishable in any of its characteristics from those of modern corn.

The scene shifts to a rock shelter in New Mexico, known as the Bat Cave, which was excavated by Herbert Dick of Colorado University Museum in 1948 and 1950. For several thousands of years the cave had been inhabited by people who practiced a primitive form of agriculture. Their garbage and other debris had accumulated in the cave to a depth of six feet. At the bottom of this accumulation Dick turned up some tiny cobs about the size of a one-cent piece. Those were dated, by radiocarbon tests (see p. 78), at about 5,600 years.

There were no living seeds, however, so it was impossible to reproduce from them. They had, therefore, to work from the evidence they had, and they found that the tiny kernels of the cob must be those of popcorn, in which the kernels are small and hard and, as every child knows, capable of exploding when heated. But it was also found that the Bat Cave maize was also a form of "pod corn," in the sense that the individual kernels were enclosed in pods or chaff, instead of the all-enclosing husk.

"Pod corn" exists today as a freak. In some parts of South America it is preserved by the Indians, who believe that it has magical properties. Otherwise it is regarded as a monstrosity and has been dismissed by a number of botanists from any role in the ancestry of corn. Professor Mangelsdorf, however, believes that it is monstrous today only because it is a "wild" character superimposed on modern highly domesticated varieties. "Today's pod corn," he said, "is comparable to a 1900 chassis powered by the engine of a 1958 car." He crossed modern popcorn with pod corn.

By reconstructing the corn genetically, the experimental botanists have been able to give a satisfactory account of how the modern corn evolved. A simple mutation produced the lowering of the position of the ear. This separated the sexes and made for a larger grain-bearing ear completely protected by the husks but no longer capable of dispersing its seeds. In the course of history man had deliberately selected the ears most suitable for his uses and in doing so had produced a plant dependent upon him and more useful to him.

(v) Structural Plants

Away back in the Dawn Age our primitive ancestors discovered that trees and plants could yield them materials, other than food, which they could put to their uses. Since forest management and the planting of trees is a development of comparatively recent times (and tragically ignored or neglected even now), this discovery had many disastrous consequences. Man remained a gatherer of trees and not a tree husbandman. As a result, whole vast areas have been deprived of their trees and turned to deserts. Entire civilizations have been destroyed by soil erosion.

Among the constructional materials collected since earliest times are the reeds. They were used for huts and shelters in Egypt 5,000 years ago.

Another of the "industrial" uses of trees was for water transport, first as wooden rafts and dugout canoes, and later as plank boats.

One of the earliest developments was the making of baskets. About 10,000 years ago, just after the Ice Age, our Mesolithic ancestors were already making nets by interlacing threads out of strands of tree bark. These were for fishing, but there is no doubt that the nets were also used for carrying—like the string bags of today. This was the origin of baskets, which were just a tighter woven net. Baskets are vessels made by interlacing two more strands in different ways. This is akin to primitive weaving, in which one set of threads, the warp, is stretched on a frame, while another set, the weft or woof, is passed through at right angles. It was only when looms were introduced much later that the crafts of basketmaking and weaving drew apart.

Leaves of cultivated palms, dates (which had to be developed by husbandry because the female flowers have to be fertilized), coconut and the wine palm were used for roofing, walling and matmaking in the warmer countries.

(vi) Fibers

Flax was cultivated at least 5,000 years ago, as a fiber to be spun or woven. Before that there is evidence that it was grown for its oil-bearing seed. Hemp was the first fiber plant of the Chinese, and hemp and fabrics were known in Egypt in pre-dynastic times. Its use as a fiber can never be entirely dissociated from its early production to extract a secretion which has narcotic properties. This, it has been suggested, explains why, in Europe and the Mediterranean world, hemp never really became established—because its narcotic properties were less appreciated among people to whom beer and wine were early available.

The early history of cotton is perplexing, partly because of the presence of cotton species of apparently Old World origin in prehistoric America. Seventy-five hundred years ago cotton existed in the Indus Valley. The Babylonian and Greek names for cotton would appear to confirm this Indian origin. The curious thing, however, is that the wild varieties of the ancient Indus Valley cotton found archeologically at Mohenjo-Daro (2,500–1,500 B.C.) have never been found among the Indian species. They have all the characteristics of modern Indian cotton, suggesting long cultivation, but they are identified with a group of plants confined to Africa and Arabia (see p. 167).

The development of fibers into threads and thence into weaving represents a very important advance in the skills of

Homo sapiens. The hunters, like the Cro-Magnons (or the Eskimos and Lapps of near-contemporary times), knew the use of threads. They used the sinews of the animals. They pierced the skins from which they made their clothes with awls and laced them together. It was a big step, and in time a long one, between that and the twisting of plant fibers or wool into threads and the evolution of weaving, which, apart from high-speed mechanization, has not changed to this day. That meant the complete departure from the traditional hunting and the development of textiles consistent with an agricultural economy and with settlement.

15 *The Kitchen*

To THE KITCHENS of the ancients, present-day technology should acknowledge a great debt. The kitchen was the laboratory and workshop to which we owe furnaces and ovens, pestles and mortars, rotary grinding and crushing, methods of food preservation and pressing seeds and fruit, and the use of alcoholic fermentation.

Up to Neolithic times—say 10,000 years ago—cooking was largely a matter of steeping food materials in water and throwing in hot stones. In the Neolithic stage, with the cultivation of cereals, cooking developed a new importance. Cereals were dried for storage and grinding. Instead of immersing stones, containers were heated by direct contact with fire. Porridge was made by heating cereals in boiling water; later, biscuits and flat unleavened cakes were prepared. The first alcoholic drinks were made. Food was roasted or else preserved by pickling, smoking and salting, and animal fats were prepared as butter and cheese. Vegetable oils from the olive and from kernels were another remarkable development. With the coming of basket-making sieves were developed, particularly to get better-quality flour. The early Mesopotamian terms for sieves clearly refer to their manufacture from reeds and rushes.

16 *Hard Liquor*

ONE OF THE EARLIEST discoveries—an interesting piece of scientific observation—was the recognition that "leavens," which were probably not recognized as organisms, when added to dough produced fermentation and a palatable change in texture.

The only fermentation process which may go back beyond Neolithic times, and which may be even older than agriculture, was the turning of honey into nectar. Rock paintings, found in eastern Spain, show honey collecting in an early Stone Age hunting community. When farming began, one of the associated industries was beekeeping.

At the very dawn of history the ancient Egyptians knew that the first alcoholic fermentation was followed by a second fermentation forming mainly acetic acid. They knew the process by which a congenial beer could be turned sour and they prevented the second fermentation by stoppering their beer jars so as to exclude the acetic organisms. As early as 2000 B.C. date wine was the tipple of the Egyptians and Babylonians. Honey was often added to the date juice and the alcohol content was high.

In early Sumerian times beer was produced by the fermentation of barley and other cereals. Five thousand years ago 40 per cent of the cereal production of Mesopotamia was used for brewing. Wine was also known over 5,000 years ago, and vineyards were a feature of early agriculture.

17 *Shelter*

SETTLEMENT implies housing. Early Man was a cave dweller; his refuge was a lair or den like those of the beasts. But it is always a mistake to assume that cave dwelling is the sign of the absolute primitive. In hot countries, and particularly in deserts, there is a great deal to be said for living in caves—notably pit dwellings, which can be compared to inverted tenements with the "apartments" arranged round a natural well. And in the New Testament, as in the Old, there is plenty of evidence of civilized living in caves, like those that recently yielded the Dead Sea scrolls.

As a condition of Man's acquiring mastery of his environment, however, he had to have his shelter not only where he could find it but where he wanted it. In the days of the mammoths their skeletons covered with skins gave our predecessors the equivalent of a tent or an army hut. Later they built huts of saplings and skins or constructed them of turf or of wattle.

When the hunting group became the settled tribe, then they needed something more. For one thing, apart from shelter, they needed defenses, not only against the marauding beasts, but against the nomadic people resentful of the tiller and envious of his stored supplies. For safety they might build their villages on piles in the lake or bog or surrounded by an excavated moat or by a palisade. Like the Red Indians or like the Dyaks of Borneo today, whole groups, even an entire village, would be content to live under one roof in a long house.

The settled farmers, all those thousands of years ago, had differentiated from the nomads and had become their rivals. Not only had they settled on the arable land which had once been the dry-season, riverside pastures of the pastoral peoples, but they were more effective animal husbandmen. They could grow forage crops and feed their flocks and herds when the range lands, the steppe country, could not support them. Moreover, by systematic cultivation, they could produce surpluses and, beyond their own subsistence, sustain "specialists"—the craftsmen, the priests and the administrators.

City civilizations at such a point of time (differing in geographical areas) were about to emerge.

18 *Footnote for Women*

WHEN ONE COMES to think of it, it is pretty obvious that Woman, not Man, was the innovator who laid the foundations of our civilization. While the men went hunting, the Woman was the guardian of the fire and, pretty certainly, the first maker of pottery. It was she who went picking the wild berries and nuts and seeds and who went poking with sticks to unearth the edible roots. In the mother-to-daughter tradition, the knowledge of plants born of long observation led the women to experiment in cultivation. Biologically Woman was more observant than Man, because the recurring phases of the moon coincided with the rhythm of her fertile life and she could observe the period of gestation not only in herself but in the animals and in the seasonal reappearance of the plants. So she had a sense of Time, and the measurement of Time was one of the earliest manifestations of constructive and systematic thinking.

The ancients were less reluctant than menfolk are today to acknowledge the role of women as the originators. In Judeo-Christian tradition Eve is reproached for eating the fruit of the Tree of Knowledge, which led to the expulsion from Paradise. Greek and Roman mythology were more generous in their acknowledgment of Athena/Minerva as the goddess of wisdom and patroness of the arts and crafts. In the societies which emerged in primitive times women held a dominant position. There is evidence of the existence of matriarchies in which the women directed the affairs of the tribe, acted as priestesses, and transmitted the succession through the female line.

PART THREE

The Watershed

1 The Black Potters

ONE OF THE MOST INTERESTING places in the world for the study of the elements of emerging society is the Persian plateau. The choice of that location also has the advantage that it evades the conflicting claims of each of various areas to have been the "cradle of civilization"—the Nile Valley, the Tigris-Euphrates Valley, or Turkestan.

At a time when the greater part of Europe was covered by glaciers, the Persian plateau was already passing through the Pluvial Period, when the region was a great inland sea into which many rivers ran. Fossil fish and shells which have been found in the high valleys show how deep and vast this sea was. Then, between 10,000 and 15,000 B.C., there was a gradual change in climate, leading to the dry period in which the plateau began to dry out until, progressively, it became a great salt desert.

At the time when the droughts began, prehistoric Man was already living on the plateau, often in the caves or rock shelters which had been the underground channels of ancient rivers or in pits dug into the mountainsides and roofed with branches. Even at this cave-dwelling stage pottery was in use. It was poorly baked and deep black in color because of the smoke in the firing.

As the great central lake shrank, its shores where the rivers left a fertile deposit of silt became rich savanna pastures. The animals descended to these newly formed grasslands and the hunters followed them and settled on the plain. From this period, about 5000 B.C., the record of material civilization can be traced.

The oldest remains of human settlement in Persia have been un-earthed at Siyalk, near Kashan between Teheran and Isfahan. At the bottom of the diggings there is evidence of agricultural activities, including stockbreeding. The remains of domesticated oxen and sheep have been found. There, too, is the black, smoked pottery, derived from the earlier cave dwellers, but mixed with red pottery, already revealing primitive craftsmanship in which the designs, including colors, were baked into the ware. Although, of course, the remains of perishable materials like reeds have disappeared, the designs on the pottery show the unquestionable evidence of basketwork. Clay spindles also give proof that the rudiments of a textile industry were already there. Both men and women wore ornaments—necklaces of shells, carved rings and bracelets, and they used cosmetics. They probably practiced tattooing and face painting. They had begun to believe in a hereafter. Their dead were buried under the floors of the houses, with their weapons, and remained a part of the family.

There is evidence even at this period—7,000 years ago—that trade had already started. The settled economy was producing surpluses. The settlers were making metal implements, but by hammering, not by smelting, copper; they were farming crops and they were stockbreeding; they had commodities to exchange. That they did so is apparent in the shells worn by the people of Siyalk which belonged to species to be found only on the Persian Gulf, 600 miles away.

About 4000 B.C., on top of the accumulations of the first settlements of plateau men, more elaborate houses began to appear. They were larger and built out of brick. Those bricks were just mud, shaped between the palms of the hands like cakes, with thumb holes to provide the mortar joints. The builders even went in for interior decoration. The walls of the rooms were painted red with a mixture of iron oxide and a fruit juice. The pottery was becoming more refined. They still did not have the potter's wheel, but they had the *tournette*, a slab of wood turned on the floor by an assistant. The pots were better fired and showed pictures of animals in full movement and most realistic, executed in black paint on a dark-red ground. Nowhere else in the world has such pottery been discovered corresponding to the same period of time. This suggests very strongly that

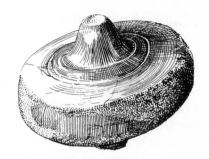

After the tournette—*potter's wheel from Jericho*

the Persian plateau may have been the original home of painted pottery. Even more significant is the fact that, contemporary with a realism of design by which it is possible to identify a horse in the process of evolution between the onager and the modern horse, these potters were already indulging in highly stylized abstract designs. In the first stage of stylization the horns of the ibex became exaggerated in proportion to the body and finally finished up as a motif without any body. The plastic artist, the potter, was beginning to produce the elements of pictographic writing.

The metal industry was developing, but now with the copper smelted and cast. Jewelry was becoming more varied. In addition to foreign shells, there were appearing lapis lazuli brought from the Pamirs and jade from China far beyond.

Consistent with this import-export commerce are the seals which were found at Siyalk. To mark the ownership of merchandise, the seal was brought into use. It was a conical stone button into which a geometrical design was cut. This was impressed upon the lump of clay which stopped the mouths of jars, which were the packing cases of the time. The geometric patterns gradually gave way to representations of human beings, plants and symbols which had the pictographic significance of pictures.

93

2 Oasis Cities

THIS SOCIAL DEVELOPMENT, 6,000 years ago in Persia, was still on a small and localized scale, because the oases were dispersed over difficult country; therefore, the great city-community life which was developing in the rich plains of adjoining Mesopotamia was retarded on the plateau.

The diggings of Siyalk show a thick layer of ash, evidence that the settlement was destroyed by fire about 5,000 years ago. The ruins served as a foundation for a new settlement in which the painted pottery had disappeared and plain red or gray pottery had taken its place. The stamp seal had disappeared and had been succeeded by the cylinder seal. On this the symbols were carved on a roller—a certain sign of the introduction of writing on clay tablets. The subsequent settlements showed a civilization which was superior, richer and more advanced but with all the signs of having been imposed by conquest. The influences were unmistakably Mesopotamian, of a kind which had already been developing at Susa, where Persian culture impinged on that of the Mesopotamian plains. At Susa there had already been the beginnings of a script and the first burgeonings of that culture which was to become dynastic Elam.

3 The Indo-Europeans

DURING THE SECOND MILLENNIUM B.C. the Persian plateau, that watershed between the Occident and the Orient, witnessed a series of migrations of great moment in the history of mankind.

From somewhere in the region of the Caucasus there was an outsurge of people who have come to be called "Indo-Europeans." One wave swept westward around the Black Sea, into the Balkans, through Thrace and back across the Bosporus into Asia Minor. A second wave moved eastward around the Caspian and established suzerainty over northern Mesopotamia and the valley of the Zagros Mountains.

Another branch of those warrior horsemen moved eastward, crossed the Oxus and the Bactrian Plain, scaled the passes of the Hindu Kush, crossed the Khyber Pass and entered India. Perhaps there was a seepage of this eastern migration into Persia about the middle of the second millennium, but it would seem more likely that there was a second massive migration of the Indo-Europeans about 1,100 B.C., which established the Persians on the plateau.

Contemporary Persia, today's Iran, is not watered by great rivers like the Nile, the Tigris and the Euphrates which by their yearly floods bring fertility to a country. It "exports" nearly three quarters of its total rainfall in the form of rivers which flow out into other countries. The only substantial river which flows into the country is the Helmand, which has its source in Afghanistan.

By an irony of nature, the modern wealth of Iran, its oil, was a condition of its perennial poverty. In Paleozoic times (say 500,000,000 years ago) seas which then covered the Middle East teemed with the organic life which became the oil deposits of Persia, the Gulf and Arabia. Then, in the convulsions of time, a deposit of clay was laid over the region and acted as the lid which prevented the evaporation of oil which happened elsewhere. Then came the upheaval which, at the end of the Pliocene Age, 600,000 years ago, wrinkled the earth's crust and formed the mountains and the plateau. Those, as has been mentioned, were largely submerged under a second sea in the Pluvial Period. When that sea "dried out" it left its salts to poison most of the central plateau. Because of the clay underlay, such rain as fell and such streams as flowed into this desert could not seep down to form underground springs but merely evaporated and left their own deposits of salt—that salt which one sees glistening like the crystals of an Arctic snow field, conjuring up mirages in the bright sunlight.

The result was country where rural communities were scattered mainly around the alluvial rim of the desert. The people were thus separated and the population was far less dense than in Egypt or Mesopotamia. This is the reason why Persia contained, and still contains, so many nomadic, seminomadic and sedentary tribes which preserve their particularism, their own dialects, manners and customs.

4 *The First Empires*

THE FIRST POLITICAL ORGANIZATION of any coherence on the plateau was that of the Medes who, with the Persians, had derived from those Indo-Europeans speaking the Aryan language which in India was to become Sanskrit.

About 750 B.C. there emerged (according to Herodotus) a Mede named Deioces.

"As the Medes at that time dwelt in scattered villages without any central authority and lawlessness in consequence prevailed throughout the land, Deioces, who was already a man of mark in his own village, applied himself with zeal and earnestness to the practice of justice among his fellows," wrote Herodotus.

He became king and his successors, though temporarily overcome by the Scythians, forged a unity which was to overthrow the Assyrians and make them masters of the entire Middle East. Under Cyrus and Darius the Medes and Persians were to extend an empire which was a synthesis of the ancient civilizations including Mesopotamia, Syria, Egypt, Asia Minor, the Greek cities and islands, and part of India. This was the empire which, in turn, Alexander the Great was to conquer. Cyrus, we might remember, was probably the wisest of all emperors. He respected the values of civilizations finer than his own and left them, in that United Nations of 2,600 years ago, to develop their own ways of life and to follow their own religious beliefs.

The Persians called him "father." The Greeks called him "lawgiver," and the Jews called him "the anointed of the Lord."

The Achaemenian Empire, the Persian civilization, was at its peak during the reign of Darius (521–486 B.C.). To maintain liaison between the different centers of the empire, Darius created a network of roads, enduringly built and elaborately policed. One, the Royal Road from Susa, his capital, to Ephesus in Asia Minor, was nearly 2,000 miles long, with 111 post stations, each with relays of fresh horses for the royal couriers, who could cover the distance in a week. Another road linking Babylon with Egypt was extended into India. These great arterial systems opened up the trade routes between the Occident and the Orient. At the junction of the Kabul and the Indus rivers, Darius built a fleet which under the Greek, Scylax of Caryanda, was given the task of sailing down the Indus and surveying the sea route to Egypt. The fleet took thirty months to fulfill its mission, and the culmination of this naval enterprise was the building of a canal between the Red Sea and the Nile. This, 2,500 years ago, was the forerunner of the Suez Canal.

"The length of it is four days' journey," wrote Herodotus, "and the width such as to admit two triremes being rowed along it abreast."

In 521 B.C. Darius began the glorification of his capital at Susa and the building of Persepolis, which was said to surpass in grandeur the magnificence of Babylon and which was destroyed by fire, by accident or design, during Alexander the Great's conquest of Persia. Darius has left his own account of the building of his palace and of the men and resources, from all over the then known world, which went into its construction. The Baby-

Ionians provided the bricklayers with their skill at making sun-dried brick; the Assyrians contributed the cedars of Lebanon; silver and ebony were brought from Egypt; the stonecutters who wrought the stone were Greeks, and the goldsmiths were Medes and Egyptians.

Weights and measures and a system of coinage were intro-duced throughout the empire. In Mesopotamia banking had been known as early as the second millennium B.C., but under the Persian Empire private banks were established, notably that of "Egibi of Babylon," who has been identified with a Jew, Jacob. This bank floated loans; its capital was invested in house property, farms, slaves, cattle and boats. Current accounts were operated and checks were in use. Indeed, the word "check" is of Persian origin. The bankers financed the digging of canals and sold the water to the farmers.

From this time dates the invention of shoes for beasts of burden, and ships of five hundred tons were being constructed. The empire was self-sufficient in metals; Cyprus produced silver, copper and iron. The Kerman region of Persia yielded gold and silver, and Seistan, on the borders of Afghanistan, supplied tin. Iron came from the Lebanon, the Caucasus and the southern shores of the Black Sea.

5 King Solomon's Mines

DARIUS USED COPPER from "King Solomon's Mines," in the moun-tains near the Gulf of 'Aqaba. These mines had been worked since 1000 B.C., and nearly 3,000 years later they are being operated again by the modern Israelis. One of the most remark-able sights in the southern Negev are the slag heaps of these ancient times—the great expanses of black crusts from the copper smelting. The smelters ingeniously exploited nature; they chose narrow valleys hemmed in by precipices, up which swept the prevailing wind; they used these natural drafts as the bellows for their smelting furnaces.

Under Darius public works were undertaken to increase productive capacities. Irrigation systems were extended and marshes were drained. With an enlightenment rarely known before and largely forgotten afterward, Darius encouraged the cultivation of trees. Although the scientific principles of modern forestry were then unknown, there was apparently selective cutting of timbers and not merely the ravaging of the forests. There is actual evidence of Darius's interest in arboriculture and in the propagation of new species. In a letter to one of his governors he orders him to transplant Eastern plants and trees to Asia Minor and Syria and gives instructions for the transfer of fruit trees from the "further part of Asia." Probably at this stage (with the opening up of the trade routes) Persia began to develop the famous medicinal gardens which culled from the Orient and the Occident plants of pharmaceutical value and, incidentally, gave us the word "drug," derived from the Persian *"drogue,"* which means the demons of disease and also the medicines which appease those demons.

6 *Pockmarks of Progress*

As YOU FLY by modern aircraft across Iran to Teheran, you get a startling impression that the countryside has been heavily bombed. For thousands of square miles the pockmarks of craters pit the landscape with an extravagance which could only be seen on the bombed battlefields of World War II. The craters are in regular lines, suggesting the results of "sticks" of bombs, except that they crisscross and interlace. This strange landscape, however, is no modern manifestation. They provide evidence of a practice which some Persian authorities claim goes back 5,000 years.

This is the *qanaat* system, an ingenious if laborious method of exploiting water. The *qanaats* might be described as horizontal wells. They are underground channels with vertical shafts—those craters which look so peculiar from the air. The shafts are at intervals of about fifty yards and, in construction of the *qanaats*, were used to remove the waste excavated by the miners, but they were also ventilating shafts to enable the miners to breathe. They can be used, of course, as vertical wells to take water from the horizontal well. These subterranean canals are devices for bringing water from the spring sources in the mountains down to the waterless plains. They can be of considerable length. The longest known is near Yezd and stretches underground for thirty miles. Vertically the deepest, at Gunbad in eastern Iran, is 1,000 feet. The average depth is about sixty feet. There are supposed to be about 50,000 *qanaats* in Persia with a capacity varying from half a cubic foot to five cubic feet a second. These *qanaats* bring the water from the well strata in the mountains to the plains where they emerge as open channels which today are called *jubes*, wide gutters which supply the farmers, the villages and the towns, including Teheran, the capital. The system of land and water rights is very complicated but in principle is a kind of joint enterprise between two sets of landlords—the owners of the high, but poor, land which contains the water, and the owners of the good land which needs the water. They usually take the precaution of marrying into each other's families.

In the time of the Achaemenian kings, notably Darius, the *qanaat* system was encouraged and extended as a form of public utility. The *qanaat* would seem to have been an original Persian invention. The need for some such device is obvious when we think back to the earliest settlers first cultivating the alluvial lands round the desert rim, with the clay pan underneath preventing the mountain waters from creating natural springs in the plain. They were also wise enough, those primitive hydrologists, to recognize the loss of water by evaporation and the need for keeping it, on tap as it were, underground.

Wherever the Persians went as their empire extended, they introduced the *qanaats*. They are to be found in Baluchistan, in North India, in Afghanistan, in Syria, in Cyprus, in the Negev and in Egypt. The *foggara* principle in Tunisia and Algeria is similar but may have had an independent origin.

A feature of the mining of these *qanaats* is the present-day use of a compass which gives the *gafeer*—the leading miner—his direction underground. This primitive compass is produced by rubbing an iron needle with a lodestone and supporting it on a pivot on something which will float so that the magnetic point will turn north. This raises the long-debated question of the place of origin of the compass. Thales, the Greek (about 600 B.C.), knew that iron ores, such as were found in Asia Minor near Magnesia (hence "magnetic"), could attract particles of iron. There is little doubt, however, that in very ancient times the Chinese had developed the pivoted magnet. The discovery would appear to have been made as a result of "geomantic divination," the practice of throwing objects on a board and foretelling the future from the way they lay. The use of the compass in the *qanaat* is so important to the miner in giving him his bearings underground, on a fixed point in the hills, that one wonders whether the first *qanaats* and the first compasses did not go together, making both very old indeed. Of course, the lodestone may have come into Persia from China.

Another important feature of the Persian water economy is what we still call the "Persian wheel." This is the wheel with the continuous chain of buckets which is still widely used in water lifting for irrigation. It is held to be likely that this method was introduced during the Achaemenian Empire.

The riches of the Persian Empire, derived from its tributary peoples and from its craftsmen of so many different cultures, were prodigious. Alexander the Great is said to have employed 20,000 mules and 5,000 camels to transport the treasures of Persepolis before it was destroyed, and with its destruction departed the greatness that was Persia.

Persia and its plateau have been deliberately chosen for this opening study of the ancient civilizations because, as a country, it is a watershed of the Eastern and Western cultures, religions and knowledge. And its development from the hunting group to empire was characteristic of the other civilizations with which it was contemporary. Each of these other cultures, however, has examples and experience of relevance to the problems of our modern times.

7 Before the Flood

LONG BEFORE Abraham left Ur to become the Biblical patriarch of a pastoral people, there existed in Sumeria a culture with delicately painted pottery. It had settled and developed on the rich alluvial silt brought down by the Euphrates.

Most authorities would now agree that the story of the Flood (in Genesis) was based on a Sumerian legend of which the oldest written versions date from at least 2000 B.C. The reality of the Flood was established in 1929 by Sir Leonard Woolley. He was excavating the graves of the kings at Ur, and he was satisfied that the civilization they represented was so far advanced that it must have had a long past behind it. He sank his shafts through one layer of archeological debris after another until he reached clean clay, uniform throughout and with a consistent texture which showed that it had been laid there by water. His expert diggers insisted that this was the bottom of everything—the river silt on which the original settlement had been founded. But Woolley made an important observation. He noticed that the level of the clay was too high above the original marsh. So he set them digging again and they cut through eight feet of clay, to find themselves in a civilization older than the one they had been investigating. This was Ur, of an older epoch, which had been drowned in the Flood, which had been overwhelmed by the waters as suddenly and as completely as Herculaneum had been engulfed by the volcanic eruption of Vesuvius. The Flood must have been a mighty one since it was capable of depositing eight feet of clay—and the proof was in the clay itself, which was not stratified as it would have been if it had been the sediment of a succession of floods. The date of the Flood could not have been later than 2700 B.C.

As we have seen, in dealing with Persia, painted pottery was already appearing there about 4000 B.C. Whether the culture at Ur in the plains had been influenced by the people of the plateau is a matter of question. But it is apparent that in the culture which developed on the clay burying the original Ur different influences were at work. In the Bible it says, "And it came to pass that as they journeyed from the East they came upon a plain in the land of Shinar, and they dwelt there." (Shinar was the name for Babylonia.) This would be consistent with a movement from India of an advanced people who brought with them knowledge of agriculture, metalworking, the potter's wheel and a script.

This deduction does not simplify, but only complicates, the problem of where city cultures first developed. It is common ground that they grew up in the valleys of the Nile, the Tigris and Euphrates, the Indus, the Oxus, the Yangtze and the Yellow River. But whether they developed independently in each region or whether by diffusion—by the migration of people and knowledge—is a question which cannot be answered with accuracy or even with approximation. (When we consider the technological changes wrought in Japan in one century of contact with the industrial world, we can see how quickly knowledge can be adopted and adapted.)

It would appear, however, that while predynastic Egyptians were still working with flints, the Sumerians, in Mesopotamia, had already advanced to the use of fine metals and delicate art work which come from long-established craft traditions.

8 *The Pattern of City Culture*

THE PATTERN of the city culture can be fairly logically determined. In the evolution of society the hunting group became the settled cultivator. The crops sown to feed Man and his domesticated beasts provided a regular food supply. In Mesopotamia, according to Herodotus, the sown wheat yielded two hundredfold to the sower, who could get two harvests a year from his grainfields as well as good fodder for his sheep. The cultivated lands along the rivers, with rich silt soils and constant sunshine, produced not only subsistence for the tillers but a surplus. This surplus became the basic commodity of trade. The tiller could use it to secure his special needs—better tools than he could make himself, better pots, better fabrics and luxuries which gradually became necessities.

These were custom-made by specialists—craftworkers—and they in turn produced their surpluses. They could trade their manufactures not only within the community but with other communities. The exchange of goods obviously included the exchange of ideas, which the craftsmen in the various communities would adapt for the improvement of their own skills. It was an accelerating process.

104

The fears which beset primitive peoples—the cavemen cowering from the lightning—became the more sophisticated superstitions of fears, discussed and shared, within the settled community. There were functional superstitions as well. The tiller had his own observations of the rhythm of nature, of germination and of the seasons, but there were natural circumstances which were outside his control and he needed means of measurement and of prediction. The coincidence of events with the appearance of identifiable stars in the heavens, or the phases of the moon, or the behavior of the sun, created a basis for an almanac. Peasant lore, while shrewd, is not always accurate or consistent. But as communities developed, observation and interpretation of events became a specialized function.

Astronomy was one of the earliest of the sciences. It was the recognition and codification of the uniformities in nature. The peasant, as he stands at the door of his hut, sees the sun rising in different positions at different times of the year, but always on the one horizon. He sees it set, but always on the opposite horizon, and so he recognizes the eastern rising and the western setting. Given any fixed point of reference—a pillar of rock, a tree or a pole—he notices the shadows which move round it, longer in the morning and the evening, shortest when the sun is highest in the heavens at noon. He acquires a sense of timekeeping because the shortest shadow conveniently divides his working day into morning and afternoon, while the heat of the noonday sun emphasizes the division.

In the wide-open spaces, before streets and alleys narrowed the vision of the sky, the pageantry of the stars followed a consistent pattern in which the star clusters, the constellations, to which people gave symbolic names, would change their positions as the night progressed, just as the solitary sun did in the course of the day. In the Northern Hemisphere they would notice that one star, the polestar, would always be seen above the same point on the horizon, in the same place at sunset and at sunrise. They would notice that, as the night passed, the other stars revolved about and above the polestar from

Primitive gnomon used by Borneo tribesmen to determine the rice-planting season

east to west, and the signal of midnight would be when a cluster, rising at sunset on the eastern horizon and setting at sunrise on the western horizon, was directly above the polestar. So to the "shadow clock" of the daytime they could add the "star clock" of the night. The regularizing of this timekeeping, in terms of the day, the month and the year, became a question of recording.

9 The Making of the Priesthood

IN THE COURSE of time the record keepers, who acquired the ability to predict, became priests. They had an insight which gave them a foresight—a collection of scientific facts which the working community, preoccupied with their own labors, would not possess. To ensure the continuity of the records, there had to be some sort of succession, and so the elements of priesthood developed—a group of people set aside, generation after generation, with special privileges to ensure them leisure of thought, maintained by the products of the rest of the group.

Complete records extending over 360 years were discovered at Ur. These show the building up of information which was the basis of an advanced astronomy 5,000 years ago—or about the time when Bishop Usher would have us believe the earth was created. They show that the Chaldean astronomers, without the help of precision instruments now at our disposal, had worked out the length of the year as 365 days, 6 hours, 15 minutes and 41 seconds—only 26 minutes and 26 seconds too long. That was valuable functional knowledge which could be socially useful, but they had also discovered the cycle which they called the saros. This was the recurrence of the eclipse of the sun. They had discovered from the recorded observations of generations of priests that there were incidents in time when the earth, the moon and the sun were in line and that precisely 18 years and 11⅓ days later they would, to the observer in the same position, be in line again. So the Chaldeans could predict to the year, the day and the hour the moment when the sun would be eclipsed. This was an important scientific fact, but it did not tell people when to arrange their mealtimes or to sow their crops or to prepare for the lambing. It did, however, with many other astronomical titbits, give the astronomer-priests a power over their fellow citizens. One can imagine the consternation of the people of Ur when, on the day and at the hour and the instant which the priest had predicted, he was able to blot out the sun.

10 *From Measurement to Mysticism*

FROM THE FACTUAL ORIGINS of astronomy came the mystical lore of astrology. The priests created the gods with whom only they were on speaking terms. From being merely the ledger clerks of events, obligingly supported by the labors of the manual workers, they became a power in the city societies which were growing up. It suited them to encourage the belief that nature could be bought off with bribes, provided that they were the intermediaries.

(Somewhere about this time in Egypt the priestly ledger clerks developed the "Nilometer." The whole life of the settlers in the Nile Valley depended on the rise and fall of the river. By making an underground channel from the river, the priests could keep accurate records from their water gauges which, over a period of years, gave them the means of predicting not only seasonal but cyclical changes. This apparent uncanny power was the basis for encouraging superstition, which became religion.)

As the priests' power increased, so did the physical manifestations of their authority. The first, and most substantial, structure in the settlements that grew into cities was the shrine. For measurement one always needed a fixed point. The shrine, once established, provided that observational base. As the cities grew, the shrines were reconstructed on a scale of ever-increasing grandeur but aways on the same hallowed site. So the foundations of the superimposed temples eventually con-

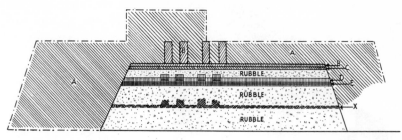

Diagrammatic section through a tell *at Erech, Mesopotamia. The lowest level* x *is the supposed foundation of the first temple built on this site. Levels* D *and* E *indicate foundations of two later temples.* C *shows a still more recent temple platform. At* B *are the ruins of the White Temple and its walls. Later still these were encased in the brickwork* A.

stituted a mount, or tell. Such a tell at Erech in Lower Mesopotamia (Sumeria) has revealed a succession of six temples, each built on top of the other.

Attached to such temples were granaries and storehouses which held the free-will offerings of the cultivators, and there were also the libraries, to which the cultivators certainly would have no access and which contained the temple records which gave the priests their vested authority. It is evident from these records that the Sumerian farmers firmly believed that they were the servants of the deities who had created and owned the soil they tilled. To buy the favor of these deities they paid tribute from the produce of their labor. These revenues-in-kind were used not only to feast the invisible gods (who had apparently a great appetite for beer) but to support the ever-growing priesthood and the army of specialized artisans who provided the equipment of the temple.

A part of the revenue-in-kind was always apportioned for export—commodities of trade which brought back to the temple foreign delicacies for the enjoyment of the priests and precious stones and ornaments for the adornment of the temple. In this way the temples of each Sumerian city became repositories and trading centers for the increasing surplus produced by the city lands, which were really temple estates, since the sovereignty of

Reconstruction of a temple at Eridu, Mesopotamia (fourth millennium B.C.)

the gods was acknowledged by the cultivators. Subject to the gods, the Sumerian land was communally owned and parceled out among the gods' people, to be worked as individual farms. But it is obvious in the earliest decipherable records that the higher temple officials owned, and could pass on to their heirs, much larger plots of the temple land than their lay brethren.

From the growth of the successive temples (as revealed by archeological excavation) it is possible to measure the growth and the wealth of the settled population. The Mesopotamian village by 3000 B.C. had grown into a city averaging 8,000 to 12,000 inhabitants. Most of the citizens were still actively engaged in farming, stockbreeding or fishing. They were supporting an urban population which already included a super-structure of priests, administrators, clerks, and specialist craftsmen. The revenues of the temples had already reached the point where their administration required not only a staff of manager and accountants but some consistent means of recording—a cipher—which the members of the temple corporation could understand. These symbols of receipts and expenditures became the origin of writing, and writing some authorities might regard as the transition from barbarism to civilization.

11 *From Priest-King to Warrior-King*

WITH THE GROWTH of the priestly hierarchy the emergence of the priest-king was inevitable. Either by his learning or by his acquisition of inherited temple lands an individual was bound, at some stage, to exercise authority over his fellows. He would reinforce that authority by identifying himself with a god and become the living embodiment of a deity to which the citizens already acknowledged allegiance.

And as the cities grew and their external trade increased, the hostility which a nomadic people felt toward the tillers turned to an envy and a predatory urge. The cities, and the accessible wealth which they represented, were likely to be raided by marauders and had to have the means to defend themselves. So, in addition to city walls, they had to have soldiers to guard them. Soldiers need officers; officers become generals; generals become rulers; "defense" becomes "aggression," and any pretext is sufficient for aggrandizement by conquest.

There was, however, another encouragement toward wars of conquest: the need for slaves. The peasant and the soil were now supporting a social superstructure as massive as the ziggurats which had been built over the first modest shrines—the craftsmen, the priesthood, the taxgatherers, the dynastic households, the tradesmen, the money-changers and the soldiers.

The produce of the soil had to be increased to satisfy the stomachs and the avarice of those who no longer worked the land. The willing tithepayer of the primitive temple, paying his dues for the land the gods had made and the crops they had given him, had now become the serf of a feudal system, but the prisoner of war could, in turn, become his slave.

Slaves were needed for the building of the cities. They were the brickmakers and, under the direction of the craftsmen-architects, they were the builders of structures like the ziggurat at Ur which, over the original shrine site, became a vast structure of staged towers which measured 234 feet by 185½ feet at its base and was 84½ high. (Such ziggurats were the "High Altars"—man-made mountains in the alluvial plains. The Tower of Babel was one, and it is clear from the Bible that prisoners of war of so many nationalities were used in its construction that there was a "confusion of tongues.") Slave labor was needed for the building of the city walls to protect the city and its wealth; the one at Nineveh is seventy feet thick.

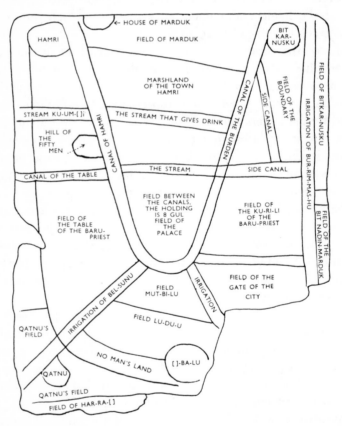

Map of fields and canals near Nippur, 1300 B.C.

Among the public works for which slaves were most needed was the construction of water channels. Once, however, irrigation systems were constructed, then, as now, competition for water rights led to violent conflicts. (We have only to remind ourselves that the word "rivalry" comes from the Latin *rivus*—meaning "a stream"—to realize that the struggle for water has always been a cause of feuding.) It called for an overlord who would not only make himself responsible for the building of canals to supply a wide area but would provide the labor force to maintain them, the laws to regulate them and the soldiers to protect them. Some of the earliest wars between the cities of Mesopotamia arose from the quarrels over competing canal systems. The systematic ruin of an irrigation system was one of the methods of punishing a defeated enemy.

When Sennacherib of Assyria vented his wrath on Babylon, he pulled down the temples and palaces and deliberately choked the canals with the debris.

Then he boasted: "Through the midst of that city I dug canals; I flooded the site with water . . . so that in days to come the place of that city, its temples and gods shall not be remembered, I completely blotted it out with flood water."

His son, Esarhaddon (681–669 B.C.), repaired the damage. "I mobilized all the artisans of Babylonia, and they cut down the reeds and the cane-breaks which throved mightily in the midst of the city. The waters of the Euphrates I dammed. I shut them off from the midst of the city, and into their former channels I directed them."

12 *Irrigation—the First Public Utility*

LONG BEFORE THAT—1,000 years, in fact—Hammurabi had included in his code of laws ordinances on irrigation, such as, "If a man opens his canal for irrigation and neglects it and the waters spoil a neighbor's field, he shall measure out unto him grain in proportion to the neighbor's field."

Irrigation was relatively simple in Lower Mesopotamia. The Euphrates, slower and more manageable than the Tigris, carries only half its volume of water and lies higher than the other river in its middle deltaic reaches. This ensures a gravitational flow between the two rivers, but where the water could not be spread by the inundation of low ground, when it was needed on higher ground, methods of lifting it had to be invented.

The simplest way of lifting water is in the hollow of the hand or, better still, in the scoop of two hands, and this system was "mechanized" by the making of a bigger "hand" in the shape of a leather bag or a wooden scoop, and the lift of the arm was also mechanically exaggerated. One of the earliest devices was a horizontal pole supported on two uprights so that the operator could work more effectively by hauling downward instead of upward. This tackle was greatly improved by the addition of a system of pulleys. The modern Arab word for pulley is found in a tablet of the fifteenth century B.C. from Alalakh, in Syria. The earliest pulley wheel yet discovered in Egypt is of the Roman period.

Another method used, and still surviving, is the swipe or shaduf. Two pillars about five feet high are set less than a yard apart. A horizontal beam is fixed between them. On this is pivoted a pole, on one end of which a bucket is suspended, while on the other end a weight is fixed as a counterpoise. The operator pulls down the bucket to fill it from the river or canal and the counterpoise lifts it so that he can tip the bucket into an irrigation trough. By this method water can be lifted six feet or more. A more elaborate system can lift it higher, by arranging the shadufs on terraces one above the other. The first operator lifts the water from the canal and tips it into a trough on a higher level, from which the next operator lifts it even higher. This system is pictured in the records of 700 B.C., but the single shaduf appears on a cylinder seal of about 2400– 2200 B.C. There is evidence of the use of chain buckets around 600 B.C. in Babylon. There was also the *kered*, a skin bucket hoisted by animal power, the animal walking down an inclined ramp.

As long as there is a river handy the problem of water is fairly easily solved. That was why intensive agriculture developed in the river valleys. But people's activities often carried them away from the rivers and into areas of scant rainfall, where perennial streams were lacking. Then any settlement had to be concentrated around an oasis well, a fertile plot in the barren desert.

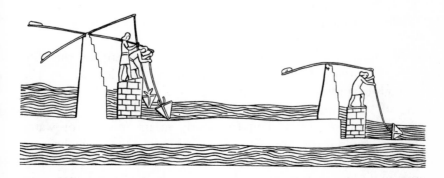

Assyrians raising water from the river by shaduf. Three men operate a double lift. The shadufs, on mud uprights, stand at two levels on the river bank, and in front of each a brick platform is built out into the river for the men who fill and empty the buckets. From the palace of Sennacherib at Nineveh, Mesopotamia (seventh century B.C.)

13 Water from the Rocks

WATER may be found where a porous rock resting upon impermeable strata captures sufficient rain and is near enough to the surface. In any depression where the impermeable rock outcrops at the surface a spring will emerge. The quantity of subsoil water will give rise to surface springs on level ground or maintain a level of water in a well sunk in the porous layer.

The method chosen by early Man for finding underground water is still employed by the nomadic Bedouin today. He looks for it in the wadi bed—the dried-up river channel. There the brief spate of the wadi has seeped down nearer to the water table (where it exists). Or he will look for it where he finds unexpected vegetation of a type which suggests that its roots are finding water reasonably near the surface. A hole is made with hoes or digging sticks. The loosened earth is piled around the hole to form a parapet to protect the well from animals or wind-blown sand. The water seeker just digs until he reaches it. If it is a good source, then the well will be lined, the wellhead made permanent, and some kind of lifting tackle erected over it.

So much for the nomad, but the development of the city cultures involved activities which could not depend on the fortuitous finding of water. The mining of metals and the quarrying of stone meant providing water for considerable bodies of men in remote places. This frequently meant mining for water before mining for ore. Circumstances might compel them to go through solid rock without the advantages of modern drilling methods. This they would do by heating the rocks and quenching them so that they cracked and could be manhandled. The quenching meant having water in advance, and establishing a mining settlement in this way must have presented considerable problems of logistics.

Few wells in the Middle East and North Africa are very deep. In the wadis water can usually be reached at twelve to fifteen feet. The shallow wells of the Libyan oasis may yield up to eight gallons a minute. When greater quantities are needed for irrigation or a large population, it is necessary to dig much deeper through rock to tap the water-bearing strata beneath. The wells of ancient Palmyra went down 250 feet—a remarkable feat of engineering.

In some places a hydrostatic pressure produces artesian wells where the water gushes spontaneously up and out of the boring. Such artesian wells, bringing water from depth, can provide hundreds of gallons a minute. In Egypt the sinking of artesian wells may date back as early as 2000 B.C. It may have originated in the oasis of Daklah, where artesian water is found at about 100 feet depth, and the experience there was probably transferred to the oasis of El Kharga, where the water is at 260 feet. The ancient method of digging artesian wells probably never varied through all the thousands of years until modern well-boring machinery was introduced. An open shaft was dug as deep as the surface water would allow. This surface water had to be bypassed, so the sides were shored up with timber. In the center a wooden tube was placed upright. This would be a hollowed tree trunk or built of acacia wood in curved sections. Like modern tube wells, they were sunk in succession and the joints sealed and made watertight. The space between the shaft and the side of the pit was filled in and packed tightly. Within the shaft drilling was then started with metal rods driven into the rock by percussion. This was a laborious process, with the debris to be removed and hard rock to be encountered. The boring would take months, if not years, and if the lining collapsed or cracked, everything would have to start again.

14 Dams to Check the Water

THE IDEA of dams for holding water on the surface would be fairly self-evident in a riverine community. This was particularly true in ancient Egypt. The Nile rises and falls at predictable periods. In the beginning of July the river is greenish with scum from equatorial waters. About a fortnight later muddy silt begins to arrive, with a redness which caused it to be attributed to the blood of Osiris, the "giver of life." The rising waters flow over the low-lying lands and the floods continue until September. By the end of October the river has retreated again into its bed, and by the end of May the river is a shrunken stream, surviving only from the constant flow of the White Nile tributary.

In ancient times the valley people moved to higher ground as the floods rose and then returned as the river subsided, to gather the edible seeds of the wild grasses or, later, to raise plants themselves. Then, with more enterprise, they would build retaining walls, to keep the water out, or in, in an enclosed area.

Out of this grew the Pharaohic system of basin irrigation. This consisted of throwing up earthen banks parallel to the river and then crisscrossing the valley plain with other banks to produce a checkerboard pattern. The sections might be anything from 1,000 acres to 40,000 acres in extent. The dikes were broken to admit the floodwaters to a depth of three to six feet and the gap was then closed. After about a month, when the ground was thoroughly saturated, another dike would be breached to allow the surplus water to drain off to permit the plowing and sowing. This drainage required canals, and once the significance of those was realized, it was a modest step in hydraulic engineering to use those channels as a means of carrying water further afield.

This system of basin irrigation, adapted to the more or less regular habits of the Nile (in contrast to the erratic habits of the Tigris or the Euphrates), had manifest advantages. Once the land had been flush-flooded, no further irrigation was needed for the wheat or barley or flax. Manuring was unnecessary, because the silt deposited by the floods brought its own organic fertilizers all the way from the equatorial hinterland and also the phosphates which the river had leached out of the upper reaches.

To Menes, the legendary first of the Pharaohs, is ascribed the first damming of the Nile to control the floodwaters. One of the attributes of the Pharaohs (aided and abetted by the priests and the Nilometers, which gave quite rational measurements, and thus predictions, of the rise and fall of the river) was that they had supernatural liaisons with the gods who controlled the river and therefore the lives of the people. Their temporal attribute was that they were the patrons of the public works which built the dikes and dug the master canals. In 2000 B.C. King Amenemhet I boasted, "I grew corn. I loved Neper, the grain god. In every valley the Nile greeted me. None hungered nor thirsted during my reign."

The deputies of the Pharaohs, the district governors, had as their chief title 4,500 years ago, "The Diggers of Canals." On them fell the duty not only of creating the canal system but of organizing patrols of all the dikes when the river reached its flood heights and of mobilizing aid when disaster occurred.

The story of Joseph and the Seven Fat Years and the Seven Lean Years is the account of a circumstance which has recurred all through the thousands of years of Nile history—the cyclical droughts, which are just as serious as the cyclical floods, like the one recorded at Luxor. There, about 867 B.C., "the flood [as a temple inscription records] rose in this whole land. The entire valley was as a sea. No dikes could withstand the fury of the waters. All the people were like water birds or the swimmers in a torrent. The temples of Thebes were like marshes."

The Nilometers, spaced up the valley, gave continuous recordings, and the priestly records provided the necessary comparison. Thus the river priests and their masters could have warning from a succession of twenty sites of the approach of the floods and gauge from their statistical records any abnormality. The archives of Nile records for the 1,300 years from the Arab conquest to the present day show that the silt deposited in the Nile Valley has raised the land by over eight feet.

In the Vatican today is a Greek statue of the Nile god holding a horn of abundance, surrounded by sixteen children, each one cubit high. A rise of sixteen cubits of the Nile waters at Memphis meant assured prosperity for any season.

15 *Storage Cisterns*

DAMS TO STORE WATER as well as to control it were another self-evident development, but the early people would learn the hard way that an open reservoir loses enormous quantities of water by evaporation under the fierce heat of the sun. That is why we should acknowledge and admire the ingenuity of those who, with no rivers to replenish their water supplies, invented the rock cisterns, the underground reservoirs of the desert.

Scattered over the Arabian Peninsula cement-lined tanks and stone cisterns of unmeasured antiquity are to be found. At arid Aden there are fifty great cisterns with a capacity of over thirty million gallons. Most of them may date only from about 1,400 years ago, but they are almost certainly the extension of a system of much greater antiquity. In Palestine stone cisterns have pitted the hillsides since Biblical times. To overcome evaporation, which not only meant a loss of water but an accretion of salt, the ancients hollowed out sunken caverns in the mountains or exploited natural subterranean reservoirs such as are found in the volcanic district of Hauran and in the fissured basalts of Transjordan. In the Negev, the desert in the south of Palestine, are to be found rock cisterns of Roman origin, such as are also found throughout North Africa, but also others which were constructed by the Nabataeans.

The Nabataeans were the pre-Semitic desert people of Arabia who came into the deserts to the north of the Gulf of 'Aqaba about 500 years B.C. They were the great rock masons of the ancient world who carved a city out of the cliffs at Petra and spread garrison cities throughout the desert where they lived, literally, in the hills. Apart from their dwelling caves and their tomb caves, they constructed reservoirs inside the hills. The cisterns were remarkable not only for their size—a tribute to their miners, masons and engineers—but for their ingenuity. The lessons which they taught to the Romans we can learn with profit today. (See also pp. 256–57).

After my desert journey through North Africa and the Middle East I learned to guess from the configuration of the hills where such cisterns were likely to be found. Once in the region of Subetta, another Negev city, Byzantine in the character of its present ruins but Nabataean in origin, I looked at a hill landscape. I wagered the desert expert who was with me that in a certain dip in the hills we would find a cistern. He consulted his charts but could find no evidence. We drove to the spot and there we found a cistern which had been broken open from the surface by the Egyptian soldiers during their campaign against the Israelis.

In Egypt, at Burg-el-Arab, I visited what had been an underground battle headquarters during the El Alamein campaign. The desert was perfect camouflage, and without a guide I could never have found the entrance. Scorpions, with their powerful pincers and poisonous sting, had discovered the cool comforts of the abandoned H.Q. and added a hazard to the visit. Underground there were twelve rooms, including a big War Room where the operations had once been planned. It was a magnificent piece of engineering and a credit to the military engineers and

121

to modern concrete. But, separated by a mile of desert and by nearly 2,000 years, there was another underground shelter. It was a water cistern dating from the Romans but similar in principle to those of the Nabataeans. It was not my idea of a cistern at all. It was a great underground cavern with vaulted halls and branching galleries. Into it from every direction fed the runlets bringing the water from the surrounding hills, which had been deliberately stripped down to bedrock. This cistern was one of many hundreds of Roman cisterns in the Egyptian desert. It, like many others, has been restored, and the nomads draw their water ration from it.

Water stored in this way, not just for months but for years, is not very fresh. It is, however, very lively; it teems with life. Nothing would have induced me to drink it after having seen at close quarters a scum of red organisms and swarms of what looked like pink tadpoles which covered the surface like a living rust. The nomads, however, are not quite so particular; they just strain off the wildlife through muslin.

16 *Stone Aqueducts*

THE STEP from earthwork canals to aqueducts was a logical one, but it involved a big advance in technology. The ancients learned the hard way that soil and rocks are porous and that the loss through seepage and evaporation is considerable. (Conversely, they discovered that unglazed pottery, with its pores, like those of the skin, could keep liquids cool by evaporation.) Sennacherib (705–681 B.C.) constructed a stone canal to bring fresh water to Nineveh from Bavian in the northern foothills, a distance of over fifty miles. This canal was, at some points, over sixty feet wide. At one place, where the canal had to cross a wide valley, a stone aqueduct was constructed, involving over 2,000,000 blocks, each of them 20x20x24 inches, and it was carried on five pointed arches across the bed of a wide stream.

The waterproofing of the canal bed was technically ingenious, even by modern standards. On an inch and a half of bitumen its builders floated a lining of concrete fifteen inches thick. The concrete was an excellent mixture of lime, sand and broken limestone. It is also clear, from the excavations of this aqueduct, that the canal bed was used for the transportation of stone from the quarries at the Bavian end. As each section of the canal was laid, it became the carefully graded pavement by which the stone blocks were hauled on wheels or on sleds or rollers. The chippings show that the masonwork of the 2,000,000 blocks was done on the site.

17 *The Fires of the Gods*

BITUMEN was used as a building material from remotest antiquity in Mesopotamia (but not in ancient Egypt until the Ptolemaic period). This early exploitation of the oil reserves which have figured so prominently in our twentieth-century politics was bound up originally with mysticism. The Babylonian word for naphtha (which we borrowed directly from the Greeks) was *naptu*, which was used in temple texts as early as 2000 B.C. It referred to prophecies based on the manifestations of oil from the ground. If fired by lightning, these flares of natural gas, or oil fractions, must have had an awe-inspiring effect. Even the escape of gas through the fissures could be terrifying, as King Tukulti-Ninurta recorded: "I camped at a place where the voice of the gods issued from the rocks." That was in 885 B.C.

The ancient Sumerians considered the world to be a vast raft floating on a sea in which the gods lived and through which they generously ejected the springs of water and, in the oil regions, bitumen and natural gas. They knew bitumen both as rock asphalt (a word which lingers from Sumerian times) and as a liquid. The King of Lagash (about 4,200 years ago) was obtaining it in large quantities from the mountains. The rock asphalt was heated in sieves and the bitumen oozed out. Hard bitumen is still found in large open "lakes" to the west of Hit, about ninety miles from Baghdad. It can be quarried, but it is also found in liquid form coming out of springs along with sulphurous water. This liquid asphalt oozing into the river forms a floating "carpet" which the ancients used to drag ashore.

The bitumen was used in building operations as a mastic. It was melted and mixed with fillers—sand, loam, lime, chopped reeds and straw—which prevented it from oozing out from between the stones when it was used as a sort of mortar. It was also used as a paint or preservative.

18 *Colossi and Pyramids*

WHEN ONE wanted, as Sennacherib did, to move great blocks of stones, not only to provide the masonry for his canals, but to transport a colossus for Nineveh, one needed haulage materials. This meant ropes. The manufacture of ropes was of the greatest importance in the ancient empires because the hauling had to be done by slaves and only a long rope could accommodate sufficient manpower. In the British Museum there is a bas-relief of haulage in Sennacherib's time which shows the block of stone for his "Bull Colossus" being dragged along on a sledge and being edged forward on rollers by men hauling on ropes at least two and a half inches thick. The other method of hauling such blocks was undoubtedly by rafts and river barges.

Even in the age of the great skyscrapers and bridges flung across San Francisco Harbor and Sydney Harbor and giant hydroelectric dams—yes, and mountains carved in the images of American statesmen—we still cannot repress an admiration for those who, without the benefit of machinery, quarried, cut, transported and carved the great blocks of stone which characterize so much of the imperial splendors of Middle Eastern and other countries.

It seems an innate urge in men when they reach a certain stage of development to express themselves in grandiose masonry. It is not confined to Mesopotamia or to the splendors that are Egypt or Greece or Rome, or even India. We find the same sort of expression in the massive monoliths of Easter Island and, of course, the British Stonehenge.

In the old Kingdom of Egypt, between 2700 and 2200 B.C., the first substantial stone buildings began to appear. The earliest impressive stone structure, the Step Pyramid of Zoser at Saqqara, shows an extraordinarily highly developed skill in masonry which indicates quite a long tradition in the craft. This massive structure, rising to a height of 204 feet, has an interesting collateral history. It was designed for the king by his architect, Imhotep, but through the centuries the Egyptians esteemed Imhotep not as a pyramid builder but as a doctor. His name signified "He who cometh in peace." He was deified as a god of healing and was later identified by the Greeks with their own god of healing, Aesculapius. In that pyramid the masonry was in small blocks, about the size of the bricks with which they had experience and which could be handled without mechanical devices.

Many ancient quarries worked by the Egyptian kings have been located and have shown the ways in which the stone was obtained. These depended on whether it was an open quarry or whether rocks were extracted underground. When it was found that the best stones were deep down, tunnels several hundred yards long were cut through to reach the required stratum.

Unfinished obelisk at Aswan, Egypt

At Aswan a giant obelisk, still unremoved from its bed, has been discovered. This giant block is over 150 feet long and weighs about 1,200 tons (in contrast with Cleopatra's Needle in London, which is about eighty feet high and weighs 200 tons). It had been abandoned in the quarry, obviously because of cracks. The obelisk was shaped and a trench around it was formed by pounding the granite with dolerite balls, very hard stones which were applied with rammers. It has been calculated that this process would take at least eight months. The quarry shows that after the trench was completed the technique was to under-cut the block. One of the methods which was employed in that period (although not in this particular case) was to drive in wooden wedges and then to wet them so that they expanded and rived the stone. There is also evidence that limestone blocks were cut with saws—copper blades fed with sand or set with emery teeth. For the shaping of the blocks dolerite, quartzite, schist, and green breccia were used.

The erection of these monster blocks still intimidates the imagination because the capstan or pulley was unknown and there is no evidence of wheeled vehicles before the New Kingdom, about 1546 B.C. The only devices that they had were levers, sledges, rollers and a method of exerting tension by twisting ropes together. Instead of scaffolding, earth ramps were built, up which the blocks were rolled or drawn toward the bed. As the wall of a building, or the pyramid, rose, the correct alignment was fixed at the joints and the remainder of the blocks were left in the rough. The final masonry on the face was completed from the top downward as the earth ramp was gradually removed.

19 *Not Forgetting Stonehenge*

A METHOD by which these giant pillars and blocks could be sunk in their foundations has been suggested by the study of Stonehenge. Here in the middle of Salisbury Plain, about seven miles north of Salisbury, is a chalk plateau. And here there is evidence of two different sun temples. The second, called Stonehenge Two, still remains in its form of the standing stones.

Two kinds of stone were used in the building of Stonehenge Two. One, sarsen, is a hard sandstone found about eighteen miles away, but the other is known as "blue stone," and that could only have come from the mountains of Pembrokeshire, 150 miles away. The outer circle and the horseshoe of standing

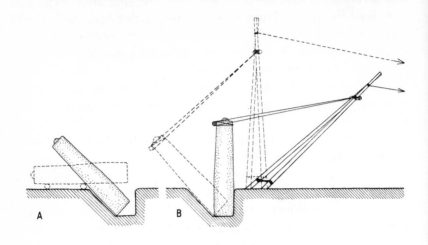

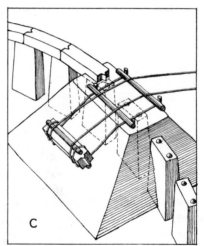

Stonehenge: possible methods of erection

stones are of sarsen, while the small upright stones are blue stones. Stonehenge Two must have consisted of a continuous circle of sarsen uprights with stones laid horizontally along them. The average weight of the sarsen uprights is about twenty-six tons, but some of them weigh as much as forty tons. This would not preclude the carrying of these stones from their quarry in the Marlborough Downs by rollers and levers. The smaller blue stones may have come by a land-sea route from the Pembrokeshire Hills, in the first instance to what is now the port of Milford Haven, and then along the coast to the Avon. The stones could have been shipped up the Avon and its tributary, the Frome, and then would have been manhandled for about ten miles to the headwaters of another river and down to the Wiltshire Avon.

The erection is conceived to have been achieved by making the pit with a vertical side and a sloping side. The giant stone would be rolled to the edge of the pit so that it would tip down the sloping side and be pulled into position by a simple device of having a pair of shear legs by which, it is estimated, 180 men could pull into position a twenty-ton stone pillar. The lintels could have been pulled up a ramp which was erected to the height of the vertical pillars. Since they had a tongue-and-groove joint, the lintels would be moved sideways and by the removal of the material underneath would drop into the pinholes which would hold them in position.

As Thor Heyerdahl has shown on his Aku-Aku expedition, a similar technique would explain how the giant stone carvings on Easter Island were erected. It is a matter of interest that people with obviously no cultural connections should have arrived at similar techniques for what would seem to be an excessive human effort for quite nonutilitarian purposes.

20 *Boasting in Stone*

THIS VAUNTING in stone which expressed itself among the Incas, the Aztecs, the Hindus, the Chinese, the Polynesians, the Babylonians, the Egyptians and the Druids of Britain is a strange urge of the human spirit. It is as though men, in their own generation, recognized their own impermanence and, contrariwise, the durability of the stones and tried to achieve immortality as kings or as cultures by an almost superhuman effort of construction.

What impressed me at Monte Alban, in Oaxaca in Mexico, was the intemperance of human vanity. There in the diggings you can see successions of terraces—like the terraces of a sports arena. Obviously each new priestly order wanted to raise its temples higher than its predecessor's and did so by building on and over the terraces, like a child playing with building bricks. But in the process they buried the carvings which were there already. They were obliterating their predecessors while building upon their work.

What we know and see of the ancient civilizations is their masonic grandeur, but it is necessary to remind ourselves that their foundations were in alluvial silt—in the soil that yielded the food and on the tillers that produced that food. The whole of the vast superstructure derived from the exploitation of the soil.

Let us briefly recapitulate:

By better husbandry, the tiller produced the surpluses which enabled him to employ others more skilled than he to make him better tools.

So the craftsman evolved and with him the auxiliaries such as miners to get him his metals.

On the surplus from the land he supported the priests, who became, as well as the mystics, men of practical learning, or science.

The temples became the entrepôts, the tithe barns of farm tributes to the gods; the traffic in those goods produced trade, and when direct barter became too cumbersome, tokens of exchange had to be created; and so money was invented.

Money became a commodity in itself, so there emerged the money-changers, the moneylenders and the credit bankers.

The export of the produce of the land and the products

of the craftsmen meant trade between neighboring cities and later distant cities.

That meant transport and communication.

Accessible wealth exposed the cities to the envy of marauders and the jealousies of other cities.

So the cities had to have defenses and the trade routes had to be protected.

Professional soldiers and warrior-kings provided this protection and, in the event, the conquering dynasties. But the whole superstructure—the craftsmen, the priesthood, the tax-gatherers, the bazaar traders, the import-export merchants, the financiers, the soldiers and the feudal system and imperial adventures of the kings—derived from the labors of the tillers and the soil they husbanded.

21 *The Soil as a History Book*

INDEED, the whole of ancient society depended entirely on the soil, and in the final test the history of these times is not written on the temple friezes, the clay tablets, the parchment rolls or the rock writings, or in the conventional history-book writings of today. It is written in the soil.

When we talk of reviving the granaries of the Ancient World, cultivating again the deserts in which the ancient civilizations foundered in their own dust, the answers of the modern schools of agronomy are too glib. We must go back to the soil itself as the textbook.

That is what the Israelis are doing when they send out archeologists as the advance guard of desert recovery, and that is what has been done in Iraq, in Mesopotamia itself.

As a prelude to the reclaiming of these lost lands a research project was undertaken by Dr. Thorkild Jacobsen and Dr. Robert M. Adams of the Oriental Institute, University of Chicago. They set out to study the 6,000-year record of irrigation agriculture in the Tigris-Euphrates flood plain. In addition to searching the ancient records of Iraq, which have been scattered throughout the world's libraries and museums, the team which they headed carried out a program of actual field work in the portion of the plain watered by the tributary of the Tigris, the Diyala.

Here they made discoveries of the profoundest importance to desert recovery. One of the greatest problems which confronts those who are trying to redeem the deserts is that of salt, which is inherent in the nature of the hot, dry deserts. Salts, of various kinds, are harmful to crops and to the texture of the soil and, as has been shown in premature adventures in resettlement, will in a few years force the farmer off his land.

These salts in the surface soils have, in a land like Iraq, got there in devious ways. A primary source of salts is the leaching or dissolving of the rocks by the rivers and their tributaries. These salts are carried with the silt to be deposited in the alluvial soil. The river-borne salts are then distributed by irrigation waters over wider areas of the land. With the thin spreading of surface water for irrigation purposes there is a high rate of evaporation, leaving an aggregation of salt in the arable soils. In the southern part of Mesopotamia the sea once reached as far north as Basra, so that the soil itself has been deposited on top of marine salt, in addition to the presence of salt borne in by the winds from the Persian Gulf.

The irrigation water of this part of the world contains calcium and magnesium, as well as sodium. As the water evaporates, the calcium and magnesium precipitate as carbonates, leaving the sodium in solution in the soil. Unless the sodium ions are washed down into the water table they affect the clay particles, turning them into "hardpan," a crumbless soil in which seeds cannot germinate or plants extend their roots and breathe and which is almost impermeable to water.

Where the water table has only a very limited flow—movement to carry away the salts—they drain from the surface and accumulate in the ground water. When irrigation waters are added successively, or there are floods and rains, this salt-laden ground water tends to rise and the salt seeps upward again into the root zone or to the surface.

22 *Salt and Civilization*

As WE have seen, however, this is not a problem of just our day and age; it must have been true throughout all the thousands of years in which Man has cultivated the soil of Mesopotamia. Dr. Jacobsen and Dr. Adams reported in the November 21, 1958, issue of *Science* (Vol. 128, No. 3334) on the progressive changes in soil salinity and sedimentation and how these contributed to the breakup of past civilizations.

Although the fertility of Mesopotamia, in antiquity, is proverbial, the traditional control of the water table was based only on the avoidance of overirrigation and on the practice of weed fallow in alternate years. The weeds were deep-rooted and had the effect of creating a dry zone in the soil, at depth, and so prevented the rise of salts through capillary action. This was a form of plant drainage; the transpiration and evaporation through the leaves of the plants could eventually reduce an artificially raised water table to safe levels.

The records show three major occurrences of the process of salination. The earliest affected southern Mesopotamia from 2400 B.C. until at least 1700 B.C. Another, less serious, one was in central Mesopotamia between 1300 and 900 B.C. There is evidence to show that the Nahrwān area east of Baghdad became salted only after A.D. 1200.

The study by Jacobsen and Adams suggests that salt, in the first of these occurrences, led to the breakup of the Sumerian civilization. It caused the northward movement of the major centers of political power from southern into central Iraq during the early second millennium B.C. Their account (in *Science*) of the decline is straightforward and persuasive:

It seems to have had its roots in one of the perennial disputes between the small, independent principalities which were the principal social units of the mid-third millennium B.C. Girsu and Umma, neighboring cities along a watercourse stemming from the Euphrates, had fought for generations over a fertile border district. Under the ruler Entemenar, Girsu temporarily gained the ascendancy, but was unable to prevent Umma, situated higher up the watercourse, from breaching and obstructing the branch canals that served the border fields. After repeated unsuccessful protests, Entemenar eventually undertook to supply water to the area by means of a canal from the Tigris; access to that river, flowing to the east of Girsu, could be assured without further campaigning against Umma to the northwest. By 1700 B.C. this canal had become large and important enough to be called simply "the Tigris," and it was supplying a large region west of Girsu that formerly had been watered only by the Euphrates. As a result, the limited irrigation supplies that could be drawn from the latter river were supplemented with copious Tigris water. A corresponding increase undoubtedly occurred in seepage, flooding, and overirrigation, creating all the conditions for a decisive rise in ground-water level.

Several parallel lines of evidence allow the ensuing salinization to be followed quantitatively:

1) Beginning shortly after the reign of Entemenar, the presence of patches of saline ground is directly attested in records of ancient temple surveyors. In a few cases, individual fields which at the time were recorded as salt-free can be shown in an archive from 2100 B.C. to have developed conditions of sporadic salinity during the 300 intervening years of cultivation.

2) Crop choice can be influenced by many factors, but the onset of salinization strongly favors the adoption of crops which are more salt-tolerant. Counts of grain impressions in excavated pottery from sites in southern Iraq of about 3500 B.C., made by H. Helbaek, suggest that at the time the proportions of wheat

and barley were nearly equal. A little more than 1,000 years later, in the time of Entemenar at Girsu, the less salt-tolerant wheat accounted for only one sixth of the crop. By about 2100 B.C. wheat had slipped still further, and it accounted for less than 2 per cent of the crop in the Girsu area. By 1700 B.C. the cultivation of wheat had been abandoned completely in the southern part of the alluvium.

3) Concurrent with the shift to barley cultivation was a serious decline in fertility which for the most part can be attributed to salinization. At about 2400 B.C. in Girsu a number of field records give an average yield of 2,537 liters per hectare (2,780 bushels per acre)—highly respectable even by modern United States and Canadian standards. This figure had declined to 1,460 liters per hectare by 2100 B.C., and by about 1700 B.C. the recorded yield at nearby Larsa had shrunk to an average of only 897 liters per hectare. The effects of this slow but cumulatively large decline must have been particularly devastating in the cities, where the needs of a considerable superstructure of priests, administrators, merchants, soldiers, and craftsmen had to be met with surpluses from primary agricultural production.

The southern part of the alluvial plain appears never to have recovered fully from the disastrous general decline which accompanied the salinization process. While never completely abandoned afterward, cultural and political leadership passed permanently out of the region with the rise of Babylon in the eighteenth century B.C., and many of the great Sumerian cities dwindled to villages or were left in ruins. Probably there is no historical event of this magnitude for which a single explanation is adequate, but that growing soil salinity played an important part in the breakup of Sumerian civilization seems beyond question.

It is of great historical importance to learn, in this way, how a civilization can die. It is more important to our present needs to know how it survived. Here were communities which had existed in spite of the salting of the soil which they had farmed prosperously for seven hundred years. The evidence is pretty conclusive that the climatic conditions have not changed in the thousands of years between them and us. There is no sign of large-scale drainage systems which might have corrected the infiltration of salt, and yet, as Jacobsen and Adams have suggested, the grain production was impressive even by present-day standards, with all our fertilizers and scientific methods.

23 *Our Debt to the Taxgatherers*

THE TEXTBOOKS in which the reclamation of these lands may be observed are in fact the temple records, the taxgatherers' accounts. Two sets of records, with a gap of three hundred years, have been examined from the mound, or tell, of Lagash, the city which was contemporary with, and near, Ur. These tax returns are in the form of clay tablets and the earliest of them date back 4,400 years. From these Dr. Jacobsen and his colleagues were able to identify the actual fields and to discover how much irrigation water was put on them and for how long, what crops were sown on them, and not only what the yields were but how far apart they sowed their seeds.

But the silt which provided the ultimate fertility was itself a problem for the ancient cultivators. We accept the fact that rivers bring down the silt and create the alluvial deltaic soils. But it is now obvious that vast areas of the plains of Mesopotamia were covered by man-made soil; men spread the silt by their systems of irrigation canals.

About 6,000 years ago the tillers had been content to take advantage of the soils of the riverbanks. Their irrigation, at best, was a system of levees to keep the river in check, with breaches in the earthworks to flood the adjacent fields when required. As they became more enterprising, however, their network of canals spread away, and for considerable distances, from the river. In switching the water, they switched the silt as well. In the course of the last 5,000 years an average of forty feet of silt was laid down over wide areas. It is obvious from the work of the archeological agronomists that only part of this deposit, although a substantial part, was due to severe floods (like the one that drowned Ur). The silt deposited in canal beds had to be dredged out and piled on the banks. When this dredged mud dried out it became wind-blown dust which was spread over a wide area. Some of the abandoned canals can be accounted for by the fact that the dredgings from other canals became moving sand dunes which choked the later watercourses. But by far the greater proportion of the deposit was from irrigation water, as it spread over the fields.

Another factor was that sedimentation, in the rivers and canals, raised the level of the channel beds. This slowed down the flow of the water so that the silt settled more readily and increased the sedimentation process; as the canals and rivers became shallower, the possibilities of the flooding were increased. Levees were scoured by the runoff, which spread the resultant silt and in the depressions caused swamps.

24 *Water and War*

IN SHORT, as has already been pointed out, when Man interferes with nature he has to maintain his mastery or nature regains it. The early tillers merely trifled with the waters, but as the villages and the cities grew, the extensions of the irrigation systems in order to produce their food meant massive interference. The individual tillers were now dependent on a water system which could only be maintained by a strong central authority and by public works which could carry water across long distances, over often unwanted "uneconomic" wastelands. They had to protect the waterways—because, in wars, the easiest way to cripple an enemy was by breaching the levees.

Wars, however, were only minor incidents, contributory but not conclusive. Writing of the Diyala region of Mesopotamia, Jacobsen and Adams drew this conclusion: "By the middle of the twelfth century, most of the Nahrwān region was already abandoned. Only a trickle of water passed down the upper section of the main canal to supply a few dying towns in the then hostile desert. Invading Mongol horsemen under Hulagu Khan, who must have surveyed this devastated scene a century later, have been unjustly blamed for causing it ever since."

PART
FOUR

The Streams of Civilization

"*The fertile Nile, which creatures new doth frame*
Long Rhodanus, whose sourse springs from the skie,
Faire Ister, flowing from the mountains hie.
Divine Scamander, purpled yet with blood
Of Greeks and Trojans which therein did die . . ."
　　　　—*The Faerie Queene* by EDMUND SPENSER

1 From Nomarchs to Monarchs

WHEN MENES founded the first Egyptian dynasty and the city of Memphis (about 3188 B.C.) and merged the cults of Osiris and Horus and Upper and Lower Egypt, the material source of his power was copper. With this metal he became a monarch instead of a nomarch.

Before then the nomes or totemic villages (identifying themselves with the animal cults of the cat, the falcon, the ram, the wolf and so on) had existed as units under a governor (the nomarch) and had lived on and traded their surpluses. Those of the Delta had used malachite as a cosmetic for their eyes and had got it from the Sinai by barter with the desert hunters. Then, around Menes's time, some experimenting metallurgist discovered that malachite was fusible and could be smelted into copper. The copper was a particularly hard variety, which did not need tin to alloy it; so Egypt did not have a Bronze Age, and the copper weapons enabled Menes to impose the will of Upper Egypt on Lower Egypt.

Menes was chief of the Falcon Clan. He took the precaution of mythologically identifying himself with Horus, the falcon-headed god, and, by the dispensations of mythology, Horus was identified as the son of Osiris, who was the god of the Nile, the source of all its fruitfulness.

Thus, by creating a god-king identity, Menes held in fief not only the lands of the Upper and Lower Nile but the farmers as well, since the fertility of their fields depended on his godlike bounty.

About this time, too, another influence had crept in. On the rocky walls of dry wadis between the Nile and the Red Sea and on the tombs of Hierakonpolis (Falcon City) can be seen pictures of sailing boats, of recognizably Persian Gulf types. On the tomb walls (in the desert) they are seen in naval battle with the reed boats of the Nile. That same scene is carved on a knife handle found at Gebel-el-Arak at the Nile end of the cross-desert route from the Red Sea. The other side of that ivory carving depicts a figure whose dress is quite foreign to Egypt but which has its prototype in a basalt stele found at Erech in Sumer. Comparative archeology would therefore suggest that there was a contact with Mesopotamia which had some influence in communicating the civilization existing there to the Nile Valley tillers and, maybe, in inspiring the idea of the god-king dynasties.

From Menes onward, through thirty-one dynasties and over a period longer than that which divides Alexander the Great from our present time, Egypt was ruled by god-kings and priests. The basis of their power, like the bases of the pyramids, rested foursquare on the soil and derived from the efforts of the peasantry tilling the alluvial soils of the Nile and its delta.

The surplus wealth which the soil yielded in the shape of food crops and fiber crops maintained the priesthood, the craftsmen, the bureaucracy, the army and the Pharaohs. This wealth was so abundant (whether the peasants found it so is another matter) that by 2700 B.C. Zoser (like the oil sheiks with their Cadillacs) had to find more and more grandiose ways of disposing of it. The god-kings of the first and second dynasties had been content with the mastabas, tombs built to hold the aristocratic remains and all the food vessels, wine jars, hunting implements and other necessities of Pharaohic afterlife. But Zoser charged his doctor, Imhotep, to build him a tomb commensurate with his wealth. This was the First, or Step, Pyramid, at Saqqara, on high ground overlooking the city of Memphis.

Imhotep was more than a great healer (which accounted for his deification); he was also a great architect, mathematician, astronomer and engineer. In its final form his pyramid was a massive structure rising in six unequal stages to a height of 204 feet. Its base measurements were 411 feet from east to west and 358 from north to south. A mile-long wall thirty-three feet high surrounded its precincts.

2 *The Great Pyramid*

THIS PYRAMID was the beginning of that funerary grandeur which we identify with Egypt. It was surpassed in the fourth dynasty by that of Cheops. His Great Pyramid at Giza is 755 feet square, rising to a height of 481 feet. It contains 2,300,000 blocks, each weighing, on an average, 2½ tons. The blocks were quarried on the east side of the Nile and were floated across on rafts during the flood season and then manhandled up a stone ramp onto the plateau a hundred feet above the river. The pyramid of Cheops demanded the labor of 100,000 men for twenty years. And into it went the ingenuity and astronomy of centuries. The perimeter of the four sides has the same ratio to the height as the ratio of the circumference to the radius of a circle.

However much we may admire the pyramids today, they were, in their day, pieces of monumental bombast, the self-glorification in stone of those who were exploiting the fertility of the Nile. By prodigies of muscle effort, men quarried and moved these great bulks of stone with little or no mechanical assistance. They went out and mined metals in the mountains of Sinai and Nubia, less for the practical uses than for the massing of ornaments and funeraries to the glory of the priests and king. They took metals out of their geological tombs of natural rock, spent laborious hours perfecting vessels and decorating them, and then buried them again in the royal vaults of the pyramids, of man-shaped rocks.

In theory the whole land belonged to the Pharaoh. That which was consumable he kept in his granaries; that which was imperishable he kept in his treasuries. He took the products of the soil and rocks and assigned a substantial share to his nobility and his priests. It is true that, like the Pharaoh of Joseph's time, he was supposed in his divine wisdom and practical stewardship to store the products of the fat years to avoid the famines of the lean years.

The Pharaohs not only controlled the bodies of their people but also their souls. When Menes became the first god-king he did it by swallowing up the totemistic clans, in which the soul of the individual had been identified with the animal which was the totem of his clan. So a Pharaoh could convince them that by ensuring his immortality, in the magnificence of his tomb, they were safeguarding their own selves as well.

As H. G. Wells has pointed out in *The Outline of History*, "These unmeaning sepulchral piles of almost incredible vastness, erected in an age when engineering science had scarcely begun, exhausted the resource of Egypt . . . and left her wasted as if by war."

3 *Slaves in Egypt's Night*

WITH GREATER food yields and with greater security from purely tribal conflicts the population increased. But, as in all urban civilizations, there were the contagions and infections of closely settled communities which in part restrain the population increase.

In an age of manual cultivation there had always to be an adequate peasant labor force on the land. As in later feudal times in Europe, there was a limit to the mobilizations for military or state work which withdrew the tillers from producing food. Therefore the only way in which the work force of laborers, craftsmen and, indeed, clerks could carry out the Pharaoh's grandiose schemes and proclaim his limitless wealth was by a system of slavery. This meant wars and foreign adventures. (The sojourn of the children of Israel in "Egypt's night" was only one instance of the subjugation and transplanting of neighboring peoples.) Foreign adventures also brought new riches in the discovery of new metals and new crafts, new spices and new cosmetics, exotic foods and fabrics, and rare woods. But they also reminded other peoples that Egypt had desirable wealth itself and encouraged them to reciprocal conquests.

In the ebb and flow of such wars throughout the Fertile Crescent the stability of agriculture was periodically undermined. If populations were carried off, or killed off, systems of irrigation and conservation fell into decay and disease and hunger followed neglect. Even in the victorious countries success imposed a burden on the farming economy. Slaves engaged on public works (like the 100,000 continuously employed on the Great Pyramid) had to be fed, and the soil which had to feed them was restricted within the valley of the Nile, since desert agriculture was no feature of Egypt even at the height of its enterprise. In many cases the slaves were better fed than the peasants who supplied the provisions. For instance, we find King Setti I recording that he provided each of the thousand laborers employed on building a temple with "4 pounds of bread, 2 bundles of vegetables and a roast of meat daily, and a fresh linen garment twice a month."

4 The Indus Civilization

Over an area four times that of Mesopotamian Sumer prevailed the Indus Civilization of 3000 B.C. It was bounded on the west by the mountains of Baluchistan and Waziristan, on the north by the Himalayas and on the east by the Thar Desert. The artificial world which was created here was just as imposing as those of Mesopotamia and Egypt. Cities have been unearthed

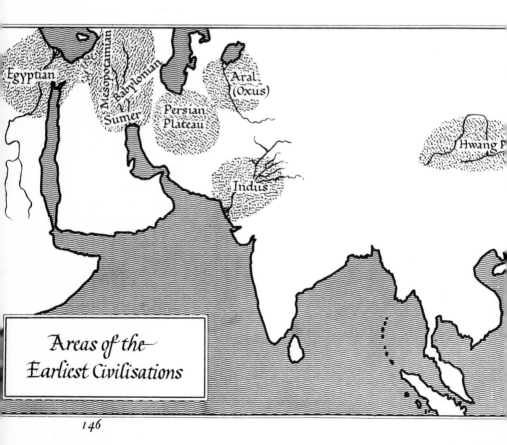

Areas of the Earliest Civilisations

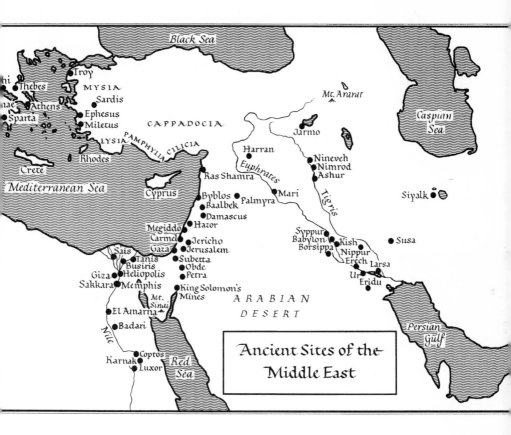

Ancient Sites of the Middle East

which were just as large as those of the Euphrates or the Nile. They were built of kiln-fired, as distinct from sun-dried, bricks, and this presumes the availability of fuel on a vast scale in an area which is now undistinguished by trees. The ruins of Mohenjo-Daro in the Sind covered at least a square mile. Before the railway builders got busy and used the bricks of Harappa, 400 miles north of Mohenjo-Daro, as ballast for the tracks, this Bronze Age city had a circumference of two and a half miles.

These cities were inundated by successive floods—those deluges which the early ancients never successfully mastered. After each flooding the lower stories of the houses were filled with rubble to provide the solid foundations for the resurgent cities, so that

147

whole quarters now rest on artificial platforms over twenty feet high.

Indus cities were supported, like the others in Egypt and Mesopotamia, by the surpluses of an industrious peasantry which cultivated grains similar to those of Mesopotamia but with the addition of rice, and their domesticated animals almost certainly included the zebu (the so-called "Brahmin ox," with its hump) and they are believed to have tamed elephants. The camel and the ass had not reached them from the Asian steppe lands.

The Indus potters had the spinning wheel; the smiths alloyed tin with copper to make brass into bronze. The weavers worked cotton but not wool or flax. The potters discovered chemical skills in glazing their pots and vases. Their craftsmen's tools are quite different—even the axes, saws, daggers and spearheads—from those of the other civilizations and show an indigenous growth and separate evolution.

They had carts with solid wheels and they had boats to move their goods around. They had external trade—external, that is, to the cities—by which they obtained their raw materials. They got their deodar from the distant Himalayas, their copper from Rajputana, and tin, gold and lapis lazuli from countries beyond the borders of the subcontinent of India.

5 City Government

MUNICIPAL AUTHORITY was well established in the Indus civilization. The streets were broad and well planned, with obvious town-planning restrictions on sporadic building. There was no obvious royal house or grandiose temple society. At Harappa the biggest building was a communal granary, and at Mohenjo-Daro there was a huge building but it gives no signs of having been other than a community center with a bitumen-lined public bath. Houses testify to "class distinctions," both in their size and in the ornaments found, but they are suggestive rather of the craft-guild merchant economy of the Middle Ages than of a ruling nobility.

Most impressive are the systems of drains. Always when one considers the growth of cities one thinks of the problems of sanitation and of contagions. Here, 5,000 years ago, was a health-conscious people. So much so that the remains of the water booths, where drinking water was sold, include huge spoil heaps of broken cups, far in excess of the casualties of the most careless dishwashers and strongly suggestive that there were sanitary laws which compelled the breaking of these rough cups. When someone bought a drink of water, the cup was thrown away like the paper cups of today.

Pictographic seal impressions from the Indus Valley showing script above the figures (2500 B.C.)

Here were the societies from which emerged early literacy—a conventional script and a numerical system. The script was pictographic but unlike that of the civilizations which were its nearest neighbors, Sumer and proto-Elam. That they had arrived at mathematics and science is manifest in their decorations—squares and circles, squares in circles, and circles intersecting with compass-drawn precision.

The illustrative material still surviving strongly, indeed inescapably, suggests rites and deities which persist in the practices of modern Hinduism, and the fashions of dress in contemporary India are foreshadowed in the prehistoric art of Indus.

Some catastrophe overtook those cities of the Indus, but there is no doubt of their cultural achievements or influence. And there is always the question as to whether, after the deluge which overlaid early Ur with eight feet of silt, the later Sumerians may not have been immigrants from Indus.

6 The Hwang-ho and Yangtze Civilizations

WITH THE REMAINS of Peking Man to remind us that the ancestral creatures of *Homo sapiens* had appeared that early in the Far East, it is a plausible argument that a collateral branch of the human race developed there and that from it derived differentiated cultures. Certainly at a time when the familiar Middle Eastern civilizations were developing, another quite distinct culture was spreading out from what is now the dry and desolate valley of the Tarim, beyond the Pamirs, and in two directions down the river Hwang-ho and down the river Yangtze.

In the Eastern Stone Age the people of Honan and Manchuria

were already living in villages and had domesticated the pig. They used axes and stone knives and arrowheads of slate, bone and mussel shell. They had developed spinning and weaving and had a pottery of the painted type which might suggest links with the cultures further to the west.

There need not have been this link; when we are talking in terms of thousands of years, inventions can be spontaneous and their resemblances are purely coincidental. But there is a likelihood of a fusion in China of two prehistoric cultural movements, one from the north and one from the south. It is also possible that a stream of Iranian culture may have flowed east and northward and made its contribution to the migration into the Americas.

One interesting feature in the Chinese development was the evidence that they used knotted strings as their records, before the evolution of a written language. These string "ledgers" reappear, as we shall see, thousands of years later as the quipus of the Incas. This might be just a coincidence—a spontaneous invention in Peru—but it is just as likely to be a throwback to the Asian ancestry of the Amerinds.

In the third millennium B.C., according to Chinese legend, there were the Five Kings. If we accept them, then, of course, there must have been a cohesive culture of which they were the overlords. But in the legends they are such exemplary beings that one suspects that they are an example of the wishful thinking in which people indulge when they are groping in the mists of their Dawn History—like the British finding their superman in King Arthur.

The dynasties which came later than these Five Emperors have certainly more historical substance. To begin with, China, like Sumer and Egypt, was a land of city-isolates. The government was at first a commonwealth of numerous kings who finally acknowledged a central emperor. The great dynasties of the feudal period were Shang (1750–1125 B.C.) and Chou (1125–250 B.C.). The bronze vessels of the early Shang period are proof enough that before that, China had arrived at a high state of culture.

The unity which China possessed under the Shang Dynasty was probably produced by the common threat to all the settled peoples of China from the pressures of the vigorous nomads of the Mongolian steppes. It had also a religious sanction, for the Emperor, as the "Son of Heaven," became a priest-king for all the Chinese.

This was the China which had already domesticated the pig, developed the spoked wheel for chariots and established the oldest system of roads we know in the world. The Shang Dynasty had its highway commissioners. Terracing, land conservation and irrigation were already well advanced 3,500 years ago. Confirmation of this and of the fact that the Chinese had become boat-builders and intrepid mariners comes from Luzon in the Philippines, where the wonderful system of rice terraces, covering an area of 250 square miles, are even by present-day standards a remarkable feat of engineering. They were first built by immigrants from China in the second millennium B.C.

7 The Great Wall of China

A POPULAR REVOLT, with support from the wilder tribes of the southwest, replaced the Shang Dynasty with the Chou emperors. The imperial ties were loose, and between the eighth and fourth centuries B.C. there were between 5,000 and 6,000 small states in the Hwang-ho and the Yangtze valleys with about a dozen feudal princes, nominally answerable to the Emperor but incessantly warring between themselves, with the war lords of the one valley joining forces against those of the other valley. From this emerged the confederation of the north, which under Chowsiang became the Ts'in (Ch'in) Dynasty, from which China takes its name. His great-grandson ruled over an empire practically identical with modern China. It was he who built the Great Wall of China which extends for 1,500 miles along what was the northern frontier of his empire. Its western end was, and is, in the deserts of Central Asia and its eastern end at the sea to the northeast of Peking. It is carried over mountain and valley, reaching in one place a height of over 5,000 feet above the sea. The actual height of the wall, including the parapet, is about fifty feet. This tremendous undertaking must have involved a diversion of peasant labor or an acquisition of slaves as great as, or greater than, that for the building of the Egyptian pyramids.

During the Chou Dynasty there emerged the period of the great philosophers—Lao-tse, Confucius and Mencius. From those days dates the Chinese respect for learning, which has always given the scholar a special place in the social hierarchy. The literature of that period—over 2,500 years ago—shows remarkable insight into the functions and the care of the human body and a system of medicine and of medical ethics much more advanced than one finds in many areas of our present-day world.

8 *African Civilization*

AROUND 3000 B.C. the inhabitants of the continent of Africa seem to have become differentiated into many races and cultures. Especial interest lies in the great variety and the genuine artistic merit of the ancient rock paintings which are widely distributed in cave shelters throughout the tropical forest belt as well as in the Saharan, Rhodesian and South African regions.

From there on, however, almost to the present time, the history of indigenous cultures becomes blurred and misleading. The trouble has been that prehistorians have been so preoccupied in revealing the ancient origins of Man in Africa that they have neglected the intermediate period. Another reason for our vagueness about "Black Africa" is that in tropical forest lands wood is the structural and artistic material. It does not have the permanence of stone or brick, and when it rots the cultural evidence is lost.

Moreover, we apply "African" far more arbitrarily than we apply "European" or "Asian," because we accept the pronounced characteristics of the Negro and forget that Africa also includes that part of the continent north of the Sahara which produced the Egyptian and, later, the Carthaginian civilizations. Because we are still mentally hampered by the "Darkest Africa" concept, which derives from nineteenth-century explorers (Livingstone, Stanley, etc.), we forget that there was a diffusion of cultures within the continent and, according to some indications, between Africa and the Polynesian Islands.

And there are still unresolved confusions about the Hamitic and Semitic relationships with the Bantu. It seems certain that the original Hamitic people spread over north Africa in an early epoch and intermingled with the Negroes. In other regions, having secured their supremacy, the Hamites maintained their superiority over the Bantu and established kingdoms in Ruanda-Urundi and in Uganda. The entry of the Semites is equally vaguely dated, but their migration into what is now Ethiopia was at its peak about 500 B.C. Over 1,000 years later the Semites, in the form of the Arabs bringing Mohammedanism, spread a profound influence over north and east Africa.

There is a missing cultural link in Africa south of the Sahara, associated with the assumption (which has been fostered by racism) that "Black Africa" stagnated until changes were triggered off by European influences. What is true is that, leaving out the effects of slavery, which is estimated to have robbed Africa of 100,000,000 people, the ill effects of modern influences were exaggerated in Africa because there had, in general, been no systematic emergence from the hunting–food-gathering stage, through the food-growing stage, to the collective community. Society continued tribal, hunting or pastoral, and in restrictive balance with nature. But the reproachful gaps in African history may gradually be filled by such things as the proper interpretation of the Saharan rock paintings, in which the wheeled plow appears alongside the giraffe—in an arid region where the giraffe does not now exist.

9 *Non-Riverine Civilizations*

CONTEMPORARILY—that is, plus or minus centuries—with the growth of the tiller civilizations—the cities which grew from the cultivation of the land—there arose different types of community in other parts. One might call them armed trading centers. For example, in the mountains of Asia Minor the land did not lend itself to the kind of extensive cultivation from which the urban civilizations grew in the alluvial plains. But there had been earlier Neolithic communities there, self-sufficient as to food, but also with access to raw materials, to metals, etc., and they had become communities. As a result of one activity or another, new centers of civilization arose on these "barbarian" locations. And, of course, each of these Bronze Age townships became itself a new center of demand which made impact on a widening hinterland. Urban arts and crafts were superimposed on the Neolithic mountain cultures but did not obliterate them. The cultures were adaptations of the existing environment and different from those of the alluvial valleys, and (another variation) cities along the coast of the Mediterranean and the Persian Gulf developed into ports.

10 *Byblos*

ON THE SYRIAN COAST, for instance, there grew up Byblos, which Sir Julian Huxley contends is the oldest continuously inhabited town in the world, from remote history to the present day. There, at the present time, is to be found the evidence of settlements well before 3000 B.C. Before the Egyptian galleys came across the "inhospitable" sea over 5,000 years ago, Byblos had already existed for centuries as a community of fishers and farmers who cultivated olive trees as well as barley and bred goats and sheep. Byblos was the best port for the Lebanon lumber trade. The woods from the forests—cedar and fir—were floated along the coasts on great rafts to supply woodless Egypt.

Before Byblos became virtually an outpost of Egypt, it had already exerted powerful influence as the chief center on the Phoenician coast of the cult of Astarte and Adonis. Astarte was the patron goddess of Byblos, while Afqa was sacred to Adonis. The legend of the two divinities is familiar. Adonis, the youthful masculine god who originally sprang from a tree, was loved by Astarte. He went off to the hunt and was killed by a wild boar, and the cult depends on the lamentations of the goddess who eventually secured his release from the underworld. With the legend went an elaborate ritual. The cult, of course, is a variant of the legends and magic which one finds in all parts of the world deriving from the agricultural mysticism of Neolithic times. Astarte is the mother-goddess symbolizing the fertility of nature. Adonis born of a tree is the masculine principle needed to fertilize the feminine element, but he is also the crop which withers in the summer and then grows out of the dark soil again in the spring. In a way, his being killed by a wild boar exemplifies the struggle between the food gatherer and animal nature.

On the site of the original temple of the local deities was built a great monumental temple by the Egyptians. It measured over 90x63 feet of richly adorned and solid masonry. The Pharaohs sent to the shrine stone vases and other offerings inscribed with their names. Egyptian ambassadors, officials, clerks and merchants frequented the temple. The native clerks were sent to be trained in Egypt in hieroglyphic writing, and, in exchange for the cedars of Lebanon and olives and dyes, Byblos received, and accepted, the elements of Egyptian civilization, manufactured articles and corn, as well as writing. (We must remember that "Byblos" gave us the word for Bible, or book. This reminds us also that all the elements of writing in fact came to us from the Middle East—pens, ink and paper—the last term being derived from papyrus. Byblos, for the Greeks, was the source for this paper and the origin of the rolls which became our books.)

11 *Cyprus*

IN THE SAME WAY Cyprus gave us our word for "copper." The wealth of metal tools in the Bronze Age tombs of the island shows that specialist miners and smiths existed then. But neither pottery nor any other craft had apparently come into local being. Nor are there any foreign craft pieces in the tombs to indicate that they got finished goods in return for the crude ingots or ore which they exported.

12 Crete

THE NEOLITHIC farmers and fishers of Crete were joined about 3000 B.C. by refugees from the Nile Delta and fresh colonists from Syria, bringing with them some of the technical and artistic traditions of Egypt and Asia. In this way they acquired the cultivation of olives, and in return they traded the advantages of the exploitation of the island's natural resources in timber, copper and shells for dyes; they were producing an exportable surplus. The island's geographical position between Egypt, Asia and the mainland of Greece and its supplies of timber for ship-building enabled Crete to become a trading nation. Little town-ships arose even on tiny islets which themselves were destitute of land to support a local cultivation. So they were essentially craft townships. Craftsmen, traders and sea captains became rich enough to acquire ornaments and to create a wealth, but there is no evidence in early Crete of an aggregation of wealth. Collective tombs were crowded with skeletons and quite richly furnished, but they were the communal burying places of the clans and not merely of a nobility. Stone axes and obsidian knives were still used side by side with metal tools and weapons. But they were dependent on trade. And the Minoan civilization was based on trade.

13 *Troy*

FURTHER NORTH the little islands scattered in the belt across the Aegean had nothing to offer farmers, but they possessed marketable resources of copper, of emery, obsidian and marble, which could be quarried or mined and exchanged for foodstuffs. So, even in 3000 B.C., they were thickly populated by people who worked metals. From the evidence of their graves they probably had a secondary trade—piracy. They had discovered not only the secrets of commerce and industry but of making a living by stealing from the cities with a surplus wealth.

Some of these cities acquired wealth purely by piratical commerce under leadership of military chiefs. The city of Troy, made famous by the epics of Homer, began as a fortified hamlet or citadel barely one and a half acres in area. It was dominated by the chief's fort. In time it expanded, until what the archeologists call "Troy II" covered nearly two acres. By now its acquired wealth had attracted to the chieftain's court potters and goldsmiths trained in the Asian schools and skilled in filigree work. Trade and plunder secured for Troy supplies of copper, tin, lead, silver, gold and obsidian, as well as manufactured luxuries. This wealth was manifestly concentrated in the personal treasury of a petty war chief.

14 Seagoing Civilization

THUS on the Levantine coast and in the mountains of Asia Minor there developed communities like Troy which had a different character from those which had grown basically from agriculture. They were either mining or craft communities without adequate cultivation to support a growing population. Therefore, they became warlike adventurers or sea traders. The peasants of Macedonia, mainland Greece and the Danube area began to be joined by Asians and islanders already accustomed to metal tools and weapons. All around the eastern Mediterranean maritime cultures arose in which the subsistence economy of barbarism was tempered by industrialized specialization and commerce. In their special character they built up new traditions of seamanship and geographical lore and transmitted to the developed civilizations knowledge of new lands, materials and techniques. These communities then served in their turn as new centers from which civilized ideas were diffused westward and northward. East Mediterranean manufactures were transported as far west as Sicily and Malta. They also exported their religious cults as well.

15 Superstitions for Export

PROFESSOR GORDON CHILDE has suggested that it was the export of superstition and ritual from the Middle East which induced the peoples of other parts to become the primary producers for the eastern Mediterranean. He points out that in Sardinia, south-eastern Spain and Portugal they mined and smelted local ores of copper, silver and lead, and they built tombs more or less on the same general plan as those used farther east. But there is little evidence that they acquired very much in the way of finished materials in return. Still farther afield, the great family vaults like the barrows and chambered cairns of Britain are scattered along the Atlantic coast of Portugal, France and the British Isles and across the North Sea in Denmark and southern Sweden, and they are regarded by one school of archeologists as clumsy attempts to copy the Spanish, Sicilian and Cretan funerary architecture and to reflect, at secondhand, as it were, the beliefs of the Levant.

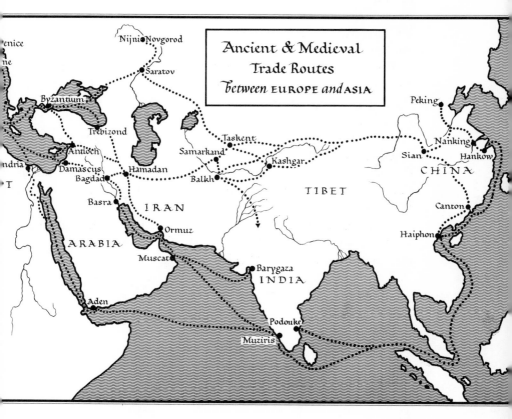

Ancient & Medieval Trade Routes between EUROPE and ASIA

In central and northwestern Europe the contacts with the traders had introduced primitive societies to superior weapons. The possession of these weapons had in turn created a ruling class which could oppress the peasantry and compel it to produce surpluses. The necessary technical knowledge for the development of arms of this kind reached central Europe, via the Danube, from Troy and probably came to Britain from Spain. Hungary and Czechoslovakia, Ireland and Cornwall could supply the copper and tin which were needed, and the trading links extended into Denmark, northern Germany and southern Sweden. A regular trade in metal linked up the whole of central Europe from upper Italy to the Harz Mountains and from the Vistula to the Rhine. With trade went piracy and the power of armed men to impress their will upon the agricultural populations. The contact also introduced the seagoing peoples to other and better-off countries than their own. This, of course, is the story of the Scandinavian Vikings.

The irony of this "commercial imperialism" was that presently the barbaric people to whom the Middle East had introduced these refinements of armaments themselves began to press upon the civilized world.

The age-old struggle between the nomads, the Sons of Abel, and the tillers, the Sons of Cain, was now exaggerated by the pressures of the metalworking barbarians on the communities which had acquired wealth and culture from the cultivation of the soil.

At this point at the end of what is called "The Bronze Age" we leave what is called the "Old World" to ask ourselves how old, in fact, the "New World" is.

PART FIVE

The Bridge

"But for the Pyramids no reason has ever been given adequate to the cost and labour of the work. The narrowness of the chambers proves that it could afford no retreat from enemies, and treasures might have been reposited at far less expense with equal security. It seems to have been erected only in compliance with that hunger of imagination which preys incessantly upon life, and must be always appeased by some employment. Those who have already all that they can enjoy must enlarge their desires. He that has built for use, till use is supplied, must begin to build for vanity. . . ."

—SAMUEL JOHNSON,
Rasselas, Prince of Abyssinia

1 The Amerinds

PICKING UP the threads of the stories of the Incas in the literature which we call "history" is like reading a magazine in a barber's shop. The last installment is there, but the previous issues are missing and the synopsis is very vague. The scene is already set in all the magnificence which excited the greed and envy of the Conquistadores but, in the absence of the back numbers, it is obvious that this wealth is only the superficial manifestation of a civilization deep-rooted in the past.

The characters are also confusing because the "heroes" are the villains and the "villains" are the heroes; Pizarro, the European, whose warrior courage we are expected to admire, is a ruffian compared with the Inca, Atahuallpa, the living sun god. The tragedy is wrought to its brutal conclusion and we are left speculating, even at this day, about an Indian culture of which the Incas were a late fulfillment.

For the rest of the story we have to go to the archeologists, still groping for the clues which the Incas themselves deliberately smudged. There is no written record of any stage of the Pan-Peruvian Indian culture except that of the Incas gathered by the conquering Spaniards from observation and hearsay. Yet the Inca phase, which extended geographically over Ecuador, Peru, Bolivia and the north parts of Argentine and Chile, lasted only 300 years. The Incas themselves had not, in our sense, a written language. There were no "talking stones" such as the Mayas had in the Yucatan or pictographs like the Aztecs'. To maintain their divine origin and to prove that civilization began with them, the Incas had deliberately suppressed the spoken tradition and consigned their predecessors to the oblivion which

165

they themselves might have suffered but for the industrious Spanish clerks, who in their ledgers of loot added their footnotes on a people.

Only the artifacts of the pre-Incas' cultures can help us, and they are eloquent in their testimony of the skills and ingenuity to which the Incas themselves were the heirs. Fabrics, unexcelled in their design and methods of weaving, have survived for untold centuries in the tombs, where the dry climate has preserved them. Excellent craftsmen in that hidden past made decorated pottery without the help of a potter's wheel and produced ornaments in gold and silver and copper and masterpieces of masonry. But even the records of the tombs and the buried remains of their material culture tantalize the seekers, for they give little help in dating. There are no calendars or coins, no parameters of time by which the various epochs can be surely fixed. There are the quipus, the knot-string records, but they are meaningless without the professional "rememberers" to whom alone they were meaningful—like the secretary who makes herself indispensable because she alone knows the filing system! Perhaps with the help of carbon 14 we may get a more systematic time appraisal.

2 Pan-American Pantry

BUT BEFORE we go back and try to trace the origins and cultural evolution of the American Indian, let us remind ourselves once again that all civilizations derive from agriculture and that more than half the foods the world eats today were first cultivated by the Indians of the Andes. From that region came maize in twenty varieties, potatoes in two hundred varieties, sweet potatoes, yams, squash, many types of beans, maniocs, peanuts, cashews, pineapples, chocolate, avocados, tomatoes, peppers, papaya, strawberries and blackberries. Some of these may seem surprising because they have been domesticated for so long, or have run wild in other parts of the world, that we forget their American origin. Yet it is not really strange that the lands of the west coast of South America should have been the plant nursery for most of the world. Latitude is compensated for by altitude. That is to say, climatic conditions vary from the torrid lowlands to the high, cold slopes and plateaus of the Andes, so that the plants at varying altitudes could be acclimatized in countries of different latitudes. The universality of the potato is an example. In Peru potatoes grow, in differing varieties, from the blistering coastal lands to as high as 15,000 feet. Thus, in terms of temperature adaptation, they can be grown in countries from the Equator to the Arctic.

3 *Tangled Thread of Cotton*

COTTON is one of the world's great mysteries—particularly South American cotton. Cotton did not enter the Mediterranean until the fifth century B.C. The first authentic proof of its use in Egypt is in 370 B.C. Before this it had been known to the Assyrians as "tree wool," but the Babylonian and early Greek names disclose an Indus origin. This is confirmed by the discovery at Mohenjo-Daro (2500 to 1500 B.C.) of a cultivated species for which there has never been found an Indus Valley wild species. Yet its precursors, in the wild state, are found in Africa and southern Arabia. Here the question arises, was the cultivated cotton taken from the Arabian Peninsula into the Indus Valley long before 2500 B.C.? But, when we turn to the South American cotton, we are confronted with a natural legerdemain which completely baffles the plant detectives. There, in Peruvian graves which, with all the imperfections of dating, cannot be younger than 2000 B.C., have survived beautifully woven fabrics from cotton fibers of highly advanced cultivation. But—and this is the snarl in the skein of cotton—there is every reason to believe that this was cotton of Asian origin—cotton which in its basic form had gone from west to east (into America) and later, in its tetraploidal form (which means that its basic number of chromosomes had been doubled), had recrossed the Pacific into Asia. This reverse lend-lease is bewildering, yet, one gathers from the experts, inescapable. But how?

The glib answer could be "Birds." Apart, however, from the distances involved, birds do not eat *Gossypium* seeds—seeds of cotton. Nor could the winds have carried them over 3,000 miles. The other strange possibility, which exceeds even the imagination of Heyerdahl's *Kon-Tiki*, with its raft settlement of Polynesia by South American Indians, is that some ancestral men migrated from Asia into South America with the elementary form of cotton and then, many thousands of years later, other interhemispheric nomads moved back again to the Old World with the sophisticated tetraploidal form. It strains the imagination, but it is anybody's guess.

4 Continents Adrift

THIS RAISES the whole question of Man's settlement of the Western Hemisphere and, indeed, of the origins of the Americas. No one today lightly dismisses, as might have been done even a generation ago, the Wegener Theory of Continental Drift. It has been restored to respectability, if not to complete acceptance, by the studies of rock magnetism.

The Theory of Continental Drift, propounded by Professor Wegener in 1912, implies that the land mass was once coherent— a vast island—and that it broke up. The fragments became, as it were, rafts of sial (the uppermost layer of the earth's crust), floating on the heavier underlying sima (the basaltic layer). Wegener's idea had at least a superficial plausibility to anyone who looked at a map.

If, bearing in mind we are dealing with a globe and not a flat Mercator projection, we fret out the outlines of the continents, we will find that some of them fit very neatly together, like the pieces of a jigsaw puzzle. For example, the bulge of Brazil fits with great exactness into the Gulf of Guinea in the continent of Africa. Fitting the North American continent back into Europe is not quite so simple. But Wegener insisted, with reasonable justification, that the breakup had been like that of an ice field, in which the floes would not only separate but would also be likely to swing. If one accepts that, then one might agree that the positions of the Spanish Peninsula and Newfoundland might have been sufficiently distorted to explain the difficulties of making them fit. In the Arctic, however, the Canadian archipelago, Greenland and Spitsbergen are all pretty consistent with the idea of land floes breaking up. Moreover, if one extends the Caledonian formation of the Scottish Grampians and of Wales, one finds a plausible conformity with the Appalachians in the United States.

In the east and south the fitting together becomes even more intriguing. If Madagascar is tucked back closely to the continent of Africa, and we assume that Australia twisted away, the Australian Bight can be made consistent with the configurations of South Africa. But even when we "tighten up" India, Indonesia and the rest, there is still a gap—a missing piece where the Indian Ocean is. If, however, one regards the Scotia Arc (the Falkland Islands and the South Shetland Islands), stretching from the tip of South America to Antartica, as a hinge, then the Antarctic continent can be swung, very nicely, thank you, into the gap.

Perhaps it was because the jigsaw seemed so simple, so un-scientific, that the Wegener theory, in spite of the professor's reputation, was not treated with as much respect as it might have been. It has been the subject of debate and, indeed, division for a great many years. But recent developments in the study of rock magnetism have lent very influential support to the theory.

5 The Wandering Pole

WHEN SEDIMENTARY rocks have been laid down in the various epochs of various geological times, the ferrous crystals in the rocks were orientated toward the poles—the crystals became like magnetic needles. The study of these compass pointers in the rocks over the past few years has produced surprising results. In successive layers, in the rocks, the crystals have changed their direction. By plotting these directions it is pos-sible to determine where the rocks were in relation to the magnetic poles when the rocks were laid down. Judging by the results, however, the north magnetic pole, for instance, must have migrated from somewhere in the region of where Japan is at the moment to its present position somewhere in the region of the Prince of Wales Island, north of the Canadian mainland. By the same token, from rocks in the Southern Hemisphere, the south magnetic pole must have been a vagrant also.

To suggest that the magnetic poles have shifted might also imply that the geographic poles have shifted—that is, that the axis of the earth itself has varied. That is much more unlikely than the alternative, which would support the Wegener theory, that the crust of the earth itself has changed in relation to the poles. That crust, the skin of the earth's surface, whether intact or rifted, must have moved, so that it was the land masses and not the poles which were creeping around. Since the sun must have remained constant in relation to the equator, this idea of movement would give a consistent explanation to the prevailing mysteries of how you can get coal from primeval tropical forests in Ellesmere Island in the Arctic. Coal deposits occur similarly in Antarctica.

The Continental Drift Theory also provides a rational explanation of the mountain systems of western North America, Central America and South America—the Rockies, the Sierras and the Andes. Those great upthrust ranges could, in fact, be the bow waves of the sial pushing against the resistance of the sima. And the theory is also very accommodating when it comes to problems of the diffusion of plant and animal species. Zoologists and botanists have always had to look for "land bridges" to account for the diversification and similarities of plants and creatures widely separated. It would, for example, account for the differentiation of the animals in Australia—the marsupials, which developed there apparently after the continent was separated from Asia and Africa. It might even account for the presence of elemental cotton in South America. Unfortunately it does not solve the further riddle of how that cotton was retransferred to the Eurasian land mass separated by the width of an ocean.

This land movement, if it happened as Wegener suggested, must have happened long before *Homo sapiens* got his urge to travel or, indeed, before he existed in terms other than of his simian ancestors. The theory could take care of the South American monkeys, akin to, but different from, their Old World relatives; but to account for Man in the Western Hemisphere, it would have to assume a separate creation. That is so unlikely as to be ruled out, and, anyway, there has never been any evidence in the Americas of anything to encourage the idea that *Homo sapiens*, or his alter ego, evolved there. Indeed, there has never been found anywhere in the Americas any evidence of Paleolithic industry, although the excavations of the campus of the University of Alaska have turned up tools like those found in Neolithic stations in the Gobi Desert. Other stone implements, defined by archeologists as "Folsom Culture," occur in conjunction with remains of extinct bison at sites in Colorado and New Mexico. Far to the south, in a cave on the southern tip of Argentina, the evidence of an extinct sloth is mixed up with the tools and refuse of men who hunted and ate an extinct type of American horse. (Remember that it is generally assumed that the horse was first introduced into the Western Hemisphere by the Spaniards.) These human vestiges, however, do not have the antiquity of Geologic Man in Europe, but Man may well have come to America between 15,000 and 25,000 years ago. This suggests a land bridge between Asia and America; and the later migrations of the Eskimos, which can be dated back 4,000 years, indicate that the land bridge may have been the Aleutian Islands, over which the Eskimos would have crossed the Bering Strait (an alternative theory has been presented that they crossed the frozen waters of the Strait).

6 Origins of the Indians

IT IS fairly obvious how the Indians came, but where did they come from? The immediate answer is, of course, "Asia," since they crossed the Strait. And, in broad terms, they would be described as Mongoloids, but in the great geographic span, from Alaska to Patagonia, the American Indian shows a great diversity. It is easy to describe the Eskimos as "Mongols" because of their physical appearance, which is indistinguishable from that of the

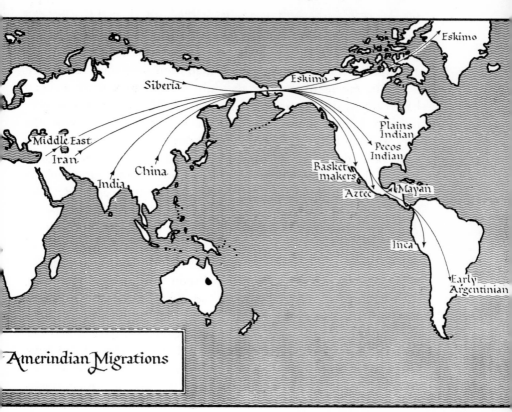

Amerindian Migrations

Chukchi, their neighbors on the Asiatic side. The Chukchi, in turn, are recognizably akin to Chinese, Japanese, Burmese, Tibetans, Siamese, etc. While the American Indian has the pigmentation of skin, hair form and facial size of the Asiatic Mongol, in general he lacks other characteristics by which we identify the Mongol. The fold of the eye, for example, is not conspicuous in any of the Indians south, one might say, of the tree line. Nor is the hawk nose of so many of the Indian tribes Asiatic in the Far Eastern sense. Indeed, it has been identified with the types of the Persian plateau, which, as we have seen, were inherently Aryan in character.

Other types of Indians have been linked to the Egyptians. For example, the skulls of Arizona basketmakers and of the Coahuila cave men resemble Egyptian craniums. This might suggest exciting possibilities of an Atlantic *Kon-Tiki* and an explanation of a kind of affinity between the Aztec and Maya calendar systems and those of the Nile Valley. This, however, would be an extravagant assumption. The transatlantic sea migration is so implausible that it can be taken for granted that any movement was by a "long haul" across the continent of Asia. It could suggest that in prehistoric Indian times there was a common origin with the Egyptians in a Eurafrican Mediterranean type. The Pecos Indians have been described as "pseudo-Negroid," and this term again goes back to remotest history and was not in anticipation of the African migration in the slave trade. Amerindian types have also been identified with the Dravidians of the Indus Valley.

Another attempt to identify the American Indians, both North and South, with a specific racial type was the temporary cult of the O blood group. At one time blood grouping, now such an important feature in blood transfusion for medical purposes, was supposed to have established the individuality of the American Indian as belonging invariably to group O. This group lacks the agglutinogens A and B. The first samplings gave a 100 per cent of group O for various types of Indians. This would have suggested a unity of the American race—an immigration of one common stock—but it was bewildering because of the enormous differentiation of physical types manifested in the Indians of the Americas. The prevalence of the B agglutinogen in Asia and its hereditary dominance over the O group with its absence of agglutinogens was explainable only on the assumption that both A and B changes in the blood groups appeared in Asia subsequent to the migrations of the Amerinds. In later surveys it was found that the "100 per cent O" was spurious. The first B group was found among the western Eskimos. Then a high percentage of group A was found among the Blackfeet, and later only 23 per cent of group O was found in the Ceraga Indians of Brazil. Later, when methods were devised for testing the blood groups of mummified tissue, it was found that all four of the blood groups appeared in Peruvian mummies. It was then obvious that the predominance of group O in American Indians had no clear bearing on the question of unity of the American race.

In the sum, all that has been discovered has shown not a unity but a diversity. Over the common bridge, and in the course of uncounted centuries, indeed, millenniums, successive waves of immigrants entered and spread over the two continents of America. They had obviously been filtering across Asia and had added to other characteristics—Eurafrican or Dravidian or Iranian—traits which they shared in common with the Mongols.

Their journeys and diffusions did not stop until the whole hemisphere had been traversed and occupied. Petrified footprints of these early peoples have been found beside the petrified footprints of bison in Nicaragua—the bison which became extinct thousands of years ago. In Brazil and in Ecuador similar imprints are found and right south to the tip of Patagonia. There, in the cave called Palli Aike, in the crater of an extinct volcano, have been found the bones of the sloth and of an extinct horse, along with the remains of the ancient Indian artifacts belonging to periods widely separate in time. Those Patagonian remains are estimated to be between 3,000 and 5,400 years old.

The spread southward may have been in part due to the pressures of waves of immigrants. But in the main one can suppose that what compelled them first to cross the Aleutian bridge from Asia, then go down through the corridor east of the Rockies and into the great plains and finally into the jungles of South America, was just that impulsive urge which today pushes men from this earth onward to the moon, to the planets and to the stars. And in the course of thousands of years they changed their ways, some drastically, some scarcely at all. Some were content to remain hunters, like the Indians of the prairies; others became settlers and formed their pueblo villages, and some went forward into advanced cultures, like the Mayans, the Toltecs, the Aztecs and the Incas. Some degenerated to become, or remain, the primitive tribes of the equatorial jungles.

At the time of the discovery of America the total population of Indians in both North and South America was perhaps thirty millions, although what is now the United States contained only some 1,000,000. Most of the North American Indians were still hunters. They consisted of over six hundred distinct societies living under conditions ranging from the warm coastlands to the Arctic ice, from the Florida swamps to the frozen tundras, from the Atlantic woodlands to the Western deserts. They were "uncivilized" only if we identify civilization with material cultures. In general they were civilized in their relations with each other and in their recognition of the innate human and spiritual values.

7 *The Confederacy of the Pine*

THE MOST important Indian grouping on the continent north of Mexico was the Confederacy of the Iroquois. In the subsequent exploitation of the Indians and of their lands, white men had to justify their own cruelty by condemning the savagery of the Indians. All brutality is relative. Indeed, we might remind ourselves that "savage" came from the French *"sauvage"* and meant merely "the woodland people" until it became connected with brutality. The Confederacy was probably one of the most enlightened institutions that the world has ever known. It came into being some time around the middle of the sixteenth century —fifty years after Columbus discovered America, or about fifty years before the first settlements of the White Man. It was a league of five tribes, the Mohawk, the Seneca, Oneida, Cayuga and Onondaga. It was brought into existence to renounce war as between the tribes. The code of the Confederacy read:

The Confederated chiefs now uproot the tallest pine tree and into the cavity thereby made we cast all weapons of war. Into the depths of the earth, deep down into the under-earth currents of water, flowing to unknown regions we cast all weapons of strife. We bury them from sight and we plant again the tree. Thus shall the Great Peace be established.

The peace aims of the Confederacy were universal. Any Indian on the continent could enter the Confederacy. The whole prospect was changed through the settlements by the whites and by their imperial struggles. Outside the Confederacy were the Cherokees. After the creation of the United States the Cherokees wrote a constitution of the White Man's kind. They established a legislature, a judiciary and an executive branch. A free press and public-school system was set up, and in their relations with the white man they kept faith, although the white man consistently betrayed them. In the end they were expelled from their lands and driven into Arkansas. On that trek 4,000 Cherokees died.

8 South of the Rio Grande

THE GREAT FLOWERING of Indian culture, however, was in the south, in Mexico and beyond that in Peru. Down the wedge-shaped plateau of Mexico the Indians came uncounted thousands of years ago. Presumably for thousands of years they lived as hunters and they moved, following their animals, to places where water or salt could be found.

Then, in a great undetermined moment, came the discovery of maize. The introduction of this plant into Mexico was the essential factor in the economic groundwork of the civilization which was established. The fibers of the maguey of the plateau and the cactus in Yucatán provided the second requisite, fibers for clothmaking. But while the Peruvians had their llamas— that strange camellike creature which somehow, like the men, had come from Asia—the Mexicans had only their backs. In a mountainous country an animal to draw the plow is not as essential as on a level plain beside a river, but it is obviously more necessary to carry the burdens up a steep, rocky road. Certainly one of the restrictions on the development of Mexican

GULF OF MEXICO

Huaxtec

Morelos
Aztec
MEXICO CITY
Puebla
Mixtec
Zapotec

Totonacapan
Olman

Mayan

Main Archaeological Regions
of Central America

culture and economy was the lack of beasts of burden. Men, or rather women, relieved the need.

With the development of maize there was food to be stored. Men no longer had to give all their time to the search for food. The story, as everywhere, repeated itself: specialization of tasks became possible; leisure, religion and art developed.

Out of the maize civilization developed three well-known cultures, the Mayas', the Toltecs' and the Aztecs'. The first may have been the most ancient of the three. The Mayas moved from the plateau into Guatemala—pushed out, presumably, by the second, the Toltecs, who in their turn were replaced on the plateau by the Aztecs.

9 *The Mayas*

CERTAIN FACTS seem to be reasonably well established. With justification we can claim that on August 6 in the year 613 B.C. the time record of the Mayas was begun. This is their year zero; it is exact and definite, founded on calculations, which remain with us, of lunar and solar eclipses. From the evidence of these calculations it can be assumed that the Mayas had been studying the stars for well over 2,000 years. It would take that long to work out that kind of calendar. Some authorities believe that the Mayas built the great pyramids at Teotihuacán. Some place the high point of the culture which built these pyramids at 500 B.C., but others date it later. About the time that Christ was born, the first Maya empire was founded in Guatemala, and it is agreed that its great period was between A.D. 450 and 600. The architecture, sculpture and painting in those Central American ruins of this period are the most highly developed, artistically balanced and beautiful yet found. We might remind ourselves that Europe at this moment was floundering in the darkest era of the Dark Ages. Rome had been sacked and Charlemagne was yet to come. At that period, during those 150 years, the Mayas were almost assuredly the most civilized people on the planet.

10 The Toltecs

IN A.D. 1191 the Mayas of Yucatán were overthrown by a great prince from the Mexican plateau called Quetzalcoatl. Although he was later identified with gods, there is no doubt that he had a temporal reality. He is blamed for blood sacrifice but he obviously conferred great boons upon the people, for he was remembered in their mythology as the redeemer who was to return and restore the Golden Age. That, we remember from our schoolbooks, was the undoing of the Indians because, according to prophecies, Quetzalcoatl was due to return to earth and glorify his people in the year A.D. 1518. Like the sun, he was to come out of the east. Cortes, his armor glinting, came out of the east and became the embodiment of Quetzalcoatl, with disastrous results for the Indians. The Golden Age became the Rape of Gold; the redemption became subjugation.

Before his apotheosis, Quetzalcoatl was the Toltec king, priest, astronomer and culture-hero extraordinary, who taught all art, wisdom and kindness to his people. He "borrowed" the Mayan calendar and reduced it to a system of signs and ideographs which could be understood by the diverse peoples of Central America.

Following a series of outrages committed by the invaders, the citizens rise in arms against the Spanish. The Spaniards and their Tlaxcalan allies are besieged in the palace of Axayacatl. In this scene a field piece is shown in action, while the horsemen are held in reserve for a sortie. Lienzo de Tlazcala

The story of the Toltecs is one of great confusion—thanks to the activities of the Bishop Zumárraga who, after the Spanish Conquest, took all the records of the library of Texcoco and heaped them on a pyre "to the glory of God." Similarly Father Landa followed his superior's example and destroyed the Maya library in Yucatán. These records contained accounts of medicine, astronomy, chronology and the histories of the pre-Aztec peoples. In two fanatical days the priests did a job more thorough than the burning of the library at Alexandria.

What they could not destroy were the enduring remains at Teotihuacán. Here is the record of the Master Builders. The

Pyramid of the Sun is 750 feet square and 216 feet high. And this is just a fragment of the sacred city which was four miles long, two miles broad, and which had a citadel courtyard of 1,700,000 square feet. The buildings were covered with and the roads laid in cement. How they prepared the masonry and cut the hard, brittle obsidian of their ornaments still baffles the investigators. Their only metal was copper, much too soft for shaping the stones. They used some kind of emery to smooth the stones (like the courtyard in Montezuma's capital, which was so mirror-smooth that Cortes's horses could not keep their feet). Perhaps, as the experts suggest (with some hesitation), they had a steel which has rusted away without trace. Nor is there any explanation of the microscopic detail of some of their gem carvings—unless the craftsmen used crystal magnifying glasses.

Teotihuacán perished in the late tenth and early eleventh centuries A.D. Its downfall has been ascribed to religious conflict, revolt and the failure of crops. Archeological evidence would confirm that. It would appear that the priesthood acquired delusions of grandeur and that in the last stages of the city, which had progressively grown, there was a sort of cancerous growth. The excessive demand for construction could, by its drain on human resources, have produced revolt. But it can be sensibly assumed that it was not only the people but nature which revolted.

To get the lime cement for this excess of piety the neighboring forests must have been extravagantly destroyed. The Indian method of producing quicklime required ten times as much wood as the limestone to be reduced. To this ten-to-one proportion must be added the fact that without metal axes or saws, of which there is no surviving evidence, the simplest way of producing charcoal in quantity is to set fire to the forests themselves, without the refinement of cutting down the trees. I, personally, would accept the evidence. The bald hills around the Valley of Mexico and around the Valley of Oaxaca in the south would testify to such destruction of forests and, in their degree, to a pre-Conquest destruction.

If this were so, then the failure of crops which starved out the Teotihuacánians could be rationally explained by the deforestation which, without the trees to filter the rains into the underground springs and by producing runoff and erosion, would dry up the streams and wreck the once-fertile lands.

Across the great lakes, which once nearly filled the Valley of Mexico, the Toltecs survived in the other great city of Azcapotzalca. This land is cultivated at the present time and the needs of agriculture have led to the razing of the ruins, but the peasants there are continually turning up the evidence of a once-rich culture. It petered out somewhere at the end of the twelfth century A.D.

Once again archeology finds eloquent evidence of the fate which overtook a people. A large cluster of baby burials, all contemporary, suggests that starvation and resulting infantile mortality overtook a culture which is otherwise distinguished by its abundance.

11 *The New Fire*

THE NEW FIRE CEREMONY was the climacteric occasion of the Aztec calendar. It occurred once in every fifty-two years. It marked the end of one phase of the universe and the beginning of the next. The altar fires which had burned continuously for fifty-two years were extinguished. In their homes the people allowed their hearth fires to die, destroyed all their household goods and fasted and bewailed their impending fate, because this could be the end of the world. Unless the gods would grant a new dispensation, their life would end.

183

Then, as the sun set at the end of the epoch, a procession of priests representing all the gods of the Aztecs would march toward the summit of Huixachtecatl, the Hill of the Star, timing their arrival at its crowning temple for midnight. The fate of mankind rested on a star, believed to be one of the Pleiades. If that star crossed the zenith, that meant survival. If it should falter, it would mean the end of the world.

When the star crossed the zenith, as it inevitably did, a human victim, specially beloved of the gods, was sacrificed. In the breast of the victim they kindled a fire—the "New Fire"—and from this fire torches were lit to rekindle the flames in every temple in the city. From those temple fires the people relit their hearth fires. Life had been assured for another fifty-two years.

By virtue of this ceremony the history of the Aztecs (in spite of Bishop Zumárraga and Father Landa, the record burners) can be accurately dated. The destruction of the household goods is represented by the accumulated potsherds on the archeological sites. There is no deposit for the cyclical celebration of 1559

A handful of the Spaniards reach the mainland. The Aztecs, instead of following up their advantages, plunder the bodies of the killed and drowned. Be it remembered, however, that the Spanish carried off the entire Aztec treasure. Codex Florentino

because the Spanish Conquest intervened in 1519, but others can be traced backward, through pottery, from 1507 to 1455; from 1455 to 1403; from 1403 to 1352, etc. Working back through nine cycles of fifty-two years, we reach the year zero in the Aztec calendar—A.D. 1091.

Into the Valley of Mexico, already culturally developed, there came somewhere about 1168 a vigorous people. At first they lived on an island on a lake in western Mexico and crossed in boats to the shore. They began to migrate. They stopped at various places, all of which in retrospect acquired a religious significance but which in fact were no more than the patterns of a shifting cultivation—the workings of primitive agriculturists wearying the soil until it tired and the yields dropped. Finally they reached the lakes of the Valley of Mexico, where they peacefully settled in what is now Chapultepec, near the present Mexico City. As they prospered they pressed upon their neighbors and their neighbors pressed upon them, and wars resulted. To their punitive expeditions they added the blood sacrifice of prisoners, a cult which they had brought with them.

This cult of human sacrifice, by which we remember the Aztecs and by which the Conquistadores justified their own excesses, had already acquired a mystical significance. Although it is hard to believe, to be sacrificed was an end devoutly to be wished. The victims who had their living hearts torn out were supposed to realize that they were the privileged of the gods. This theory was apt to confuse their neighbors whom they raided to secure sacrificial victims.

For example, in their early days in the valley, the Aztecs were seeking to curry favor with a powerful chief, Coxcox. They sought the hand of his daughter for their own chief. He gave his consent, but when she arrived she was so beautiful, and his gift was so great, that in humility they regarded her as too good for them. So they made her the Bride of the Gods, sacrificed her and draped her skin on a priest to impersonate a nature goddess called Toci. The father, who had been invited to a ceremony of marriage, not with the gods but with the chief, did not appreciate the honor which was thus conferred upon his daughter and summoned his armies to exterminate the Aztecs, who fled back to the islands on the lake. There they lived as outcasts in a Mexican community of cultures which had not been disfigured hitherto by the sacrificial cults.

On these cramped islands they confronted the problem of survival in an ingenious way. They created the "floating gardens," the chinampas. These were man-made islands contrived by scooping up mud from the marshy borders of the lake and by holding it in place by a breastwork of reeds. Then trees were planted, the roots of which bound the earth solidly together. Between those extensive "baskets" of soil the water flowed in a regular system of canals. Fresh mud was always added before each planting so that the organic matter was continually renewed. In this way the Aztecs converted the otherwise unproductive marsh into a grid of canals and fields of rich fertility. Thus they inverted the process which we find in the Nile Delta, where the rivers created the silt beds and the Egyptians cut the canals through them. This system of chinampa agriculture still exists in the districts of Xochimilco and Chalco, where most of the vegetables and flowers are still grown for the needs of Mexico City. They are still a rural Venice for the tourists who meander through the network of gardens in garlanded boats.

12 *The Lake Civilization*

IN TIME there grew up a lake civilization based on the island on which the Aztecs built their city of Mexico-Tenochtitlán. Standing in Lake Texcoco, linked to the shore and surrounded by the green and colorful islands, the chinampas, that city inspired the rude soldiery of Spain to rhapsody—and rapine.

"It is like the enchantments they tell of in the legend of Amadis," hymned Bernal Díaz del Castillo, the companion of Cortes. "Are not the things we see a dream?"

Here was paradise. As the Spaniards looked down into the valley they saw the oval island and its three causeways from the center of the city to the mainland. It was like a jeweled ornament, with the white opalesque buildings of the temples of the city surrounded by the emerald and ruby clusters of the green fields and red-flaming gardens pinned on the blue bosom of the lake.

Above the square blocks of the houses rose the truncated pyramids, like the Babylonian ziggurats, each with their temple on top and the plazas around. It was a city of patios, cloistered courtyards, and arcades. Apart from the extensions of the lake causeways, the city had no roads, but it was interlaced with canals, along which the peasants brought their canoes and supply boats. There were no wheeled vehicles because the wheel, except in the calendar sense, did not exist among the Aztecs. Nor, until the Spanish invasion, were there any horses. Movement was by water or on foot.

Into this fabulous city rode the Spanish invaders. At the head came Cortes, the bearded white man in his glistening armor, mounted on a horse, an animal the Aztecs had never seen. Obviously this was the reincarnated Quetzalcoatl, the Plumed Serpent, the God of Civilization! Behind him came the 400 Spaniards. They rode across the causeway, a remarkable piece of engineering, executed with geometrical precision and composed of huge stones well laid in cement and wide enough for ten horsemen to ride abreast. As they marched on this dike they passed several large towns resting on piles and reaching far into the water. The lake populations, apart from their crops, maintained a trade from the manufacture of the salt which they extracted from the waters of the lake. The waters swarmed with canoes. The sixteenth-century Spanish historian, Antonio de Herrera, estimated 50,000

of them. Near the approaches to the capital they encountered
Fort Xoloc, a battlemented gateway flanked by towers which
was the outer defense of the city a mile and a half away. Where
the causeway reached the island there was a drawbridge which
gave onto a broad avenue, and the Spaniards passed among the
temples whose altars were blazing with the fifty-two-year fires.
As they marched down the spacious street the troops crossed
bridges over the canals on which the Indian boats glided backward and forward with their cargoes of fruits and vegetables.

*The Spanish flotilla puts to sea. These galleys, equipped with oars and a sail
and armed with a cannon in the bow, could play havoc with the Aztec war
canoes.* Codex Florentino

TEMPLE OF THE SUN *Aztec pyramid of Tenayuca, Mexico* [American Museum of Natural History]

13 *The Halls of Montezuma*

FROM THE PYRAMID of the War God, Montezuma gave Cortes a godlike view of the city. Bernal Díaz wrote:

Then Montezuma took Cortes by the hand and told him to look at his great city and all the other cities that were standing in the water and the many other towns and the land around the lake. . . . So we stood looking about us, for that huge and cursed temple stood so high that from it one could see over everything very well, and we saw the three causeways which led into Mexico . . . and

TEMPLE OF THE WATERS *Hydroelectric powerhouse, Kemano, British Columbia, being excavated out of solid rock, a quarter of a mile inside Mount DuBose* [Aluminum Co. of Canada, Ltd.]

we saw the aqueduct of fresh water that comes from Chapultepec, which supplies the city, and we saw the bridges on the three causeways which were built at certain distances apart . . . and we beheld on the lake a great multitude of canoes, some coming with supplies of food, others returning loaded with cargoes of merchandise, and we saw that from every house of that great city and of all the other cities that were built in the water it was impossible to pass from house to house except by drawbridge, which were made of wood, or in canoes; and we saw in those cities temples and oratories like towers and fortresses and all gleaming white, and it was a wonderful thing to behold.

Thus Montezuma received Cortes as the ambassador of a great monarch. He made the Spaniards his honored guests with hospitality which they abused. They abducted Montezuma and subjected the superstitious priest-king, already doomed by his own astrology, to psychological torture which modern brain-washers have never surpassed. When he was no more than a zombie, a walking corpse, drained of his spiritual lifeblood, he was killed. It is irrelevant whether the blow that killed him was a stone thrown by his outraged people or whether he was actually murdered by the Spaniards. In the sequel, his nephew Guatemotzin was put to torture in an effort to force him to reveal where gold was hidden, and he was hanged by Cortes.

14 *Tenochtitlán and Hiroshima*

How A SMALL BAND of Europeans could subjugate a "great empire" can no longer be regarded as a miracle or a mystery. Montezuma was no monarch. He was the leader of a group of tribes with a mystical, but not constitutional, authority. He was not the head of a hegemony of the other tribes of Central America but merely identified with a small but strong group which could periodically intimidate others into paying tribute but which had no administrative authority of feudal powers or of military levy. No one doubts the desperate courage of the small band of Spaniards, but their initial advantage was gained by "psychological warfare." This was fortuitous—the myth of Quetzalcoatl and the coincidence of his prophesied return with the arrival of the white man; the appearance of the unknown horse (with Cortes subtle enough to realize the terrifying effect of the bellowing of a frustrated stallion); and the effects of edged and

ycpolínhq̃ mexñca

Cuauhtemoc, who conducted the defense of Tenochtitlán, is received with all the honors of war by Cortes and his consort, Marina. In the upper right Cortes may be seen greeting Cuauhtemoc's wife and family. The legend translated reads: "With this event, the Mexicans were finished." Lienzo de Tlaxcala

burnished steel, with the coincidental superstitious significance of plumes, which the Spaniards could not have foreseen. The subsequent disruption of the Indians was not the result of their defeat in battle but of famine through disintegration of an agricultural economy and of disease, introduced or released by the White Man.

As many were killed in the three months' siege of Tenochtitlán by the Conquistadores as were destroyed by the atom bombs on Hiroshima and Nagasaki. (Estimates in both events vary between 120,000 and 240,000.) Yet the horrific story of that ruthless slaughter and destruction is still only an incident, not a culmination. We have already seen how the burning of forests for charcoal for the cement of the temples and cities had bared the mountains. Now, in their conquest, the Spaniards accelerated the process. They destroyed the capital and other lake cities, but Cortes wanted to build again to the glory of Spain, and he chose the site of Tenochtitlán, Montezuma's city which he had so thoroughly destroyed.

15 *The Death of a Valley*

PRESCOTT, who goes on record in his *History of the Conquest of Mexico* as saying, "The empire of the Aztecs did not fall before its time," gives an account of the rebuilding of the city in four years—on the Spanish model and on a grandiose scale.

The labor was to be performed by the Indians, drawn from all quarters of the valley, and including the Mexicans themselves, great numbers of whom still lingered in the neighborhood of their ancient residence. At first they showed reluctance and even hostility when called to this work of humiliation by their conquerors. But Cortes had the address to secure some of the principal chiefs in his interests, and under their direction and authority the labor of their countrymen was conducted. The deep groves of the Valley and the forests of the neighboring hills supplied cedar, cypress and other durable wood for the interior of the buildings and the quarries of *tetzontil* and the ruins of ancient edifices furnished an abundance of stone. As there were no beasts of draught employed by the Aztecs an immense number of hands was needed for the work. All within the immediate control of Cortes were pressed into service. The spot so recently deserted now swarmed with multitudes of Indians of various tribes. . . . The prophecy of the Aztecs was accomplished. . . .

(This prophecy was their taunt to the tribes which had become the allies of the Spaniards. "Go on," they said to the Indians who were destroying the capital. "The more you destroy, the more you will build again. If we conquer, you shall build for us; and if your white friends conquer, you will do the same for them." All the Indians, ex-allies and ex-friends, were reduced to peonage.)

Prescott continues:

And the work of reconstruction went forward with a rapidity like that shown by an Asian despot, who concentrates the population of an empire on the erection of a favorite capital.

But Prescott, who justified almost anything because of the human sacrifice practiced by the Aztecs (a practice which had prevailed in various degrees during less than two hundred years of the history of the Central American Indian), saw no connection between this frenzy of despotic building and his description of the lake and its adjoining cities:

But a generation had scarcely passed after the Conquest before a sad change came over these scenes so beautiful. The town [Iztapalapan] was deserted and the shore of the lake was strewed with the wreck of buildings which were once its ornament and glory. The [floating] gardens shared the fate of the city. The retreating waters withdrew the means of nourishment, converting flourishing plains into a foul and unsightly morass, the haunt of loathsome reptiles. And the waterfowl built her nest in what had once been the palaces of princes.

The ruined gardens? The retreating waters? Cortes had impressed 400,000 Indians, the people who had made a lake arable with floating gardens. He had cut down the timbers for the glorification of his palaces and churches. And he had built in stone and stucco which, remembering the Indian proportions of ten tons of charcoal to one ton of limestone, meant the devastation of forests by firing.

"The retreating waters withdrew the means of nourishment." The level of the lake fell through the loss of springs, suckled by the forests. The lakes, as they became shallower, became more and more salt, until in the end they became just salt pans. And the process thus started went on remorselessly through the centuries until Lake Texcoco withdrew her skirts from Tenochtitlán and the Mexico City of today stands on a dusty plateau, once water-filled.

16 *The Unhatched Egg*

THUS A PEOPLE who may have originated from the Persian plateau or the Indus Valley, and who during the aeons of time had traversed Asia and North America to establish a civilization in Central America, became the serfs and the slaves of a people who had taken a shorter cut, across the Atlantic.

It has been said by Stuart Chase, "In astronomy the American mind reached its climax and the Mayas were its high priests." Over 4,000 years ago the first material which went into the creation of the Mayas' calendar must have been collected and built up into a system in which it is possible to distinguish, without duplication, any given day in 370,000 years. They had discovered the zero, the symbol indispensable to modern science, higher mathematics, and our mechanical age. It is generally claimed that zero, the "unhatched egg," was derived by Europe, from the Hindus, through the Arabs. But, in Hindu terms, the discovery was made not earlier than A.D. 600, while the Mayas had discovered it centuries before. Of physics and geometry the Mayas had a practical knowledge, and they were exceptionally highly developed draftsmen.

These people, the Mayas, the Aztecs and the rest, had an advanced medical system in which they employed herbal remedies, including a digitalis (which the English doctor, Withering, was to rediscover in the eighteenth century, as a treatment for heart disease). They had an extensive knowledge of the working

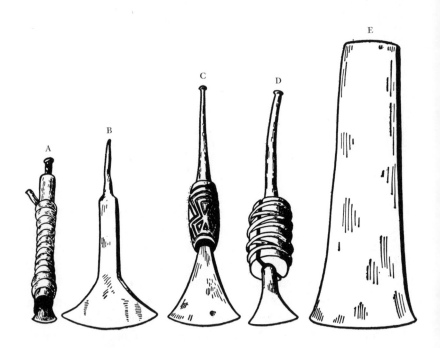

Inca surgical instruments. These were found in graves with gauze bandages and a form of primitive but very effective tourniquet. A *Bronze scalpel, wrapped with leather thongs.* B *Bronze* tumi *for making incisions in bone.* C *Another form of scalpel with ornamented bone handle.* D *Bronze scalpel with wooden handle.* E *Larger bronze scalpel; specific use unknown.*

of the human frame, of its skeleton, its muscles and its nervous system. The Mayas were particularly skilled in treating diseases of the eye. The Aztec hospitals and refuges for veteran soldiers evoked the admiration of the Spanish conquerors, who discovered that these "barbarians" had a sanitary system far in advance of anything they had left behind them in Europe; in the capital city there were over 1,000 street cleaners.

The Mexican tribes, each in their various ways, had impressive and diversified social systems. Even in what, geographically, would appear to be close proximity, they kept their diversity.

For example, the Zapotecs on Monte Alban were practicing human sacrifice (which they passed on to the Aztecs) while the people of Mitla, only a few miles away, were contemporaneously practicing a religion which abjured human sacrifice. It is also obvious from the archeological remains that the Indians had mass-production factories a long way ahead of the Industrial Revolution.

But, above all, they had brought agriculture to a high degree of efficiency and (in the breeding of maize, for instance) of sophistication.

17 *The Fate of the Inca*

To THE SOUTH, beyond the Isthmus of Panama and Nicaragua, flowered the civilization with which this part of the book started —the Incas'. They, too, were the heirs of previous cultures. The Andeans appear to have had little, if any, contact with their neighbors in Central America. But they were to suffer the same remorseless fate.

There are few uglier stories in history than the fate which overtook the Inca, Atahualpa. It is true—another of those grim coincidences—that when the Spaniards arrived, the empire of the Incas which had survived and grown in the stability of three centuries, with little recourse to war, was in the throes of a dynastic struggle between Atahualpa and his half brother Huáscar.

Atahualpa had emerged triumphant and was on his way to the capital, Cuzco, to be installed as the Inca, the Living God. On his progress he had stopped to take the sulphur baths at Cajamarca. There he heard of the arrival of the small band of

Spaniards under Pizarro. Again the element of superstition comes in; there was a legend that the Inca's Creator God, Kon-Tiki Viracocha, had forsaken his people because he was dissatisfied with them and that one day he would return. Atahualpa believed that the Spaniards were the gods themselves, coming to conduct him to Cuzco to invest him as the Inca. But presently, when he heard how they raped the Virgins of the Sun in one of the temples, he suspected that they were no gods. But, either because he felt secure in his supremacy as the Sun King or because of native Peruvian hospitality, he gave instructions that the newcomers were to be received everywhere with honor and friendship. He then invited them to meet him in the plaza at Cajamarca. He ordered his own warriors to come unarmed so as not to give offense to their visitors.

On the evening of November 16, 1532, at the hour of the Christian vespers, the Inca was carried in his litter, surrounded by his unarmed bodyguard, into the plaza. On three sides of the square were low ranges of buildings, with spacious halls and wide doorways. There, in concealment, Pizarro had already stationed two divisions of his cavalry on their horses, those animals unfamiliar to the Incas, and had posted guns.

There is the fantastic story of the priest who challenged the Inca in the name of the Pope and commanded him to turn to Christianity. He propounded the nature of the Trinity and bewildered the Inca by trying to prove that three in fact was four. In the upshot the priest lost patience, accused the Sun King of insulting the Bible and the Pope, and rushed to Pizarro and said, "Do you not see while we are standing here wasting our breath, talking to this dog, full of pride as he is, the fields are filling with Indians. Set on at once!" Pizarro obeyed the injunction. The White Men's guns roared and the cavalry dashed from their ambush to massacre the helpless Indians and to kidnap their Inca. Only one Spaniard was wounded, but some 10,000 Peruvians died that day.

Then came the Inca's fatal mistake over the ransom. He had issued orders, to avoid further bloodshed, commanding his people not to avenge the massacre or the indignities to his person. But he had formed a pretty shrewd estimate of the Spaniards and realized that their desire to convert him to their religion was less than their rapacity for gold. He decided to appeal to the avarice of his keepers and told Pizarro that, as the price of his freedom, he would fill a room with gold. The apartment to be filled was seventeen feet broad and twenty-two feet long, and the height he agreed to fill was nine feet above the floor. In

The litter was the principal transport for the nobility. The Inca and his Coya-queen being carried by Rucana tribesmen.

199

addition to filling this with gold, he agreed to fill another room twice over with silver. He undertook to do it within two months.

The couriers of the Incas went out over the land, traveling fast-foot across the Andes and down to the coastal plains, and the gold arrived within the stipulated period. By modern estimates the gold that filled that treasure room was worth £75,000,000.

The Inca had sentenced himself to death. If he could command such riches at such short notice, there was obviously much more that he could withhold. So the pretext was found that he had used the gathering of the ransom to communicate with his people throughout a vast empire and to alert them for a rising against the Spaniards. He was condemned to be burned at the stake.

Two hours after sunset on August 29, 1533, Atahualpa was led out, chained hand and foot. Father Valverde, whose argument on the Trinity had led to the kidnaping and the massacre ten months before, was at his side. As the Inca was bound to the stake with the faggots piled around him, the priest held up the cross and demanded that he renounce the faith of his fathers and embrace Christianity. In return, the priest promised he would be spared the fire and merely be strangled.

According to the Spanish account, which of course was useful in persuading the Indian peoples that their Inca had set an example, Atahualpa was converted and garroted.

In that blasphemous moment the Incas' civilization might have been strangled like Atahualpa. It did not die; it persists to this day, not as monuments and ruins, but as a culture and a way of life, with which European power and religion has had to compromise.

In its permanent effects the empire of the Incas left an imprint and an influence as profound as that of the Romans in Europe. We can call them "the Romans of the Western Hemisphere." This is not just a question of dimension; even by modern standards, and measured by the shortcomings of most of the world today, the system of government was remarkable.

18 The Andean Civilization

THE CRADLE of the Andean civilization was Peru but not one Peru—three Perus, all lying parallel to each other. First there was the Peru of the coastal desert; second, the Peru of the high Andes and the plateau; and third, the Peru of the jungle.

Along its coasts flowed the Humboldt Current, the Gulf Stream of the Pacific, of which Heyerdahl took advantage on his *Kon-Tiki* expedition (named for the "Uncreated Creator" of the Incas). This current brings to the coasts of Peru a strange compensation for the deserts which lie ashore. The waters are alive with swarming plankton, which make the sea fecund with fish, and this sea-life attracts birds in fantastic numbers. Those birds in turn complete the cycle of nature by depositing on the islands and along the coasts enormous quantities of guano dung, the accumulations of which once constituted the world's richest reserve of natural nitrates. The ancient Peruvians applied this fertilizer to the infertile deserts.

Into the valleys, running from the desert into the mountains, filtered a succession of immigrant peoples, who in their isolated valleys formed separate cultures. In their subsequent diffusion, and each in their own way, they extended their agricultural practices over the Andes and onto the plateau. From one of these group settlements around Lake Titicaca spread the Incas to become the rulers, but also the heirs, of the other cultures.

The earliest Inca chief known to history was Sinchi Roca, the beginning of whose rule may be fixed at A.D. 1105. Without wars and until his death, Sinchi Roca slowly extended his own tribal area along Lake Titicaca. His son then ruled and advanced, again without war, and his grandson, Mayta Capac, further enlarged the territory and the Inca influence without more than local skirmishes. That was true of all their subsequent history— they established a hegemony, not by wars of conquest, but by force of example and the authority of respect.

19 *The Golden Digging Stick*

THE BASIS of the Inca empire, as of all civilization, was agriculture. But, whereas in so many other civilizations the soil and its people became the slaves, in Peru the soil was paramount. The structure of society was rooted in a nature mysticism. There was no such thing as dead earth; all nature must be nursed into life. The sands of the desert and the highest slopes of the mountains were a challenge, and their cultivation was a sacred mission. The symbol of the soil, the huaca, or place-shrine, was everywhere. We can marvel at the wonderful terraces, stone aqueducts and rock reservoirs which remain to this day from pre-Conquest times, but they are a tribute not only to the technology and social system which created them but also to the religious zeal which sanctified the soil as the giver of all life.

The Inca governmental system was based on the village, but the village was not only a community of people but also a communion of the soil with these people. There was a complete identification between these people and their land. These villages might combine with others to form confederacies and accept leaders whose authority was hereditary. Before the coming of the Incas some of these had acquired a kind of feudal system, but it was a system based not on warriors but on farmers. The Incas had the sense, as they extended their influence, to

*Men and women plowing the fields together. The men use the foot plow,
called* taclla; *the women break up the clods of earth. Another woman brings
corn-*chicha *to drink.* Redrawn from Felipe Huaman-Poma de Ayala

preserve the social structures of their neighbors, while producing a general conformity of design.

In an oversimplified form the administration was something
like this: 10 households under an official, nominated by higher
authority but taken from their own number; 50 households
under a higher official; 100 households under an official who
was a minor lord, and so on—500, 1,000 and 10,000 households.
Over 40,000 the supervising officials were called "They-who-see-

all." Above these were what might be called viceroys, the governors of the four quarters of the empire.

Authority stemmed directly from the Inca to the peasant (or vice versa, since the Inca was the god-king embodiment of the soil and its workers). There was a nobility, an aristocracy of Inca royal blood, who were the keepers of traditions and who were trained for service through an intensive and, one gathers, extremely liberal education. Below the governors, the *apa-cunas*, no horizontal interrelation existed between the officials; the chain of command was vertical.

In August, which is the Peruvian season of plowing and sowing, the Inca and his nobility sacramentally returned to the soil. The season opened with a festival in which the Inca plowed the soil with a gold-tipped digging stick. This digging stick, which in the case of the peasant had a fire-hardened or metal tip, was a long pole, in principle like a spade because it had a footrest by which the cutter could be driven into the ground. The men worked backward; the women worked forward, breaking up the sods. All field work was manual, since they had no draft animals.

Thus the Inca system depended upon the ayllu, the village, which controlled the lands communally. These lands were divided between those which were earmarked for the Inca, i.e., state lands, the lands of the Sun, and those which supplied the village itself. The peasant tended his family plot, but at the sowing and the harvesting all the members of the ayllu worked in each other's fields. They shared the work, so that sickness of a breadwinner was never a burden on the family. No one in the group went hungry unless the whole group was hungry through some failure of the crop.

In their criminal law the Incas made a distinction between two forms of stealing. If a person stole from malice or avarice the punishment was death. But if he stole through want or necessity, then the official of his ayllu was punished for his lack of administration which provoked the crime. Honesty was

a basic creed. The Indians left the doors of their houses open—
a welcome to all comers—but if the owner was not at home,
a stick was laid symbolically in front of the door and nobody
would enter. The other cardinal crimes were murder, violence,
lying, adultery, and laziness. This penalty for laziness was like
the inescapable exactions of our modern income tax. Since there
was no money in the Inca economy, taxation or *mit'a* was in the
form of work service, and anyone who "slacked on the job"
was evading his taxes at the expense of his neighbors.

20 *The Work Levies*

APART FROM the usufructs of the Incas and the priests which
were piled up in the tithe houses of the villages, the peasants had
other citizen duties in the form of work levies. They were expected to supply labor for the mines, for the roads, for the
building of the rope suspension bridges across the gorges and
the public utilities like the extension of terracing, aqueducts and
reservoirs. If, for example, a rope suspension bridge (like that
of Apurimac-chaca, which was the subject of Thornton Wilder's
Bridge of San Luis Rey) had to be built or repaired, word would
be sent by the runners of the courier service to the ayllus to provide the levies.

The recruitment was on a decimal system. If a thousand
Indians were needed to cut the agave to get the fibers to be spun
into the thick cables and to undertake the adventurous work
of slinging the bridge across the gorge, then each headman of
ten villages would be asked to furnish a hundred Indians. The
men would be immediately mustered, for time was the essence
of obedience, and would be marched to the site. Scrupulously
fair records of such work service were kept in the knotted-string

The Apurimac-chaca—*the bridge that crossed the Apurimac River. Known in literature as the Bridge of San Luis Rey. It was one of the greatest engineering feats of the Incas. Although the fiber cables had to be changed every two years, the bridge survived from 1400 until 1880.* Drawn from a daguerreotype taken by E. George Squier in 1865

"ledgers" of the quipus. The work in the mines was recognized as a hateful form of service, and the hours of work and the term of duty were correspondingly short. Being sent to the mines for longer terms than those demanded by *mit'a*, or work taxes, was a form of punishment but not of slavery. All authorities are agreed that the basic work philosophy was: "All should work; none should work too much or too long and none should suffer want." This, the land and the labor, was the real wealth of the Incas, not the gold and silver which, by provoking the avarice of the conquerors, destroyed the empire.

In this enlightened society there was one law for the rich and one law for the poor, but in many respects it operated in the opposite sense to that in which we apply it today. The aristocracy, deriving their privileges from the blood of the Inca royal house, had exemptions from many of the laws which applied to the common people. For instance, they were allowed polygamy and concubinage while a rigorous monogamy, with the death penalty for adultery, applied to others. But in Inca society the people of the upper classes were given much more severe penalties than the lower classes for offenses against the mores or ethical laws. An offense which would call for the humiliation

The quipu, *as drawn by the Inca-Spanish chronicler. The dominolike figure to the left suggests the manner in which its decimal system of counting should be understood.*

of a public rebuke among the peasants would mean the loss of privileges and banishment for the noble who had failed in his example; a crime which would be punished by mutilation such as the loss of an eye or an ear among the common people would mean death to a noble. The code of law of the Incas, although it specified drastic punishments, was basically an appeal to the collective conscience and the sanctions of public opinion.

As we have seen, in Mesopotamia and elsewhere, the extension of agriculture beyond the self-evident arable lands depended on public utilities providing common services for groups of communities which could not provide for themselves unless they did so by rivalry or by encroaching on their neighbors' rights. In Peru the ultimate point of reference of all public utilities was the Inca himself. In principle and, one gathers, in practice the Inca was responsible for the building of the terraces, those living pyramids of basins of soil hewn out of, or built on, the mountain sides, which even today hold the soil which was accumulated there long before the Conquest. He was responsible for the great aqueducts, for the rock reservoirs and for the irrigation-canal systems. Woe to the governor or the official who betrayed the Inca by failing in his duty to safeguard these systems. There is evidence of instructions from the Inca himself being carried by couriers to remote parts of his empire, commanding specific ayllus to clear a specific section of a canal.

21 *The All-Seeing*

THIS SENSE of the All-Seeing Inca was maintained by an elaborate system of communications. In time of emergency fire and smoke codes were used by lighting dry-cotton tinder with concave mirrors. By this means news of some crisis could reach the Inca in Cuzco from places 2,000 miles distant in less than three hours. These were just forewarnings. For messages involving more information, the Incas had another system which was the fastest on earth until the invention of the telegraph. The Incas has an elaborate service of *chasqui*—couriers—who could run in relays between Quito and Cuzco, a distance of 1,250 miles, in five days, although the route traversed mountains 6,000 to 17,000 feet high, altitudes at which anyone, without the effort of running, would suffer from shortage of oxygen. They could run an average of 246 miles a day, which is two and a half times faster than the speed of Roman couriers. Even at great heights they could maintain an average speed of a mile in six and a half minutes.

Modern physiology can account, in part, for this prodigious capacity of the Andean runners. We find, today, a people adapted to great heights by having much bigger lungs than people of lower altitudes. Dr. Carlos Monge, the Peruvian biologist, has shown how they have become physiologically adapted in other ways; even reproduction at such altitudes is a matter of acclimatization.

Lung capacity was supplemented by extraordinary physical endurance which has been accounted for by the chewing of the leaves which provide cocaine. The drug apparently made them insensitive to both fatigue and hunger. The worshipful title held by the queens of the Incas was "Mama Coca"; the qualities of the coca plant were prized by the Incas as "a solace second only to women."

Just as the Romans maintained their grip over a far-flung empire by an elaborate system of roads, so did the Incas. The Roman system covered 56,000 miles through Europe, the Middle East and Africa, and that of the Incas, through the forbidding mountains of the Andes and up the entire length of desert coast, totaled over 10,000 miles of all-weather highways. The German scientist and author Baron Alexander von Humboldt has claimed

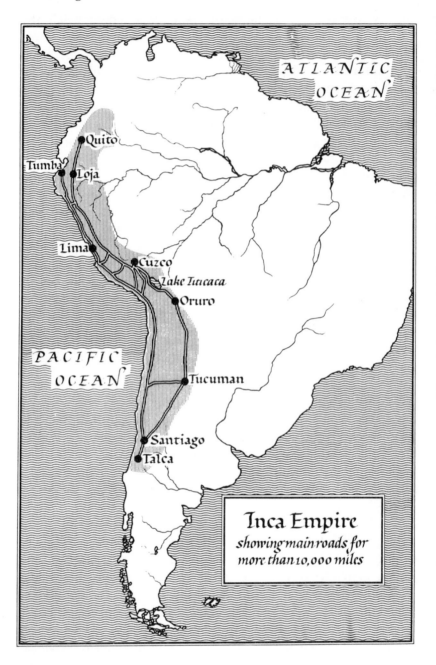

Inca Empire
*showing main roads for
more than 10,000 miles*

that as an engineering feat the Inca system surpassed that of the Romans.

There were two main arteries. The Royal Road ran through the Andes from beyond the equator, south through Ecuador, Peru, Bolivia, Argentina and Chile—a range of thirty-six degrees of latitude, or 3,250 miles. This makes it longer than the longest Roman road, from Hadrian's Wall, which divides England from Scotland, to Jerusalem. The Peruvian coastal road began at Tumbes, three degrees below the equator, and ran through the blistering desert, 2,520 miles, deep into Chile. In addition to these arterial roads there were link roads into and across the mountains which were prodigious feats of engineering, shelved out of the mountains, traversing gorges and in one case climbing to a height of 17,160 feet. There were roads to the mines and there were military roads, like the one which was pushed four hundred miles through the mountains, a road of masoned stone, for the purpose of subduing a tribe of Chanca outlaws.

The standard width of the Inca coastal road was twenty-four feet. It was not metal-surfaced because the desert soils could be packed hard enough for the foot and llama traffic, and wheeled vehicles and iron-shod horses had not yet arrived. But where the road passed over marshlands it was solidly built on a raised causeway and it was flanked on either side by walls to prevent sand drift and to contain the formations of marching soldiers. Another feature of this road engineering was the remarkable drainage methods which were embodied.

Even the Conquerors had ungrudgingly to admire the road system and to concede not only the ingenuity of the Inca's engineers but their humaneness. The roads, as De Léon wrote in 1550, were constructed "without increasing the death rate or causing excessive labor." Again each ayllu and each province were responsible for their sections, under the direction of the professional road builders who did the surveying and gave the instructions and left the local groups to complete the job under the distant All-Seeing Eye of the Inca.

In essence these were military roads, but for pacification,

not for wars of conquest. The armed police force, the professional army, never numbered more than 10,000. This was supplemented in times of danger by a civilian militia, automatically supplied by the ayllus.

Just as remarkable as the engineering work was the system of posts. Apart from the relay posts of the *chasqui*, which were one and a half miles apart (all each courier was expected to run), there were *tampu-chuna*, or inns for travelers. The main room of such an inn was from 100 to 300 feet long and 30 to 50 feet wide, with private apartments adjoining and continuously replenished food stores. These inns were built and serviced by each locality and were maintained at the expense of the Inca—a "ledger" transaction by which their maintenance and supply of the inns rated as part of the work-service tax.

22 *Welfare State, A.D. 1500*

THE SOIL belonged to the community of the people, but the metals beneath that soil belonged to the Inca. Since there was no conversion of that metal into coinage, no one could possess metal except the Inca and those to whom he delegated it for the purposes of ornamentation of temples, etc. Thus, although the nobility might have the perquisites of their position in the shape of concubines, rich clothes and princely establishments, they had no material wealth. They were landlords, not landowners, and could not hoard.

Prescott, who in general justified the Conquest for religious and romantic reasons, was nevertheless constrained to say:

If no man could become rich in Peru, no man could become poor. No spendthrift could waste his substance in riotous luxury. No adventurous schemer could impoverish his family by the spirit of speculation. . . . No mendicant was tolerated in Peru. When a man was reduced to poverty or misfortune (it could never be by fault) the arm of the law was stretched out to administer relief. Not the stinted relief of private charity nor that which is doled out from the frozen reservoirs of "the parish" but in generous measure, bringing no humiliation to the object of it and placing him on the level with the rest of his countrymen. . . . Ambition, avarice, the love of change, the morbid spirit of discontent, those passions which most agitate the minds of men, found no place in the bosom of the Peruvian.

After the Conquest, *mit'a*, the work-service tax of the Incas, became forced labor for the Conquerors. In the land where "all should work; none should work too much or too long," the slave Indians worked a twelve-hour day on a six months' stretch. In the areas of Lima and Charcas the number of Peruvian Indians declined from 1,490,000 in 1561 to 612,000 in 1754. Men and women, young and old, were forced to work in the mines without rest, and a people whose civilization had made hunger a crime were allowed a pint of maize a day. Outside the mines a people who had shared the wealth of the soil became debt slaves, eventually to be forced off the land and into the factories of the later industries.

Pretexts for conquests can always be found in history— if the history is written by the conquerors. But the soil speaks more eloquently than the written word—of an Inca population which lived in balance with nature, a population probably greater than that which exists today, on the same land, using the same waters. None was in want, where millions are today impoverished. From generation to generation the resources of the soil increased, where today they are diminished. The Indians of the Incas practiced that philosophy which says: "Live as though you would die tomorrow; farm as though you would live forever."

23 *From the Incas to the Eskimos*

AND NOW we pass from the high altitudes to the high latitudes; from the tropical heat of the Equator to the snow-covered barrens of the Arctic.

As far as one can judge, the Eskimos, as we know them today, were comparative late-comers to the American continent—much later than those who filtered through to Central and South America. They have, however, been there for at least 4,000 years.

On the Firth River, at a spot about twenty miles from the Beaufort Sea, there is what Dr. R. MacNeish of the National Museum of Canada has called the "Grand Central Station of the North." There, at a caribou crossing, have been found the relics of at least nine different cultures. Over 8,000 artifacts were discovered in one season's digging—implements of bone and stone, scrapers, arrowheads and pottery. Some were identical in design with those unearthed in eastern Siberia. This site had obviously been a favorite stopping place for a whole series of great migrations across the Bering Strait and into the western hemisphere. And for a very simple reason: this, for uncountable centuries, was where the caribou deer forded the river. With the blind constancy of the natural compulsions which remain the feature of caribou migrations, the animals had funneled through here year after year, and all that successive hunters had to do was to wait for them.

The "Grand Central Station" had probably been used by those immigrants via the Bering Strait who earlier traveled south to become the Southern Indians. But there are two main migrations of Eskimos. They have been generalized in the categories of the "Dorset" and "Thule" cultures. The Thules have been regarded as the direct ancestors of the present Eskimos, although some authorities identify the Thules with the Tunnits, whom the present Eskimos claim to have displaced. On the other hand, other authorities argue that the Tunnits were in fact the Dorset people.

An expedition organized by the Arctic Institute of North America, together with the University of Pennsylvania and the National Museum of Denmark, excavated a site at Alarnek on the northern tip of the Melville Peninsula where, as at Pingerkalik and at the Igloolik (69° 24' north, 81° 49' west), were hunting villages of the Tunnits of Eskimo lore.

Alarnek is 200 miles north of the Arctic Circle. There the site revealed over 200 houses built in terraced rows. They were rectangular and quite large, 20x45 feet, in contrast to the round houses of the modern Eskimos. The houses were heated by stone indoor fireplaces and were lighted by oil lamps. One can assume that the inhabitants of the site always built on the water's edge and that the bands or terraces of "real estate" indicate seven different eras. As the water of the sea retreated, the Eskimos built on lower ground. The highest row of houses on these terraces was fifty-six feet above the present water level, and the lowest was twenty-four feet above it. Dr. Jorgen Meldgaard of Denmark, leader of the expedition, reckoned that it would take the sea about 2,000 years to recede that much. This would indicate that Alarnek existed as a settlement at least 3,000 years ago, and it is significant that, in the lower row of houses (nearer the sea), the older implements and relics of the higher rows are found mixed with "foreign" artifacts—those which had not belonged to the culture of the higher settlers. Presumably, therefore, the original people were invaded and displaced by another people, and that presumption, in turn, lines up with the Eskimo lore of the Tunnits being driven out by the ancestors of the present Eskimos.

24 Lore of the Long Night

THE ESKIMOS have had in the past no permanent language—no books or tablets—but they are great talkers and they have, of course, plenty of practice during the Long Night (the sunless winter), so that their legends are retold from generation to generation and are fairly consistent although, of course, they are well embellished with colorful exaggerations.

Throughout the whole of the Arctic and in Greenland the legend of the Tunnits is well repeated. Some accounts make them a race of giants (*Tunnit* in Eskimo means "big"). But their size is probably just the natural exaggeration of a race which is diminutive itself and would like to think that they had beaten bigger fellows. The accounts, however, agree that they had extraordinary strength and fleetness. This, in fact, is supported by material evidence in early settlements. Their strength enabled them to carry great rocks and heavy burdens, and their fleetness enabled them to chase the caribou deer on foot, outstrip them and kill them with spears. The remains of the early habitations certainly include huge rocks, and there is evidence of thrust spears but not of bows and arrows.

The relics on the retreating beaches (as at Alarnek) also underline the stories of the present-day Eskimos about how the Tunnits had no boats and were walrus hunters and not whale hunters. Nor had they any dogs. Stripped of the mythology with which the stories have naturally been ornamented—one-legged, one-armed men; monsters with enormous bellies; one-eyed goblins; spirit trappers, lurking under the ice; werewolves and giants—the legends obviously have some ethnic authenticity which is only now being disentangled.

Among the 3,000 implements recovered at Alarnek were tools, weapons and art work made from flint, slate and walrus ivory. There were no bows and arrows, but spears and harpoons (although no sign of boats). Surprisingly there were the remains of a few wooden implements. One says that it is surprising because there is not a tree within eight hundred miles of Alarnek at the present day and it is difficult to imagine where the drift-wood could have come from 2,000 or 3,000 years ago; and, of course, there was not the flotsam and jetsam of wrecked ships from which, in recent centuries, Eskimos have contrived wooden implements. This raises very interesting speculation as to whether, when this culture existed, there were trees far beyond what is now the northern limit of tree growing.

25 *The Copper Eskimos*

ONE THING which tends to confirm that the Dorset and Tunnit people were one and the same was that the early people of Alarnek buried their dead and used gravel mounds unlike the rock burials of the Thule culture. This raises other interesting questions. For example, the eastern Eskimos in Baffin Island and other areas, and the Alaskan Eskimos, have different physical and linguistic characteristics from the central Eskimos; a Baffin Islander is more likely to understand the conversation of the Alaskans than the Eskimos in the center. These central Eskimos are also, on the average, taller and better looking. Their ancestors have been vaguely described as "Copper Eskimos" and "Caribou Eskimos." Such names are descriptive rather than explanatory. It suggests rather that the later migrations traveled in an arc south of center into the eastern Arctic, bypassing a race in the center. As we have seen in discussing the Indians of the south, there is a plausible case that some of the migrations came out of Asia farther away than Mongolia (for example, the Iranian plateau) and were of a type at least slightly differentiated from the shorter, squatter, heavily lidded Mongols.

This might explain the Tunnits and the differences in the central Eskimos who may be the survivors of the Dorset culture and not, as some have suggested, of a later migration which simply filtered into the center.

At the tip of the Melville Peninsula, near Igloolik, there are some typical Thule houses built from stones and whalebone. I saw such houses much further north on Cornwallis Island. In the permafrost foundations of one house at Igloolik was found a store of frozen meat, refrigerated countless centuries ago. The Eskimos, who have periodically excavated such whalebone houses to get weathered whalebone as sleigh shoeings, claim that the Tunnits did not use the bones of whales, which they could not hunt without boats, and this would appear to be another argument why the Tunnits were the Dorset-culture people and not the seagoing, whale-hunting Thules.

Historically and geographically there has been a clear dividing line between the Eskimos and the Indians. It is the tree line. That is where the forest ends. The trees thin out and shrink until, as someone has said, they "get down on their knees and crawl." Willows become vines creeping over the ground. And finally they disappear altogether.

This tree line wanders very erratically across Canada from within a few miles of the Arctic Sea in Alaska and the Yukon to latitudes south of that of Edinburgh on the Hudson Bay and Labrador side. Beyond that tree line, to the north, lie the Barrens, the great snow deserts which have been the habitat of the Eskimos. Rarely, if ever, have the Eskimos ventured beyond the forest line, and just as rarely have the Indians ventured into the Barrens. When either has done so—in pursuit of the caribou, for example—there have been conflicts. And as far as one can judge from the accounts, the Eskimos have invariably lost or at least have retreated before the Indians. This is remarkable, since the Eskimos are a people of extraordinary courage; but they are also a people who have no word in their language for "war" or for "battles." Those who admire the Eskimos (and I am one) would like to think that one of the reasons why the Eskimos have persisted as the people of the Barrens instead of migrating south like the other Indians is just this peaceful characteristic of theirs which made them prefer their own life to conflict or imposing their will by force on others.

26 *Stone Age Mechanics*

ONE THING is manifestly true: that the Eskimos' life in the Barrens and in the Arctic Islands has condemned them for thousands of years to an existence which has been hazardous and precarious. It has kept them a hunting people. In parts of the Arctic the twentieth century was contemporary with the Eskimo Stone Age. Around the coasts, Hudson Bay, Baffin Island, etc., and in Greenland and Alaska, the Eskimos—the fishers, the whalers and the sealers—have had contact with the white man for several centuries. But in the center many of the Eskimos had never met a white man until thirty years ago.

I myself know Eskimos who thirty years ago were living completely in the Stone Age. About that time the Hudson Bay fur traders, followed, as always, by the missionaries, made their first contacts with these people. They were hunters of the caribou, the musk ox, the walrus, the seal and the whale, and they hunted them with weapons which they had to contrive out of difficult materials.

The Eskimo bow was a powerful weapon. It was made in sections. In some cases they would take matching antlers and join them with a third section which they would rivet with bone. Deer sinew was stretched along the upper and lower sides and the whole bound with sinew. Another typical version was the laminated bow. This would consist of a long strip of bone to form the upper and lower surfaces, with shorter sectional lengths sandwiched in between. This would be interlarded with sinew, bound with sinew, and with sinew as the bowstring. They made the best of the material which they had available, and if in later times they found jetsam with nails, these masters of improvisation would use them as metal rivets.

Having no metals (except for some native copper along Coppermine River in the central Arctic), they were wonderful artificers in bone. Their snow knives, for slicing the blocks of snow to make their igloos, were like scimitars fashioned from tusks; their hammers were deer antlers with the snags blunted. They contrived harpoons and fishhooks out of bone. They fashioned their basins for their oil lamps out of soapstone and tipped their spears with slates or flint. To reduce the blinding glare of the sun on the white snow they made spectacles of walrus bone in which narrow slits (about an eighth of an inch broad and an inch long) were cut. It is remarkable how effective these slit spectacles are. They give a surprising range of vision while reducing the glare and have advantages over snow glasses of sophisticated modern types. On my Arctic travels I found conventional glasses quite useless because the breath freezes on the lens and blacks out vision. Having tried the Eskimo bone type and being unable to beg, borrow or steal a set for myself I took a pair of sun glasses, cut similar slits out of the plastic lens with a razor blade and covered the rest of the lens with surgical sticking plaster. The result was entirely effective and, what is more, I got my companions to autograph the spectacles, as if signing a plaster cast, and I could contemplate the Arctic through my friends.

27 *Snow Engineers*

ALTHOUGH it is obvious that the Eskimos at various times have contrived houses out of stone, turf and the skeletons of whales, the igloo, the domed snowhouse, is their architectural achievement. As snow engineers they are superb. The technique consists of finding a patch of firm snow, of depth and consistency, and marking out in it the circumference of the igloo. With their snow knives they cut snow blocks and remove them by the simple device of using the toe of their *mukluk* as a wedge and splitting the snow along the lower plane. They then arrange the blocks in a circle—cutting them always from inside the intended snowhouse. When the wall is three or four blocks high, they slice it down like a curving ramp, on which they lay the next snow blocks so that they coil into a spiral. In this beehive structure there remains eventually a gap at the summit of the dome, for which they fashion a key block, which locks the whole structure into position. They fill the interstices between the blocks with snow.

The builder has "built himself in." At the base of the wall he cuts himself an escape hatch, which becomes the door, from which he constructs a dog-legged tunnel, with its outlet turned away from the prevailing wind. Inside, the removal of the snow block has left a semicircular pit. The remaining arc is built up into a snow bed, on which are laid thick layers of fur on which the Eskimo family sits or lies with their legs stretched out to ease the blood circulation. The pit traps the drafts. The heat of the stoves and of the human bodies keeps the igloo reasonably warm. This surprises only those people who think of the igloo as an icehouse, instead of a snowhouse—forgetting that the snow is full of air which acts as an insulator against the cold outside.

One of the tricks which is played on a tenderfoot taking the Arctic Survival Course is to put him into an igloo built by an Eskimo guide and, with grim warnings of carbon monoxide poisoning from the stove, leave him to ventilate it. Invariably the novice cuts a hole in the apex of the dome and then finds himself in the middle of the night gazing at an open expanse of sky. The reason is that the heat generated in the igloo zooms through the hole and, by melting the snow, enlarges it. No Eskimo would make that mistake; he makes the ventilating hole well down the curve of the wall where the upper hot air mixes with the cold drafts from the doorway and goes out cool.

Igloos can be very commodious and eight to ten feet high,

but also, of course, they can be built in series and joined by snow tunnels. A family can inhabit one for the whole of the winter, but it is no great hardship for an Eskimo to rebuild an igloo—one of my guides, anticipating a blizzard, built a snowhouse in thirty-five minutes.

In modern Arctic settlements incomers devise all kinds of structures to meet the conditions, but in the end they come back to the dome, whether they use modern plastic materials or not, because manifestly the Eskimo experience of centuries must have some validity.

Similarly with clothes. As hunters, the Eskimos had no fabrics and no alternative to pelts as a form of clothing. They arrived at the most effective answer. Their inner shirts and pants were fashioned from the soft furs of the deer faun, with the fur turned to the skin. Their outer garments were of older caribou, with the fur outward. Their boots were sealskin, which gave a grip on the snow. Fur hoods provided the headgear, and trimmings of wolverine around the hood provided protection against blizzards, because this fur has a peculiar quality of holding the snow and frozen breath loosely so the shake of the head can get rid of it. All clothes were loose.

When white men felt compelled to go to the Arctic and had to dress for the conditions, they naturally regarded the Eskimo dress as primitive. They invented Arctic outfits. One type consisted of a kind of boiler suit made of nylon fur, with zippers. The result was disastrous, because the zippers froze and the victims found themselves sealed in their suits and stewing like a casserole in their own body juices. (That is something one learns in the Arctic: that more dangerous even than the below-zero external temperatures is one's own body heat. A sharp wind, and the result can be deadly.) So they had to learn that the "sloppy," loose-fitting clothes of the Eskimo had the sanction of the wisdom of centuries. When an Eskimo, running after his dog team, finds himself getting overheated, all he has to do is to flap the slack hem of his parka and his body steam escapes through his loose collar.

This sort of thing, and much else, newcomers to the Arctic

learn by bitter experience. That is why the Eskimo is entitled to call himself *Innuit*, the Real Man, as far as his familiar Arctic is concerned.

28 *White Man's Pap*

HERE IS a race which has never had the material concomitants of a settled civilization—no accessible metals to bring them out of the Stone Age and no crops through which they could have become tillers. Instinctively they have used as food plants which, though scarce, grow in the summer months. Their only fruit was bilberries—the one thing which would give them sugar. (They are, as far as I can judge, almost the only race which has never had an indigenous form of fermented drink, because they had no source of plant carbohydrate and, in the aseptic cold of the North, no microorganisms to produce ferments.) Their food, therefore, was entirely animal, but it meant that they took their body sugars in the form of fats and had all their vitamins already packaged. Fish oils, for example, stored the summer sunlight in the form of vitamin D. Their primitive food ecology might have been hazardous—feast or famine—but it was adapted to them and to their conditions. Their eyesight was the finest in the world (it had to be to survive in the Barrens) and their teeth were the finest in the world; this was due in part to the compacting of their teeth by the hard work they gave them: the women chewed the pelts to soften them; the men held their implements in their jaws, and all of them had to chew raw meats and fish.

On a medical tour of the Arctic I traveled with a flying dentist. In his temporary surgeries the only dental troubles which he could find in anyone above teen age were traumatic—a broken tooth—but no caries. In the old people their teeth were worn down like those of an old dog. As I looked at the heart-shaped faces of the young Eskimos, I asked him when the bone formation started to change to produce the square jaws of the adults. He pointed out that there was no bone change, that the squareness was entirely due to the development of the muscles—because they used their jaws as a third arm to hold their snow knives, their fishlines and even their dog reins.

Among the young, however, there was evidence of caries and even of defective eyesight. Invariably the case history showed that the youngsters had been to mission schools where they had had White Man's diet. This is becoming increasingly true of the adult population as well. They have acquired a taste for "White Man's Pap"—flour, sugar, lard and canned goods. They have also acquired a taste for "hard liquor." They have contrived their own hellish brew—using dried fruits and baker's yeast to ferment a hooch which has fatal results.

The life of the Eskimo has drastically changed in this century. Although there were the early contacts with the White Man around the coasts, the associations were through hunting and fishing—things they understood. Then white women discovered a liking for white-fox fur. This is the only fashionable fur of the Eskimo's Arctic. The vogue produced a revolution in the Eskimo way of life. The traders persuaded them to become trappers and, consequently, to reduce their hunting. From their trap lines they could get the furs and, accordingly, the credits which could obtain for them the store foods and store goods. They could have guns to make their hunting easier, and later they could have outboard motors to make their fishing and sea hunting easier. They did not have to go ranging for hundreds of miles in search of caribou. They could stay nearer to their trap lines, to the settlements and to the fur posts.

It all depended on the value of the white fox. Before they realized that, however, the Eskimo was already caught up in White Man's economy and had to become the victim of it. It was hard for the Eskimo to understand that a white-fox fur worth fifteen dollars at the store one year was worth only four dollars the next. It was not easy for the traders to explain to him that his family had to go hungry because the whim of the white women, thousands of miles away, had changed toward the white fox. Theoretically he could go back to the hunt, but it was not so simple. The gun had given him a quicker and surer means of killing the caribou, but in a hunting economy that can be a very bad thing. The massacre which produces the feast of one season can produce the famine of the next. At the beginning of the century the caribou population ranging over 600,000 square miles of the Canadian North was estimated at 1,750,000; today it is officially reckoned at about 300,000.

The Eskimos in Greenland have had contact with the Danes since the tenth century when Eric the Red first called it by that name and when perhaps, at least in the south, it was a "green land." But the closer association, which now includes Eskimos in the parliament of Denmark, dates back about 250 years. The result is that very few of the original strain of Eskimos now exist and the others call themselves "Greenlanders" and not Eskimos.

Something similar happened in the western Arctic when the Americans took over Alaska from the Russians.

29 *Stone Age Atomics*

THE ESKIMOS who have been less exposed, until recent times, to White Men's cultural influences are the 10,000 or so of the Canadian North. Now the impact has hit them and hit them hard. They have, in the space of a couple of generations, stepped out of the Stone Age into the Atomic Age. The grandson of the spear hunter of thirty years ago may still use his ancestral sledges and dog teams on his treks across the snow desert, but he takes with him a Geiger counter to find uranium and a wireless receiver to keep in touch with the news and with the sophisticated music of the modern world of which he feels himself inescapably a part. The Eskimo child, though he may never have seen a wheeled vehicle, like a train or motorcar or a handcart, can identify the types of aircraft flying overhead. The hunter-trapper of a few years ago has discovered himself, and has been discovered, to be a first-class mechanic.

He belongs to our mechanical times because he is the heir to his ancestral instincts. To survive in the Arctic he had to have a blueprint mind, recording subconsciously the vestiges of his snow-covered landscape. He possessed also those manipulative finger skills which made his ancestors the masters of improvisation. The combination made him a "natural" as a mechanic.

This means, in terms of the Eskimo, that we have a race which has culturally leapfrogged all those phases which we have traced in the development of other civilizations. We must make no mistake about it: the Eskimos are a civilized people, although their culture has not given material expression to this. If, as it must, the Frozen North is to become part of our habitable and developed world, it can only be by a conscious partnership between *Innuit* and *Kabloona*, between the Real Man and the White Man, because both are taking short cuts in the Arctic and will lose their way without each other's experience and help.

Perhaps we can find some confidence and reassurance in the fact that the first Chairman of the Senate of the new state of Alaska was an Eskimo.

PART SIX

Hobnails of Chivalry

1 *Cultural Cummerbund*

By the year 500 b.c. civilization, in the sense of city cultures, extended westward from the China Sea to the Atlantic and, if we are to believe the evidence of the Mayan calendars, to Central America as well. It was a kind of cultural cummerbund, round the waist of the globe. North and south of it there were still the barbarian peoples.

The characters of the civilizations, however, have drastically changed since we left them in the Bronze Age, or, as one might call it, the Soil-City Age. The city cultures of the alluvial plains had waxed and waned. The ancient cities of the west, though not those of China, seemed to have lost any capacity for progress and had become increasingly decadent. They had, in fact, reached the limits of their technology and were the hostages of their environment. Although the framework of civilized life was maintained, the crafts, art and literature had become conventionalized and religion, which had passed through the stage of rational compromise with nature, had become buried in an increasing mass of ritual and had, in fact, reverted to superstition. Much had been lost and forgotten. Astronomical observation, which had been kept up and had been developed had been corrupted into astrology, and the sciences had degenerated into cults.

The other corrupting influence—which was to become even worse in civilizations which succeeded them—had been the increasing importance of slavery. Slave raiding on other cities, or more easily and profitably, on barbarian tribes, had become an accepted practice. The existence of the landless and rightless slaves had a serious effect on the conditions of the free workers. In competition with slave labor the peasants and the craftsmen had little incentive to improve their techniques, and the growing upper class treated all three classes as menials. There was a separation of the brain aristocracy and the ruling nobility from the practical problems of living. Mathematics, astronomy and medicine were indulged in as intellectual exercises, although, as we have seen, they derived from the observations and expedients of those who had work to do. Moreover, the effects of slavery undermined the security of the city cultures. The more a city depended on slaves, the less it was able to defend itself. Oppressed freemen and depressed slaves had little to gain or to lose by the change of masters—like the Jewish slaves in Babylon, welcoming Cyrus as a liberator.

The great revolutionary factor, however, in the change in the character of the civilizations was the introduction of iron. The widespread availability of a metal much more common than copper or gold or tin changed the conditions of war by providing weapons more readily. The warlike aspects of iron, however, were almost incidental to the change in technology which occurred. It opened up whole new areas to agriculture. The fact is too often overlooked.

In the alluvial plains, the open lands of silt-deposited soil, cultivation was relatively simple with wooden implements. Conditions were vastly different in the stony uplands of Asia Minor or in the forest belts of central and northern Europe. The earlier uses of metal had been essentially for the luxury products of city life and for arming the bodyguards of the aristocracy. Bronze had always been too expensive for ordinary people, who had had to rely for the most part on stone implements from their Stone Age ancestors. Iron, however, although at first inferior to bronze, could be mined locally and worked by village smiths.

The effect of the abundance of the metal was to open up whole new continents to agriculture. Forests were axed; swamps were spade-drained, and the resulting clearings could be plowed. The rocky uplands, which would have defeated the resources of the earlier peasants, could now be mastered with iron-shod implements. Europe could now become a wheat land.

*Greek plow. From a black-
figured Nikosthenes (sixth
century* B.C.*)*

This had quite a drastic effect in altering the balance of power between the dry farming of the Western countries and the irrigation cultivations of the East. Apart from the expansion northward, with cultivation in the clearings of the European forests, the iron revolution was important even on the doorstep of the ancient civilizations.

One does not usually think of the effects of iron on the shipping of these ancient times. We think of iron in terms of the iron ships of the nineteenth century. But the effect of the new tools in the shaping and building of ships drastically altered the geography of the ancient world.

2 Trojan Horse Traders

WE HAVE SEEN how the Cretans had taken the initiative in shipbuilding in earlier times. The breaking up of their sea empire, first by the land-based Mycenaeans and later by the Achaeans

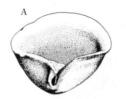 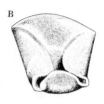

Saucer-shaped pottery lamps.   A *Phoenician.*   B *Carthaginian.*

from the Balkans, was a sign for piracy and the sacking of cities by Iron Age barbarians. This, of course, was the inglorious story of Troy which Homer made glorious. When Helen's face "launched a thousand ships" and gave us the great romantic story of *The Iliad*, it was no more than pillage and counter-pillage. The rude ancestors of what we call the "classical Greeks" had settled on the inhospitable islands and on the mainland of Thrace and Asia Minor. They had already their god Hephaestus, later the Romans' Vulcan, as their deified form of the ironsmith. Ships had brought these islanders of Levant into conflict, and on occasion combination, with each other. The excavations of Troy have given historical substance to the Homeric legends, but it is a history of a clash of petty chiefs and brigand lords. However, pillage and piracy not only strengthened the resources of the islands; they created, in the Levant, the technique of sea trade.

Out of the hinterland of the older civilizations emerged new Iron Age peoples. The Assyrians, the Medianites and, as we have seen, the Persians found the effete city cultures of Mesopotamia and the Nile an easy prey. The Iron Age also coincided with the development of the cavalry horse among the people of the steppes—the barbarians on the outskirts of civilization.

The growth of maritime cities and of seagoing peoples, like the Phoenicians, meant colonization along the whole of the Mediterranean and adventures as far afield as Cornwall in distant

Britain. In 600 B.C. Necho II, one of the last of the native Egyptian Pharaohs, commissioned a captain of the Phoenicians, whose ships by this time were stationed in the Gulf of Suez, to sail around the continent of Africa. According to Herodotus, this remarkable journey took three years. Another Carthaginian, Hanno, made a voyage along the northwest and west coast of Africa about 520 B.C. with a fleet of sixty ships.

3 *East Moves West*

CARTHAGE was founded by the Phoenicians about 822 B.C. or some seventy years before the founding of Rome by the Etruscans in 753 B.C. (This raises the long-debated question as to whether the Etruscans were not themselves Phoenicians.) The Phoenicians from Tyre and Sidon had already founded, in 1100 B.C., the city of Utica, which occupied a site at the mouth of the Magada River in northeast Tunisia. Other cities founded by them about the same time were Lixus, on the Moroccan coast, and Cadiz, in southern Spain. Then in an upheaval in Tyre (in 822 B.C.) a party of refugees fled under the leadership of a princess called Elissar. She was the daughter of the king of Tyre and has been identified as Dido, who was immortalized for us by Virgil. She is said to have fled from her native city after her brother, on succeeding to the throne, had murdered her husband for the sake of his wealth. Virgil tells the story of Aeneas and his followers escaping from burning Troy and making their way to the coast of Africa. He tells of the meeting between Dido and Aeneas, how she fell madly in love with him and how, when he came to return to Greece, she built a great funeral pyre and destroyed herself. This is taking poetic license with history,

Cisterns at Carthage

for Troy must have been destroyed at least three hundred years earlier.

In the beginning the Carthaginians and the Etruscans were close allies, so close, in fact, that Aristotle alleges that they had combined to destroy Greece. The first treaty of friendship between Carthage and the Rome of the Etruscans is said to have been signed in 509 B.C. and, according to Livy, a Carthaginian embassy came to Rome in 340 B.C. Thirty years later the Etruscans were defeated in naval battle by the Greek colonists of Syracuse at the same time as the Gauls invaded Italy from the north. Etruscan power vanished; the Romans, or Latins, emerged as the masters of Italy, and Carthage not only lost an ally but discovered an enemy.

Around 300 B.C. Carthage was a metropolis of grandeur and pomp. It contained a great fortress, imposing temples and many magnificent public buildings. It was encircled by a triple line

234

of fortifications, and immediately above the towering walls were rows of tall houses, six stories high, on either side of three streets which led down to the harbor. Its suburbs had beautiful villas and lovely gardens, the homes of prosperous maritime traders. Its population numbered more than 70,000. It had libraries, baths, restaurants and theaters.

4 *Garden of the Hesperides*

WE HAVE COME to accept North Africa as the fringe of the desert, but in the days of Carthage the character of the hinterland must have been very different. Mythology makes it so. The Garden of the Hesperides, where, as his Eleventh Labor, Hercules slew the dragon so that he could steal the golden apples "in the land far away in the west where the sun sets," has been identified with the present oasis of Gafsa. This lies to the south of Carthage (Tunis) and still supplies a livelihood for 12,000 people. The island of the lotus-eaters of *The Odyssey* is believed to have been the island of Djerba, just off the coast, in the Gulf of Gabes. These links between Greek mythology and the Phoenician trading posts show how both the seafaring nations of the Levant were competitors for rich prizes in what we might now regard as an inhospitable part of the Mediterranean.

Perhaps the clue lies in the early Phoenician settlements of Lepcis (later Leptis Magna of the Romans and Homs of today), Uai' (later Oea and now Tripoli) and Sabratha. These were trading posts. Lepcis had a good anchorage at the mouth of Wadi Lebda and a fertile area in Wadi Caam to feed it. Uai' stood (as Tripoli does today) at the mouth of Wadi Mejenin, with a protective reef as a roadstead for ships and agricultural land around. Sabratha was established at the head of an important trade route which came up to the coast through Gadames. The deep indent in the North African coast line made those three "emporia" that much closer to the African interior, where gold, ivory, ostrich plumes and Nubian slaves and other commodities prized in the Levant were abundant.

But how were those trade routes into the interior possible? There was the Sahara in between and no "ships of the desert." Sir Julian Huxley, in *From an Antique Land,* points out:

It is a curious fact that the camel does not seem to have been regularly employed as a beast of burden in the Nile Valley until about 300 B.C. though camels had, of course, been used in desert caravans in Arabia and Mesopotamia from the time of Abraham and earlier. It is still more curious that camels were not known in North Africa proper until the beginning of our era. We know that Marius, just before 100 B.C., used horses in his campaign against Jugurtha, which he certainly would not have done if camels had been available, and Sallust records that the first time Roman soldiers ever saw camels was in Asia Minor when Lucullus was fighting Mithridates between 88 and 84 B.C. Somehow camels reached Africa by 46 B.C., for in that year Caesar captured a score from Juba at Thapsus, but they did not become abundant there until the 4th century A.D.

Yet in the eighth century B.C. when Carthage had gained sovereignty over the three ports, Lepcis, Uai' and Sabratha, they were sea outlets for the overland trade routes to Equatorial Africa. Without camels the traffic must have been either by human porterage, by donkeys, by horses, or perhaps by the long-horned cattle of the Garamantes of the Fezzan. In any case, they could not have gone long distances without water and food. (The donkey is capable of going four days, maximum, without water, compared with the camel's twelve.) The only possible explanation is that the Saharan water holes and oases of vegetation were much closer together than they are today.

5 Hannibal's Elephants

THERE ARE other presumptions to support the view that North Africa was not as desiccated in Carthaginian times as it is today.

On a twentieth-century Saharan expedition I went armed with an apparently fatuous question: "Where did Hannibal get his elephants?" But it was a heads-I-win-tails-you-lose question; it could not go wrong.

Hannibal's elephants had always fascinated me since I first encountered them in the classroom and learned how they scared the Romans when they came trampling out of the snows of the Alps through the back door into Italy. How did the Carthaginians acquire those primitive "tanks"?

If they got them from Asia (because some people suggest, against modern experience in the Congo and in zoos, that the African version could not have been tamed for battle purposes) how did they transport them? If they were marched from Asia, then the deserts of the Middle East must have been different. If, on the other hand, they were a tamed version of the African species from central Africa, then the Sahara could not have been what it is today—the elephants could not have traversed the present distances between the oases. If they were brought from east Africa up the Nile, then the Western and Libyan Deserts could not have been the thirsty places they are now. Lastly, if Hannibal found them in his "own back yard," in North Africa, what is now desert must have been forest or jungle. So whatever answer I got, the simplest must be, "The deserts were different."

Amusingly that question, "Where did Hannibal get his elephants?" was the password which gained me the freedom of the French Sahara. I had to get the permission of the military commander at Colomb Béchar. It was a very unpromising inter-

237

view with a poker-faced "brass hat." Then, in despair, I asked
the question. It was like removing the mask of a dark lantern. His
face lit up. He bounded from his desk to the operational map on
the wall and said just, "Là!" He went back to his desk, pulled open
a drawer and produced a manuscript—an account by Suetonius
Paulinus who, before he became the general who beat the British
Queen Boadicea, had been a military intelligence officer in
Africa and had written, in A.D. 47, about the great Forest of
the Guir, describing the elephants, lions and other wild beasts
which inhabited it. The commanding officer, in his enthusiasm
to convince me, immediately ordered a command car and an
escort and sent me off to Fort Abadla, the military post in the
Guir, a desert enclave which thrusts into the mountains of
Morocco.

There I asked the same question of the commander, who
was as great an elephant enthusiast as his superior. He was
equally emphatic that Hannibal had got his elephants from
North Africa. I asked him what had happened to the forest.
He led me to an embrasure from which we could see nothing but
desert desolation and he pointed to a hilltop on which was a
white dome. That, he explained, was the tomb of Sidi Tayeb,
a powerful Moslem holy man or Marabout. I gathered that
Sidi Tayeb was a kind of Arab St. Patrick. Backed up by another
manuscript produced from another desk in another military
command post, he explained that Tayeb was bitten by a horned
viper in the Forest of the Guir, and as he lay dying he invoked
Allah and cried to all the animals in the forest, "I order you at
once to leave the region of the Guir which I take under my protection." And within six days of his death all the elephants,
lions and reptiles had vanished into oblivion.

But the really important part of the legend was in the tailpiece:
"And his followers to whom he bequeathed the forest cut it
down." That, I was to find in all my journeys through North
Africa, was the litany of the man-made desert. "They cut it
down."

The legend of Sidi Tayeb belongs 1,200 years after Hannibal, but it helps to confirm the assumption that in Carthaginian times the vegetation of North Africa was more abundant than it is today. Yet, although the forests must have modified the climate to some extent, there is other evidence that, by and large, the basic climate was much the same as it is today—that the people of those times were coping with conditions which made irrigation and water conservation measures necessary. But the Carthaginians were not conspicuously an agricultural people until the defeat by the Romans in the Second Punic War drove them out of the Mediterranean as traders. Then they turned upon their hinterland with a thoroughness which made them the outstanding agronomists of ancient times. Their wadi cultivation methods gave yields of grain as high as those of the alluvial plains of Babylonia. Moreover, as well-traveled and observant people, they had borrowed experience from as far away as the Indus, and their great contribution was the introduction of scientific fruit farming. They brought into North Africa the almond, the fig, the peach, the pomegranate, the vine, and the olive. And their agricultural prosperity so excited the envy of the Romans that they destroyed Carthage but borrowed their Phoenician agricultural methods.

6 Odysseus, the Plowman

THE ADVENT of the Iron Age meant the return to smaller-scale economic units than those of the river civilizations. Early Iron Age cities rarely had populations of more than a few thousands as against the hundreds of thousands of Thebes, Babylon, etc. By the fifth century B.C., with the spread of slavery, much larger cities had begun to grow. Athens had, at the limit of its

Greek women taking shower bath

power, a maximum population of 320,000, of whom only 172,000 were citizens, while Rome at its supreme moment had over a million. The first Greek cities formed were just a conglomeration of a dozen or so villages. They did not, however, have to "start from scratch." They inherited the arts and many of the habits of the older civilizations. But they did not have the compulsions of great public works—like irrigation systems—which made it essential to have an overlord or a suzerain. Their public works could be limited to fortifications, harborage, aqueducts and drains, with such public buildings as the Acropolis or the Parthenon, and they gave the world politics.

It seems almost disrespectful, if not irreverent, to speak of the classical Greeks, whom we invoke as the originators of our Western civilization, as though they were a race of blacksmiths. But they were definitely an outcome of the Iron Age. In *The Odyssey* we see kings living on their domains, but it is obvious that they are rather like squires than royalty. They employ free labor and slaves, but like Laertes, who knows how to dig around a vine, and Odysseus, who boasts he can drive a furrow as straight as any man, they were gentlemen farmers. We see the Queen Arete of Phaeacia weaving by the light of the fire, and Penelope of Ithaca is, of course, the world's most famous weaver, who kept her importunate wooers at bay with her loom. Homer introduces us to two trades, that of the smith and the potter. The Homeric picture is one of an advanced form of tribalism. It is recognizably European. Agamemnon is no Oriental despot ruling with the authority of an earthly god—he is an appointed leader; and there are the signs of an assembly of the people to be consulted on important occasions.

7 *Greek Pocket Boroughs*

WHEN WE COME to the age of the Classical Greece, of Socrates, Plato and Aristotle, this picture has changed. In Ionia, Peloponnesus, central Greece, and south Italy and Sicily, the colonies, the districts, are divided into a large number of quite independent and autonomous units. Because we have glorified their culture so much, it is difficult for us to realize their insignificant size. We find Plato ordaining that his ideal city shall have 5,000 citizens and Aristotle demanding that each citizen should be able to know all the others by sight. When Hippodamus laid out the Piraeus, he specified that the ideal number of citizens was 10,000. But, of course, the figure refers to "citizens" and all the inhabitants were not citizens—there were the wives and families, but also the slaves and resident aliens, so that Piraeus might have a total population of about 100,000. In fact, only three city-states had more than 20,000 citizens—Syracuse and Acragas in Sicily, and Athens. At the outbreak of the Peloponnesian War, the population of Attica was about 350,000, half of them Athenian (men, women and children), about a tenth resident aliens, and the rest slaves. Sparta had a much smaller citizen body, although it was larger in area. The important commercial city of Corinth had a territory of only 330 square miles. The small island of Ceos was divided into four city-states. It had four armies, four governments, and possibly four different currencies and systems of measures.

The term *polis*, which is the basis of our word "politics," has been applied to the city-state, but it really referred to the people. It could mean the whole communal life of the people, political, cultural, moral and economic. Even religion was bound up with the polis. Each polis had its patron god or goddess.

The culture which we inherited from the Greeks was synthetic. It made use of every element of culture which it could find in the countries with which it had contact, with which it traded, and which it later occupied. That does not mean that it was merely a continuation of what had happened before. It was as a synthesis something quite new.

Great contributions which it made were in political institutions, particularly democracy, and in natural science, especially mathematics and astronomy. What differentiated it from all previous civilizations was what we now call "the scientific method." This was not just the knowledge or practice of science but the capacity to separate facts and verifiable information from emotional and traditional statements. It had the quality of rationality and realism.

The original culture of the mainland Greeks was that of the simple European type. It had the merit that it was unable to comprehend or absorb or take for granted the highly sophisticated and, by then, effete systems of its predecessors. The Greeks selected or absorbed or discarded various features. Remember, however, that the base, like all other Western Iron Age cultures, was quite different from that of the older irrigation cultures. Its economics depended on a rather poor kind of dry farming of small peasant holdings, supported by vineyards, olive groves, fishing and seasonal sea trading. Indeed, the city-states relied to a great extent on exports for the maintenance not of luxuries, as in the older civilizations, but commodities for common consumption. For example, Attica was so short of good corn-growing land that it depended on its exports of pottery, olive oil and silver to buy food for the population of Athens.

The Greeks were realistic. They did not rely (too much) on gods or on tradition but encouraged, originally at least, the enterprise of citizens. They were realistic, too, in their approach to art. In Egypt statues had been magical, but the Greek sculptor was trying to suggest an ideal which could be aimed at in human bodily perfection. In Greek culture the athlete, the artist and the doctor all worked closely together. It was the "Age of the Eye" in which, for instance, Praxiteles, the sculptor, and Hippocrates, the founder of medicine, arrived at their results, either in statues or in treatment, by direct observation and not by booklore.

8 The Age of Dialectic

It was, moreover, the age of dialectic—the capacity to argue. Some may think, in the light of further developments in Greek science, that this love of argument for its own sake became a vice. The traditional presentation of Greek science is in the form of arguments based on general principles rather than on examples drawn from particular problems of technique. Mathematics, especially geometry, was the field which the Greeks regarded as the highest attribute and in which they used their methods of deduction and proof. The belief that the universe was rational and that its details could be deduced from first principles by pure logic helped to deliver the Greeks from superstitions.

Perhaps the fault lay less with the Greeks themselves than with the absurd and complete acceptance of their findings by later generations. For example, Aristotle, who was essentially an instigator of research, became the final authority for generations of intelligent people who accepted his findings. Nevertheless, this Greek emphasis on pure logic, "thinking off the top of the head," led to the growth of an intellectual aristocracy to the detriment of the craftsman. This was in part due to the extension of slavery because, although much craftwork was done by freemen, they were degraded by competition with slaves so that they, too, became an inferior class. In the same way a slave society debased the social position of women. Indeed, the position of wives and daughters of Greek citizens was far worse than it was in the older civilizations. They were precluded from taking part in public life and were little better than domestic slaves themselves. As a result, all domestic work, which included far more arts than it does now, such as weaving and the preparation of simple remedies, was beneath the concern of the philosopher. There was little scientific contact between the men who did the thinking and the men who did the work.

Yet the general problems from which science grew, such as the understanding of the heavens or man's body or the workings of the universe, were first defined by the Greeks. In the scholastic subservience of later times, however, it was unfortunate that the Greeks were regarded as "having a word for it." The first task of modern science, after the days of Francis Bacon, was to show that much of what the Greeks had expounded had been misleading.

9 *Alexander the Great*

THE CONQUESTS of Alexander opened up Asia to Greek trade and Greek colonization, and we can read into them something more than just the ambitions of Alexander himself or the glories of military conquest.

He imposed his imperial will on the city-states of Greece which, even before his time, were falling into decadence. The general level of Hellenic prosperity was declining and, although individual fortunes of the aristocrats and plutocrats were bigger than ever, the number of slaves relative to the total population had increased and the peasants had sunk into poverty and serfdom. The soil itself had suffered, and it has never fully recovered. The limestone hills had once been clothed in woods and vegetation, but the demand for charcoal for the making of iron and for cement, and the pressure of population, extending cultivation by clearings, had removed the forest cover and had already led to the erosion which is the affliction of Greece today. The soil was scoured off by the rains no longer tempered by foliage and herbage, and the springs failed because the water no longer seeped into the ground to replenish them but ran off torrentially to the sea. The social structure had also degraded the craftsman. The arts and crafts which we regard as the material "glory that was Greece" were the products of social inferiors.

Even by the time of Alexander, the contradictions of the social and economic structure were as naked as the hills of Greece. There was unemployment and a shortage of foodstuffs. Many small peasants were conscripted into prolonged military service, or their holdings were devastated by hostile armies or expropriated for debts which circumstance had forced them to incur and had left them no means of repaying. There was no alternative work for them in the factories because slave-manned industries had gradually crushed the individual enterprise of the small craftsman. Just as the artisan of the twentieth century sees his skills being reproduced or replaced by automation, so in Greece skills were broken down into processes. The potter had once been the individual perfectionist, molding the clay, designing the artwork, executing the painting and firing the ware. Latterly those became the separate functions of teams within a factory, and the specimens which are the pride and joy of Western museums were the repetitive factory products of team workers who were not even recognized citizens.

Furthermore, as the internal market contracted because poverty reduced purchasing power, so did the external market. Greece exported industries instead of consumer goods. With no prospects at home, craftsmen emigrated to new colonies, and around the Black Sea, for example, there grew up successful manufacturing centers which competed with the old-established crafts of Greece itself. Thus Greece could not export its wares to get, in return, the wheat and foodstuffs from overseas.

In the fourth century B.C. there was no option for the dispossessed or superabundant peasantry but to sell their services

Athenian pottery establishment (sixth century B.C.*)*

as foreign mercenaries. Xenophon's epic story of the Ten Thousand, recruited by Cyrus the Younger to drive his half brother off the Persian throne, is, stripped of its military romance and glamour, just the same story as the Highland Clearances which emptied the glens of Scotland in the eighteenth century A.D. and sent the dispossessed clansmen to settle in Canada or serve in the armies of France or Russia; neither the Greeks nor the Scots had any option.

10 *Greek Colonialism*

THE CONQUESTS of Alexander made Egypt and the Middle East a province of Hellas. Greek became the *lingua franca*, so ideas began to circulate freely. Alexander took over the whole of the Persian Empire and extended the concept of the city-state as far as the Indus and the Jaxartes.

Alexander began founding, in his widespread domains, military colonies for his veterans and cities akin to those of Greece. They followed a pattern—the market place, theater, public buildings, schools and fountains. Most of them were laid out on a grid system (like so many American cities today) but in origin they observed the Platonic-Aristotelian principle of the small polis—Pergamon, in Asia Minor, although a capital, was only 222 acres in extent; Heraklea, at Latmos, was only 245 acres; Alexandria, when it was founded as the Greek capital of Egypt, was of the same order.

They all had municipal government on the models of old Greece. They were administered by Greek officials, financed by Greek bankers, supplied by Greek merchants and borrowed their arts and crafts from Greece. Nevertheless, the old Oriental cities with native commerce, industry, religion and science were not destroyed (if we concede, as some do not, that the burning of Persepolis, during Alexander's sojourn, was an accident). Greek institutions, customs and gods were accommodated in the existing cultures, and when Alexander's successors, the Ptolemaic Pharaohs, took over Egypt, they took over all the perquisites of deific and temporal power, with no concepts of Greek democracy, which anyway had already been supplanted in old Greece by the acceptance of the tyrants and the elite.

In spite of the conventional history books of dates and dynasties and our sentimental attachment to Greece as the inspiration of our Western institutions, Alexander's adventures were impelled by economic circumstance—to salvage Classical Greece from its own decadence and poverty. It was expansionism which provided an outlet for a surplus population and for reciprocal trade which redeemed a country no longer self-sufficient. Greek cities were dependent on imported corn, but places like Egypt now offered export-import facilities by offering staple foodstuffs in return for olive oil, salt fish, pork, honey, cheese, dried fruits and nuts; Greek jars which have been found as far apart as Susa, in Elam, on the Lower Danube and in Sicily and Carthage are evidence of the export of oil and wine from the Greek mainland and islands.

The landlords of the Greek Empire and the Hellenic fraction-empires which succeeded Alexander's were different from the old aristocrats or temple bursars. The rulers and the priests still got their "rake-off," but farming became capitalized and commercialized. Specialized farms, producing for the (Greek) world market, were spread right through from Russian Turkestan and India to Sicily and Tunisia. They were worked by slaves or serfs on reasonably scientific lines. They tended to correct the balance between crops and livestock, which is hard to maintain on small holdings, and by proper rotation and conservation helped to preserve the soil. Another gain was the acclimatization of animals and crops which became possible on a wide scale. Cotton, apricots, citron, geese and buffaloes were

248

introduced into European Greece; sesame, horses, asses and swine spread from Europe across Asia to India, and lucerne, Oriental fruit trees, melons, beets and barnyard fowls were trafficked through Greece into Italy and Spain.

Secondary industry, that product of the Greek Iron Age, spread along the military roads and trade routes. And again the pattern was modified. It is true that factories had grown in Classical Greece, but they had been attached to landed estates, temples or palaces and worked by bondsmen or slaves. Now they were industrial entities. They were manned by masses of slaves, not to make use of machinery or even to facilitate teamwork or work flow, but for convenience of supervision. Specialization, which had been mentioned in old Greece, now became the feature of the factory economy in other parts. In place of the freeman craftsman, master of all his skills, there was now the composite craftsman made up of semi-skills—a foretaste, in the pre-Christian era, of the production line. In the team each worker had his own limited function. The joiner, who would make the door, would not set up the doorposts; the stonemason would not sharpen, much less make, his own tools; the spinner would not weave; the pot maker would not paint. Shades (all those centuries ago) of trade-union demarcation!

This, of course, could have completely stultified advance in techniques, because imitation is a poor incentive to invention. Nevertheless, a series of major advances did take place. After 330 B.C. there is evidence of rotary flour milling, driven by donkeys but sometimes by water wheels (which the Persians had already introduced). This rotary milling was a revolution, in more senses than a pun, because hitherto each household had crushed and ground its grain in querns. Now flour millers and community bakers came into existence but, more important, it was the first extension of nonhuman motive power since the Bronze Age, which had produced water-lifting devices, sailboats and wheeled carts.

11 Greek Science

THE FIRST PHASE of Greek science was in the sixth century B.C. and is associated with the legendary figures of Thales and Pythagoras and other nature philosophers who speculated on how the world was made and how it had come to be.

The second phase was between 480 and 330 B.C.—between the end of the Persian Wars and the suppression of the independent Greek cities by Alexander the Great. It was during this period that we have Socrates, Plato and Aristotle and the study of the nature of man and his social duties.

The third phase was when the empire of Alexander brought Greek science into contact with the older sources of culture in the East, as far as India. Alexandria, in Egypt, became a new home for science, and the result was a development of mathematics, mechanics and astronomy which we associate with Euclid, Archimedes and Hipparchus. This period was the bridge between all that was past and all that was to come.

The two centuries beginning in 230 B.C. were more fruitful in mechanical inventions than any period until the seventeenth century A.D. Archimedes of Syracuse, although as an aristocrat he would have resented the description, was an applied scientist, a technologist and an inventor. In an age when the elite despised the practical, he discovered and applied the hydrostatic principle. Every schoolboy knows the story of how, in the public baths of Syracuse, he made the discovery and rushed, naked, to his home, shouting, "Eureka! Eureka!" ("I have found it! I have found it!") What he had found was the answer to a problem put to him by his relative Hiero, the Tyrant of Syracuse, who thought the jeweler, in making his crown, had cheated him by using an alloy instead of pure gold. The answer which Archimedes had found in his bath was that if a body is immersed in a fluid, it will experience an upthrust which will be equal to the weight of fluid it displaces.

He also invented (or at least gets the credit for inventing) the Archimedean screw for raising water. This was formed by winding a tube spirally around a cylinder. When such a screw is placed in an inclined position with its lower end immersed in water, its rotation will raise water to the higher level. He is also supposed to have been the inventor of the compound pulley and to have elaborated the principle of the fulcrum, the point about which a lever turns to give a lift. He boasted that if he had a fulcrum or standpoint he could move the world. He set fire to the Roman fleet attacking Syracuse by using burning glasses to focus the sun's rays. When the Romans carried the city by assault, he was slain by the uncouth soldiery while contemplating mathematical figures which he had drawn in the sand.

Around 250 B.C. Ctesibius invented a perfectly good pump fitted with valves and cylinders and pistons which would have been capable of mechanically raising water to much greater heights than the devices which existed then and for many centuries afterward. Yet there is no evidence of its being used for draining mines or irrigation. Even the Romans, perhaps owing to the limitations of their lead pipes, never thought of transporting water under pressure but created instead the giant aqueduct systems.

It is a sobering thought that nearly 2,000 years ago Hero of Alexandria invented a steam engine which was quite practical and embodied the principles of the turbine and of jet propulsion, all those centuries before Parsons (turbine) and Whittle (jet). The basis of this was a sphere of metal with two right-angled tubes set in it, with the outlets pointing in opposite directions. There was a cauldron from which steam entered the sphere through the tubes which acted as the axis. The force of the steam escaping through the angular tubes forced the sphere to spin.

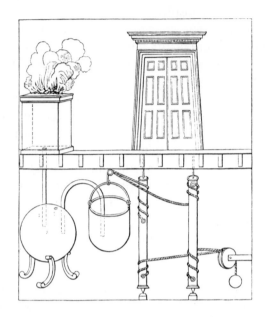

Hero's device for opening the doors of a temple when the fire is lighted upon the altar. Expanding hot air in the altar drives water from the container into a bucket which, in descending, turns the door spindles by means of a rope raising the counterweight.

He also invented a jug which, by applying a siphon effect, produced a conjuring trick. In his *Mechanica* he showed a complete understanding of a transmission system. By employing a handle to turn a screw, which revolved a cogwheel, which acted as a winch for a multiple-pulley system, which dragged on a lever, hinged on a fulcrum, he had a device which lifted a weight far in excess of the muscle effort of the handle turner.

They were merely toys, or magical appurtenances of the temples. A progenitor of the steam engine could be heated by the altar fires and its steam power used mysteriously to open doors and disclose the gods. And why? Because this was the age of slavery, when muscle power was abundant and mechanical power was unnecessary. Hero's discoveries were "uneconomic."

12 *Soil Enslaved*

By 200 B.C. the number of tenant farmers throughout the Greek world was declining. Big landowners were displacing them, converting them into serfs and employing slaves in greater and greater numbers. The same thing was happening in the crafts. Factory owners were using hired or slave labor, and on public works contractors rather than individual craftsmen undertook the work. Slave masters contracted to supply the labor and the money lenders financed the projects.

It is necessary here to remind ourselves once again that the basis of all this panoply of pomp and power and pelf was the soil and those who worked it. No matter how many slaves there were, they had to be fed from the same plots as the freemen.

Proper husbandry is the personal nursing of the soil and not its impersonal exploitation. The records of Alexandrine Egypt in 196 B.C. showed how far the system had declined from these truths. Peasant lands were farmed for the moneylenders so that they were producing crops which had a market value but which could bankrupt the soil. The land workers were oppressed by taxes and the prisons were full of debtors. Land was expropriated for debt or tax evasion and passed into the hands of those whose soil it was not. To escape from their debts or from imprisonment peasants, to the alarm of the Pharaoh, were fleeing their patrimonial acres and taking to robbery and violence. There were mass strikes by the land workers, who sought public relief from the temples while their grievances were being ventilated. The net result was that, although there was an abundance of slaves, scarcity of peasant labor, the depopulation of the villages, the abandonment of arable land, the neglect of dikes and fields and a progressive decay brought about the eventual collapse of empires.

The gross effect of all this on Greece itself was, of course, disguised for a long time. The opening up of new export-import markets, which followed military expansionism and the distribution of the hoarded wealth of the Oriental kings to Alexander's soldiers, masked the disequilibrium. But the migration of craftsmen to the new colonies presently restricted the export of consumer goods. The import of foodstuffs, indispensable to the metropolitan economies, reacted on the local peasantry. The competition of foreign (colonial) industries and slave-owned factories relegated the individual craftsmen and producers to debt slavery and often to actual slavery. Civil war in Sparta and in the states of old Greece followed demands for the cancellation of debts and redistribution of lands.

Ships were improved and lighthouses helped navigation. So did the cartographers; and trade by sea and land, in spite of the hazards of piracy and brigands, spread more quickly. After 300 B.C. tin from Cornwall was being regularly shipped across France to Marseilles; gold, furs and forest products were being transported from Siberia and central Russia; perfumes, ivory, spices and drugs, across what are now deserts from central Africa; amber, from the Baltic, and silks and spices from China.

13 *Desert Protectors*

THOSE TRADE ROUTES were themselves the creators of new types of cultures—not merely of a new set of nomads, itinerant merchants beset by the old set, the barbarians, but of professional "protectors."

Among those "protectors" were that rather remarkable race,

the Nabataeans. Somewhere about the time of the Captivity, when Nebuchadnezzar (588 B.C.) destroyed Jerusalem and carried off the Jews to Babylon, a wave of desert Semites surged into the lands of the Edomites, who retreated into the adjacent territories and left the invaders in possession of the southern caravan routes. Those routes ran from Arabia Felix, the land of the Queen of Sheba, to Syria and to Egypt and the Mediterranean ports. Along them traveled the Oriental caravans with their riches of frankincense and myrrh, pearls from the Persian Gulf, ivory, gold, and black slaves from Africa, and spices and silks from China. From the tip of the Arabian Peninsula the camel caravans traveled northward along the eastern coast of the Red Sea, through Mecca and on to 'Aqaba. From there they followed the Wadi Arabah to Petra, where one route diverged westward to Gaza and another continued north to Damascus and from there to Tyre and Sidon, Aleppo and Antioch.

The Nabataean capital was Petra, which is a monument to their ingenuity, their craftsmanship and their ultimate wealth. This is a city hewn out of the living rock—temples, tombs and public buildings cut into, and out of, the precipices. On this point the caravans converged or were shepherded by the desert gendarmery. It was the exchange center between East and West, a desert "port" where the riches of the Orient were unshipped and transferred to the caravans of the Occident and vice versa. It obviously became a market for wholesale transactions. There were great caravansaries to house the voyagers and bonded warehouses to store the goods on which a "police tax" was collected.

In return for what was almost surely trade under duress, the Nabataeans provided safe-conduct and immunity from the desert hijackers, by means of a series of desert garrison towns and escorts. There were six considerable cities in the Negev, the southern desert of Palestine, with a combined population of at least 100,000.

14 Desert Cultivators

THOSE CITIES are noteworthy because they were virtually self-supporting in a desert which was, on present-day research evidence, as climatologically inhospitable as it is today. It can be assumed that they did not grow their own grains—at least in adequate quantities—but imported them into the desert. But there seems no doubt that they supplied themselves with fruits and vegetables.

Obde, in the middle of the Negev, was a hill city of 10,000 inhabitants. A 400-foot-high mountain was honeycombed with man-made caves—homes, stores and tombs—and on the flattened top were fortress walls within which the dwellers could retreat and within which also were massive public buildings. More interesting than the ruins today are the eloquent testimonies of the landscape. One looks down on a desert, which merely dismays, until out of the grayness of the dust one begins to see the vestiges of the fields which the dust has all but buried. A whole textbook on desert recovery can be read in that landscape.

The rainfall during the 1,000 years in which the Nabataeans maintained themselves in the desert could not have been much more than the 100 millimeters of today. That much the plant archeologists can tell us. And then, as now, it would come in sudden downfalls, to run off the hills and waste itself in the gullies which rend the countryside between Obde and the Dead Sea. The Nabataeans knew that it was futile to try to cultivate the Valley of Zin through which the spate would pour. So their cultivation was done in the offshoot valleys. Round their fields, each usually a quarter of an acre in extent, they built massive check walls, sometimes ten feet high and twelve feet thick, to impound the water. In the tributary wadis they made diversion dams to switch the floods into those walled fields. And they demonstrated how erosion, a bogey word to us, could be turned to advantage.

Those fields were not only dams, but also silt traps in which the soil naturally scoured off the hills would be deposited. Those ancient soil engineers noticed something else. The hills were encrusted with "desert pavement," a meringuelike crust compounded by the alchemy of sun and atmospheric moisture. This thin, hard skin protected the loess underneath. If this shield were removed, the loess, this incipient soil, would be swept into the silt traps. So they systematically broke the "pavement" and raked the hillsides, and the rains sluiced the soil off. One of the wadi fields, I was instructed, had silt to the depth of fourteen feet—created over a period of perhaps ten generations, although this is disputable.

Another interesting feature of Nabataeans' "desert plumbing" was their rock cisterns which held, underground, away from the heat of the sun, the water which was run off the hillsides for storage purposes.

Most intriguing of all are the mounds which surround Obde and S'betta, its sister city. They are heaps of pebbles, now choked with dust, and there is still a debate as to what they were originally. They are arranged in geometrical rows and obviously according to a deliberate design. One theory, suggested by evidence of fossil plants, was that they were dew mounds. That is to say, they were piles of loose pebbles on the cold surface of which the dew condensed and seeped into the soil below, making a wet sump of soil, protected by the mound during the heat of the day; in this mulch they planted vines, figs and olives, which rooted in the dew-replenished soil. Other experts maintain—again from suggestive remains—that they were storage bins like potato clamps or like the piles of stones which the Eskimos use to cover their caches. A third school of thought dismisses them merely as scrapings of the desert pavement. They could be one or the other, or all three. I still favor the dew-mound theory.

The Nabataeans maintained their independence against the

attempts of the Seleucids and Ptolemies, Alexander's successors, to conquer them. Their heyday was around the time of Christ. But after the Jewish revolt of A.D. 67 the Romans extended their domain over the desert areas, including the stamping grounds of the Nabataeans. This changed the fortunes of the Nabataeans and of Petra. Not immediately, but gradually, the caravan routes were diverted and the Romans increased the traffic from the Persian Gulf, away from the Red Sea. Palmyra instead of Petra became the main center. The southern trade routes languished, but it was not until A.D. 500 that the disciplined rule of the desert relaxed and the Nabataean traditions and cities fell into final decay.

15 *Rome Takes Over*

ROME replaced Greece as the dominant Occidental empire in 146 B.C. The Romans had come out from the Second Punic War victorious and had found occasion to interfere in the affairs of Greece. Philip V of Macedon having allied himself with Hannibal, the Romans sent Flaminius to punish him, and in this war the Achaean League joined with the Romans. Philip was defeated in 197 B.C. and was obliged to recognize the independence of Greece from Macedonia. The Achaean League became a puppet government of the Romans until finally in 146 B.C. the Roman consul, Mummius, defeated the city-states at the Battle of Corinth and Greece finally lost its independence and formally became a Roman province.

But even at this stage the stresses which had been apparent in the Greek Empire were already apparent in Italy itself.

They were sharply defined in the story of the ill-fated Gracchi.

The brothers Tiberius Sempronius and Gaius Gracchus were the sons of a historic house. One of their ancestors had defeated Hanno in the Carthaginian War in 214 B.C. Their father had been consul and had married the daughter of Scipio Africanus. Tiberius Sempronius, the younger, had served at the Siege of Carthage and in the Numantian War. In 133 B.C. he offered himself as candidate for the tribuneship, an office which made him inviolable as long as he was invested with it. It provided him with his opportunity. He used his office to make himself the champion of the plebs, the common people and the farmers, against the patricians, the aristocrats.

His first efforts were directed to a reform of the Roman land system by the restoration of the old Licinian Law, which enacted that no one should possess more than 500 acres of the public domains and that the overplus should be divided equally among the plebs. This was now called the Agrarian Law. He was violently opposed by the aristocracy, and the veto of Marcus Octavius stopped the passage of the bill. Tiberius, however, exerting all the prerogatives of his office, managed to pass the bill, and three commissions were appointed to carry it into execution—himself, his brother Gaius and his father-in-law, Appius Claudius. At the same time Attalus, King of Pergamus, died, bequeathing his treasures to the Roman people. Tiberius proposed that these should be used as a fund to help the recipients of land under the new law, and he also proposed to give the popular Assembly, instead of the Senate, the management of the state. This was too revolutionary. He was accused of having violated his office and of conspiring to be king, and at the next election for the tribuneship he was murdered with three hundred of his followers at the entrance of the Temple of Fides. Ten years after his death his younger brother won the tribuneship. He renewed his brother's law and avenged his murder by expelling many of his most violent enemies from the city. Several popular measures gave him favor with the people, but in the end the intrigue of the aristocracy caused his downfall. He did not obtain a third tribuneship and, faced with the threat of a popular uprising, the Senate took strong measures. Armed soldiers attacked the followers of Gracchus, and nearly three thousand were slain. Gracchus escaped to the Grove of the Furies, where he was slain at his own request by a slave who then killed himself.

16 *Spoils of Office*

THE DOMINION of Rome over the Mediterranean brought an uneasy peace but not, at first, prosperity. Indeed, it was the opposite. The peoples in the cities of Italy had been organized as a union of allies; after 88 B.C. all Italians were admitted to Roman citizenship, but the annexed territories overseas were treated as estates to be exploited as tributaries, like the conquests of an Oriental monarch. Enlightened Oriental kings, like Cyrus, however, had had the sense to recognize that their revenues depended upon the prosperity of their subjects. They usually ensured that their governors, while exacting royal tributes, were also responsible for the general well-being of the land, its soil and its people. That was not true of the magistrates sent out for a year as governors by republican Rome. Since the Senate was composed of time-expired governors, it was scarcely a brake on the rapacity of those whom it appointed. After 121 B.C. a governor, if impeached, would be tried by his peers who themselves owed their wealth and their rank to the exploitation of the provinces by tax farming, usury and concessions. At the same time election could only be confirmed by bribes "to the Roman People." Any governor had to make three fortunes in a year out of his province—one to pay his election expenses, another to bribe his judges at his trial on his return, and the third to live in comfort for the rest of his life. In the last century of the Republic senators and proconsuls amassed great fortunes.

Pompey, in Roman talents, was the equivalent of a dollar millionaire; so were Crassus and Brutus. Such fortunes were not acquired by promoting and encouraging the creation of productive wealth but largely by extortion, usury and financial manipulation of the provinces.

In Rome itself the empire enriched only a very small class. Debts and conscription had driven a large proportion of the peasantry from the land. Their small holdings were taken over by great landlords and worked by slaves. The dispossessed peasantry could not find employment in industry because the city working class was also being impoverished and socially degraded by competition from the slaves who were brought into the slave markets by each imperialist enterprise.

This was the situation which helped Julius Caesar after he had added to the empire the Celtic lands of the Rhine and the Channel and Britain. He seized supreme power as the Greek tyrants had done. Two years later he was murdered in the name of the democratic freedom, but after twelve more years of civil war his grandnephew, Augustus, became in fact Emperor. Julius Caesar was, of course, deified, and in the old Oriental tradition Augustus accepted divine honors in his own lifetime and identified himself with the gods throughout his empire. He was now the monarch of a single state extending from the Euphrates and the Black Sea, the Danube and the Rhine to the Atlantic and from the North Sea to the Sahara and the Arabian deserts.

17 *Pax Romana*

JULIUS CAESAR and Augustus put an end to the worst excesses of the senatorial governors. They created a reasonably efficient and honest administration and they gave an empire peace. Following them, for 250 years the expanding Empire enjoyed an internal peace never hitherto found in so large an area. There was also a conscious concern for ensuring the reasonable well-being and prosperity of the conquered peoples.

The immediate result was a revival of prosperity and an increase of population in the new western provinces. In size the average Roman city was not much bigger than the Greek polis. As laid out in A.D. 100, Timgad in North Africa covered only some thirty acres. Caerwent in South Wales measured forty-four acres, and Cirencester in England was about the same size. Roman London was 300 acres; New Carthage reached 1,200 acres; Alexandria, 2,275; and Rome, about 3,060.

Roman cities enjoyed municipal self-government wherever

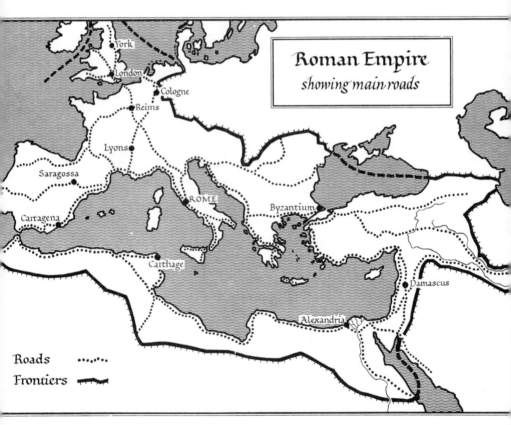

Roman Empire
showing main roads

Roads   ••••••
Frontiers   ⊢⊣⊣

they were and were modeled on a common pattern. They included a public water supply, handsome public buildings, baths, theaters, colonnades, market halls and assembly places adorned with statues and fountains. The private dwellings, at least of the well-to-do, were large and tastefully built and furnished. A middle-class house with a terraced garden could occupy a block a hundred feet square, and the main reception room would be about forty-eight feet long. The small retailers, craftsmen and laborers lived in flimsier houses with one or two rooms and in the big cities in tenements which could run up to sixty feet in height. At Caistor, near Norwich in Britain, houses adjacent to the potter's kiln, presumably occupied by the master potters, were made elegant with tessellated pavements.

In the early days of the Roman Empire the amenities of life were fairly generously distributed, at least geographically. Bronze bowls made in Capua have turned up as far north as Scotland, and in Denmark, Sweden, Hungary and Russia. Trade existed beyond its boundaries. Artisans and industrialists from Italy and Greece migrated westward and established factories in what had been the barbarian provinces. Fine red-glazed molded ware in the Greek tradition was produced in Western Europe. Pottery manufactured in Italy found its way to Asia Minor, Palestine, Cyprus, Egypt, North Africa, Spain and south Russia. Products of factories in Gaul reached North Africa and Egypt as well as Spain, Italy and Sicily. Syrians established glassmaking in the Rhône Valley and in northern France.

The barbarians of the north supplied slaves, amber, furs and other materials. In return they acquired wines, pottery, metalware, glass and coins. Trade routes radiated from the Black Sea ports and distributed similar commodities across the Russian steppes to the Urals themselves.

Regular caravans of camels brought spices, aromatics, oils and jewels across the deserts of southern Arabia and Mesopotamia. Under Roman auspices, a direct sea route between Egypt and India was encouraged as a check on the monopoly of the Nabataeans and others in policing the land routes.

CLOVERLEAF B.C. *Intersection of five Roman aqueducts.* From a painting by Zeno Diemer. CLOVERLEAF A.D. *Woodbridge Interchange of Garden State Parkway and New Jersey Turnpike* (New York Times)

After A.D. 50 the Romans began to exploit the discovery of a Greek sea captain, Hippalos, that the monsoons provided a regular means of direct transit across the ocean to India and shortened the time. The southwest monsoon in August provided both the motive power for crossing and a guide as reliable as a compass. The northwest monsoon in January ensured the return voyage.

This mercantile navy brought to the Roman market not only Indian goods but also Chinese products carried so far over land or by sea in Indian and Chinese ships. The imports were mostly luxury goods—dancing girls, parakeets, ebony, ivory, pearls and precious stones, spices and perfumes, silks and drugs.

These products could not be paid for in mass-production goods or in agricultural products. And so there developed in the opposite direction a trade in luxuries which could be carried in small bulk. The balance of trade between Rome and India was adverse and was made up by exporting gold coins. These still turn up all over India and have been found as far away as Ceylon and China. The Greek and Roman agricultural science based, as has been suggested, on the Carthaginian system, was usefully applied in extending the agricultural belt of North Africa further inland and also encouraging the growth of agriculture all over France, the Rhine Valley and southern England. Even in the north, Mediterranean techniques were applied; for instance, vines and vine growing were introduced into Britain. As an interesting example of man's adaptation to his environment, we find ingenious systems of central heating in the villas of Britain, designed to temper the rigors of the climate to the Mediterranean overlords.

18 Roman Science

As an administrative system the Roman Empire was remarkable. The intensity of commercial intercourse between all its scattered parts and the relations which it established between the civilized and barbarian worlds produced the results which are reflected in the habits of the Western world today. Besides traders, wandering craftsmen and slaves, civil servants and military officers were continually being exchanged between the remote outposts of the empire. A huge standing army was needed to guard the long frontiers, and soldiers were recruited in every part of the empire and the cautious practice followed of sending them to serve away from their home country. Ambassadors and missionaries came from the East to Rome, and Marcus Aurelius sent an embassy to the Han dynasty in China.

Yet there is a remarkable shortcoming in the Roman story. Imperial Rome made practically no contribution to pure science. What passes for science is largely the compilation of volumes of other people's knowledge, and the direct or original observations seem to be remarkably absent.

Having, for example, at first despised the Greek medicine of Hippocrates, the Romans eventually came to regard the Greeks as custodians of medical knowledge. Galen, the outstanding physician of Rome, was a Greek. He had originally come to Rome as a surgeon to the gladiators and had built up a fashionable practice as a physician before the jealousy of his professional colleagues drove him into exile and back to Asia Minor. He became eventually physician to Marcus Aurelius (A.D. 161–180). Galen was a braggart and, unlike Hippocrates, reported only such cases as were successful and redounded to his credit. Nevertheless, even if we discount a large proportion of his claims, he was a remarkable physician. He wrote more than 300 books, of which only 118 survived a fire in his own lifetime. He kept

266

twelve scribes continuously busy recording his anatomical observations, his selective case histories, the drugs he prescribed and also his boasts. His thinking was derivative from the Greek "humors." His anatomy was quite misleading because, in spite of his experience with gladiators, he was influenced by the prevailing objection to human dissection and drew all his human analogies from the studies of animals. Moreover, his works are full of superstition. But one feels that this was in a way deliberate, because he was simply accommodating himself to the fashions of his time. In his own right, and in his own time, Galen was a great physician. Unfortunately the reputation which he left behind him was to corrupt and prevent the advance of science for another fourteen hundred years. As late as 1559 the College of Physicians in London condemned one of its Fellows, Dr. John Geynes, and forced him to recant when he dared to suggest that Galen's works contained errors.

The great contribution which Rome made to medicine was in its military hospitals and its remarkable drainage systems, aqueducts of fresh water, and public baths.

In applied sciences, too, the advances made in Roman times were disappointing in comparison with the enormous opportunities which were offered. Roman architects, builders and engineers superbly applied and amplified processes and techniques inherited from the Greek world, but one finds very little evidence of revolutionary innovations or novelties.

19 *Disease and Decay of Empires*

WE CAN PAUSE with Marcus Aurelius and with Galen, because here was the last of the great Romans as well as the last of the great Greeks and, indeed, their professional relationship—Emperor and Court Physician—was itself symbolic. By this time the Roman Empire was already in decay. Rome and the cities were full of peasants who had been driven off their farms by malaria. One of the factors in this movement was that the great lands of fertile, well-drained soil and farms on the uplands had passed into the hands of landlords who had cultivated them by slave labor while leaving the poorer areas to the pagans—a word derived from *pagi*, or marshes. In these marshes the malaria mosquito bred, and the disease and the poverty drove their victims into the cities to spread the infection. The disease apparently extended to the frontiers of the empire, decimating the garrisons, depopulating the towns, and, in a climax which some authorities think was an outbreak of pestilential disease (it may have been smallpox), led to the final break-through of the barbarians.

It is significant that simultaneously the same thing was happening to the Han dynasty in China; the frontier defenses of a well-organized and well-administered culture collapsed and left the way open for the invading Mongols.

In the process of decay, even before the death of Marcus Aurelius, the Roman provinces had begun to become more and more economically isolated. This was due to the fact that they had imported immigrant craftsmen and experts and had established their own industries in competition with the original centers of production.

At the same time, to avoid the city plagues and taxation, the aristocrats had moved into their country villas and had established themselves on a basis of near self-sufficiency. As a result of the new developments, even as early as A.D. 50, the agricultural system was being changed to estates worked by dependent tenants, or share farmers, practicing subsistence agriculture and giving services and surpluses to the landlord. This was the characteristic, later, of medieval Europe and the manor system. But these Roman estates would include hired craftsmen, such as weavers, fullers, smiths, carpenters, bakers and so forth. Whereas originally the country households had turned to their villages and local towns for such help, now they were practically self-contained.

This led to a very serious decline in the urban industries and the impoverishment of once-flourishing cities. The process can be measured by the actual contraction of urban areas. After A.D. 275 Autun had shrunk from nearly 500 to less than 25 acres. In Verulamium (St. Albans) the decline of city life was equally clear in the third century. When the town walls collapsed and the theater fell in, nothing was done to repair them. At Wroxeter the town center was burned and was never rebuilt. This was the beginning of the ruin of the smaller tradesman and was the corollary of the decline of the primary producer—the peasant farmer.

By A.D. 250 all semblance of prosperity throughout the empire had vanished. The bankruptcy of the Roman economy was quite clear to all. It showed itself in the spreading of famine and disease, which are the concomitants of poverty. In the 150 years before barbarian invaders from Germany finally disrupted the political structure of the empire and began the Dark Ages of Europe, attempts were made to rescue the machinery of government by an even more intensive form of centralization. But the impoverishment of the empire and the decline of its population naturally reacted on the state itself. A great army was needed to defend the frontiers. And the army had to be equipped and paid. The cost increased as the emperors were forced to hire barbarian mercenaries from abroad to make up for the shortage of native recruits, owing to population decline. Administration and collection of revenue required an elaborate, costly civil service. The emperors spent vast sums on public works, not only on roads or the useful amenities of life, but also on luxuries like the great architectural showpieces. While the economic system was expanding it could easily stand the strain, but when it reached its limits the central treasury began to collapse.

20 *Premature Fascism*

NERO EMPLOYED a trick which was to be repeated by governments in our times—he fiddled his deficit by debasing his currency. Not only was taxation increased, but compulsion was applied to industry and commerce. The guilds of craftsmen and merchants, originally free associations, became, as in Fascist Italy and in Nazi Germany later on, the organs of the state for ensuring the "loyalty" of their members and the supply of workers and materials. The employees in the public services were in fact civil conscripts who were bound by employment, often branded physically, and allowed to marry only into families of fellow workers. No one was now free to adopt or ply a craft but was compelled by law to follow one.

The fraternities of shipowners, teamsters and transport workers in general were brought under military discipline. The food supply and civil amenities of the city of Rome had to be maintained because the emperors had to rely on the support of its people for their appointment and for their continuance. In Rome bread was supplied gratis and circuses were given on 175 days of the year. Rome became no more than a glorified court of the emperors whose hangers-on had to be kept humored by exactions imposed on the subject peoples.

Prices were fixed throughout the empire by edict; so were maximum wages. And the right to strike was forbidden by law. This, of course, left banditry or beggary as the sole resort of the oppressed tenant trying to escape from serfdom or from debt. In A.D. 332 the first Christian emperor, Constantine, made the attachment of the share farmer (*colonus*) to his landlord enforceable by law. In 371 the Emperor Valentinian decreed: "We do not deem that the share farmers are free to leave the land to which their condition and birth attached them. If they do, let them be brought back, put in chains and punished."

270

The results were inevitable. Agriculture is a way of life. It cannot be maintained by reluctant farmers or by slave labor. It is essentially the identity of the peasant with his soil. It means nursing his holding for his posterity, and if he sees no future, the soil is no longer his child. Neglected, it becomes sickly and dies. That was the fate of the granaries of the Roman Empire. It was like a great estate administered by an absentee landlord, who had neglected its fences and its steadings, oppressed his tenants and extorted their products to feed people whom they had never seen and who meant nothing to them. The soils, like the empire itself, began to crumble at the edges. It was allowed to become exhausted, and its conservation systems fell into decay. Unlike those garrison farmers who had pushed out into the North African desert, had conquered the soil and had built the fortified farmhouses to defend their lands against all comers, the peasants on the perimeter of the empire had no possessions to defend and there was little to choose between the ravages of the barbarians and the exactions of their imperial landlords. In the decline of the conservation systems, diseases like malaria afflicted and decimated the people and the military garrisons. The way was wide open for the barbarians.

21 *Candles in the Dark*

IN THE COLLAPSE of the wider empire the Roman capital was moved to Byzantium (Constantinople). So, in the eastern Mediterranean, which had been the cradle of previous civilizations, survived a part of the empire which had been Rome. In the Byzantine Empire some of the vestiges of high culture and refinement (albeit corrupted) were retained. Most crafts were practiced with the technical skill and equipment evolved in Greek and Roman times. Barter, to which communities elsewhere were compelled to revert with the collapse of the Roman monetary system, did not entirely oust the money economy. Nor did the stringencies of local self-sufficiency paralyze export trade completely. Greek medicine continued in the public hospitals and was preserved, to be carried into the Arab tradition later on. The Jews, in their dispersal after the destruction of the Temple in A.D. 70, took with them not only the common bonds of their religion but the knowledge and skills of the civilizations of which they were the disinherited heirs. Thus from Palestine derived not only the new religion, Christianity, which was to give its character to Western civilization, but also the wandering Jews, the landless exiles who practiced as traders, bankers, skilled craftsmen and doctors, scattering the seeds, often on inhospitable ground, of the material values of the past.

In the northern provinces of the empire, however, the cultural losses were much more serious. In the fractionation of what had been the Roman system, communities retreated into isolation. Their world narrowed and the lights dimmed in the Dark Ages. In separation and in conflict the social units were driven back into local self-sufficiency, a precarious condition where a seasonal failure meant famine, for which there was no relief now to be obtained from imperial surpluses and imports.

The vogue of modern scientific history is to remind us that the Dark Ages were not as dark as we used to think they were. That is true, particularly since in our parochialism we think only of the era in Europe. Elsewhere civilizations were flourishing or reasserting themselves. In China, for example, our Dark Ages were the Golden Ages. In India it was the age of *Susruta*, the encyclopedia of Hindu science. In it we find them practicing "rhinoplasty," which means turning down a flap of the skin of the forehead to repair unsightly nose defects and also demonstrates that they knew what the modern immunologist learned, that the body system rejects alien cells. So if an attempt is made to graft a piece of skin or flesh from someone else, the graft will not take. Only like will repair like—the graft must come from the person of the patient or from an identical twin. The Hindus at the time of our Dark Ages knew this and used the flap method, taking a patch from the patient, nourished by the person's own blood supply. They had a range of 120 surgical instruments, any of which might belong to modern surgical practice. They used anesthetics, could diagnose 1,120 diseases and knew the medicinal values of 760 plants.

In Iran, in A.D. 530, was founded the University of Jundishapur. In Mesopotamia the caliphs of Baghdad were the patrons of learning and of such men as Rhazes, the lute player, one of history's great doctors. Rhazes anticipated Pasteur by more than 1,000 years, because when he was ordered by the caliph to build a new hospital, he hung up pieces of fresh meat in various parts of Baghdad and chose the site where the meat putrefied most slowly, because, as Pasteur was to demonstrate, the atmosphere was purer and bacteria less active.

From the springs of knowledge thus preserved in the Middle East came the Arab medicine which spread through North Africa and reached its highest expression in the great University of Cordoba in Moorish Spain. In addition to this stream there were others which converged, in the case of medicine, on the College of Salerno, near Naples, which was the first medical school in Christendom. The Church, however, had no part in its foundation. Reputedly it was started by four masters: Elinus the Jew, Pontus the Greek, Adale the Arab, and Salernus the Latin—an index of its medical sources.

The lights were not entirely out. The barbarian hordes in Europe had not destroyed all the men of learning or the craftsmen and merchants. The Church itself kept alive the techniques of writing and of numbering and the measurement of time, as in clocks, and refinements such as glazed windows. And in the monastery gardens and in the church glebes they practiced scientific and exotic agriculture. While the trading and garrison cities fell into decline from their original importance, they were replaced by the cathedral cities with their permanent beauties of craftsmanship, the dedicated expression in stone, wood and glass of the arts of free men.

In another way the collapse of the empire had a perverse value in agriculture; it compelled peasants, and their feudal lords, to find farming methods more consistent with the local conditions of northern Europe, to work out their own soil salvation.

22 *Celtic Overpopulation*

WHEN THE ROMANS arrived in Britain they had been preceded by the Celts and the Belgae. The Celts had already developed settled farming with stockaded yards, including the farmstead, barns and byres, and they had tilled the ground with a primitive plow. The Belgae, from the Continent, had introduced the heavy eight-ox plow, with colter, share and moldboard, and had, alongside Celtic square-field cultivation, practiced strip-farming with surplus yields of grain.

Modern air survey has shown the widespread cultivation practiced by those pre-Roman Britons. The groups of fields are shown usually on the uplands where the natural forest, if it existed at all, was more easily cleared than the dense oak woodland of the valleys. (This, incidentally, was the same reason why the Pilgrim Fathers settled their farms on higher grounds, while forest valleys, cultivated since, were then avoided.) This, of course, is in contrast to the development of the alluvial river basins of the ancient civilizations. Cultivation in Britain, with its higher rainfall, was not dependent on irrigation. Where springs did not exist on the uplands (for the watering of stock and not for irrigation) the ancients developed the system of dew ponds, as on the downs.

It is quite clear from those aerial surveys that all the British land capable of access and productivity in terms of existing methods was already settled when the Romans arrived.

Professor Dudley Stamp has estimated that the area cultivated and cropped may have been about 4,000,000 acres, with additional sheep and cattle pastures. There is evidence that Britain, in Roman times, was already growing wheat as bread grain and that rye, which was to become the bread of the poor, was introduced later by the Anglo-Saxons.

The Romans are believed to have introduced the chestnut, the walnut and the vine, but their impact on British farming was significant only in terms of the introduction of the "villa." The villa was the ancestor of the country estate. It was always within reach of a city, which to the Roman overlord was the center of civilized life. The owner cultivated the adjoining fields with the aid of slave labor but probably let off part of his estate to tenant farmers or sharecroppers. He cultivated for the market. But away from the Roman towns and the Roman roads agriculture remained very much what it had been in pre-Roman times.

After the Picts and Scots broke through Hadrian's Wall and the Roman farms and villas became exposed to attack, the Romans withdrew to the towns. Finally all Roman troops and officials were withdrawn in the middle of the fifth century.

They had come to Britain as empire builders, convinced that the Roman way of life was the best of all possible for victor and for vanquished alike. Therefore, it was something to be imposed even if people were unwise or ungrateful enough not to want it. The Romans left their permanent imprint on Britain in the form of towns and magnificent roads. But they changed the rural picture scarcely at all, unlike the Anglo-Saxons who followed them.

23 *Anglo-Saxon Overpopulation*

THE IMPACT of the Germanic invaders was quite different because they came as settlers and not as the proconsuls or policemen of an empire. Like the Pilgrim Fathers entering New England, they came in village groups, established a settlement, cleared the land and worked it on a communal basis. They came as farmers who knew the value of good land, and they always placed their settlements near streams or springs so that they could have waterside meadows for summer grazing and hay for winter feed. This communal form of life resulted in villages (in contrast to villas). Like the Belgae, they favored strip cultivation rather than square fields, and their plow strips account for the quaint names of British land measures. They plowed so that they turned the sods toward the center of the strip, and this sod strip was 16½ feet wide, giving us the rod, pole or perch. "Furlong" is the length of an Anglo-Saxon furrow—220 yards long. Given the length of a furrow and a width of four perches, we have one acre. An acre, on loamy soil and with the Anglo-Saxon plow, was the extent of one day's plowing. The larger unit of land was known as a hide, which can be taken as a variable unit of measurement, the area which, under differing conditions, could be plowed by one ox team in a year. The smaller yardland, or virgate, was the area which could be farmed with one pair of oxen. A small holding of about five acres was what could be cultivated by hand by part-time farmers (with other work to do on the estate). It is interesting that the average hide of the Anglo-Saxons (about 120 acres) is still about the average amount of land held by the present-day British farmer.

Village plowlands were held in common. Each man was responsible for the strips which were allotted to him annually, but the plowing was done by ox teams shared by the village. Rotation of crops was practiced even in those days. Each village had three common fields—one in bread corn, another in drink corn (barley), and the third lying fallow.

The Anglo-Saxon farmers were not keen on the red and black soils of the chalk lands which had been favored by the Celts. The deep iron plows would have turned up the chalk. They appear to have avoided coarse, sandy soils and gravel, with their loss of water, and also the clays of the forest lands. They looked for lands free from flooding, with the good, deep loam which they found in East Anglia and along the flanks of the Sussex downs and the Chilterns.

One thing is clear: before the coming of the Normans, the Anglo-Saxons, the Jutes, the Danes and those among whom they had settled had farmed most of the land which it was possible to cultivate by their existing methods of technology. Apart from the arable land, the available woodland pastures were already being fully grazed.

"The evidence is steadily accumulating that lowland Britain was, according to the agricultural knowledge and farming systems of the time, already densely populated, even overpopulated," writes Professor Dudley Stamp in *Man and the Land*, referring to the time of the Norman Conquest.

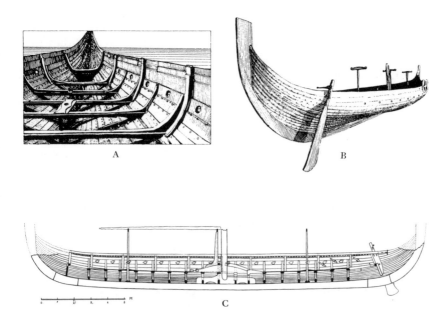

A

B

C

A *The restored Gokstad (Viking) ship, seen from the starboard stern (circa* A.D. *800). Length 78 feet over-all, beam 16.7 feet, depth 6.75 feet. The stump of the mast rises in the center, with three supports for awning. Four shields still hang on the bows. The steering oar has a tiller handle.* B *Interior of the vessel.* C *Longitudinal section showing method of stepping the mast.*

24 Norman Overpopulation

THE NORMAN CONQUEST produced one of the most remarkable documents in history. It is called the *Domesday Book*. After he had been reigning for nineteen years, William the Conqueror decided that he must have a stocktaking, or inventory, of the land over which he ruled.

He then sent his men all over England, into each shire, and caused them to find out how many hundred hides were within that shire and what the King had himself of land and of cattle and what rights he ought to have yearly from that shire.

It was done so thoroughly that not a single hide or yardland went unnoticed. "Nor was there an ox, or a cow, or a swine that was not set down." So there is a complete and permanent record of the farms and the stocks of England nearly nine hundred years ago.

Dudley Stamp draws an amusing parallel between the *Domesday Book* and the Farm Survey which the British Government carried out in the Second World War. Investigators went out to get a complete record not only of the distribution of the land but also of how farmers were treating it. These records were "brought to the King afterward" with the help of punch-card machines and in the form of soulless statistics quite unlike the colorful records of the Conqueror. That 1940 survey has had to be kept secret because it classified farmers as A (good), B (average) and C (poor), and the latter could proceed for libel in a British court of law!

It is, however, a safe and comforting generalization that British soils which were worked at the time of the *Domesday Book* and before are in as good "heart" today as then and are probably much improved.

278

Another thing which Dudley Stamp brings out is the profound effect which the Normans, who came as aristocratic settlers, not as pickets of empire, had on the English countryside. They stabilized the feudal system. They pinned down the landscape with their strongholds. They confirmed the village system by replacing the wooden Saxon churches with the enduring stone of the Norman churches; thus, just as in the case of Mesopotamia and Egypt, the tillers stayed with their altars, and the pattern of rural settlement became a fixed one. And the Normans made the hunt the quasi-sacred ritual which its pink-coated hierophants observe to this day.

Only now in the twentieth century can a good word be found for the harsh Forest Laws of the Norman kings. It is difficult for anyone brought up on *Ivanhoe, The Adventures of Robin Hood* and the *Children of the New Forest* to realize that the Normans were public benefactors and that agricultural England today owes them a permanent debt. The Forest Laws were ruthless. They divided the land into two parts—the settled part where the ordinary laws of the land applied, and the forest, which was reserved for the King absolutely. Those "forests" were not continuous woodland, as the name might suggest, but were tracts of wild land, often open, rough ground as Exmoor and Dartmoor are today and probably were then. Indeed, some of the well-timbered lands, like the oak forests of Kent and Sussex, were not scheduled as "forests" in the royal sense. Hunting grounds were on light, risky soil, which like Sherwood and the New Forest is still classified as "marginal."

If we accept the fact that by the time of the Normans England was already overpopulated in terms of land which could be worked by the then existing methods, it can be assumed that there was already pressure on those marginal lands and that there were unwise attempts to settle them. The chances of successful farming were remote, and it is an ironical fact that the ruthless Forest Laws, wittingly or unwittingly, were, as *1066 and All That* would say, "a good thing." Even the compassionate Dudley Stamp says of the forest dwellers, "Perhaps their dispossession was for their own good."

279

It certainly was for the good of the soils of England, because it preserved the balance of nature at a time when indiscriminate agricultural settlement might have drastically upset it. It preserved land which could be "coaxed" by later developments in husbandry.

Nevertheless, as social measures the Forest Laws of the first Norman kings were harsh to the point of the intolerable, and it needed the Magna Carta and the Forest Charter, two years later, to restrain the abuses.

He would be a rash man who would extend this justification of the Normans to later but similar enforcements in Scotland. Scots, looking at the empty glens of their highland ancestors, would be more difficult to persuade that the clearances which followed the Jacobite Rebellion in 1745 were also "all for the best." When Scottish exiles, scattered all over the world, don their tribal garb and invoke their clan origins, they keen the lament for the abandoned glens and foresaken hills. They recall how their forefathers were driven out of the Highlands into far countries. They talk of the people who were driven out of the glens to make room for sheep, to supply the wool mills of the south, and how the sheep later gave way to the deer, for the sport not of kings but of wealthy English businessmen and visiting Americans. They denounce those who emptied the Highlands and turned them into scenery. In their reproachful nostalgia they are not likely to be persuaded that it was really a kindness because the Duchess of Sutherland, who was responsible for the first evictions (1820), had been advised by a group of agriculturists that the lands were unsuitable for humans but suitable for sheep. Today nearly four million acres lie desolate "and stranger lords, by vagrant pleasure led, track the lone deer." This, whatever may be said of the Forest Laws in England, was a running-down operation in Scotland—a perverse lesson in ecology.

25 Black Death and the Black Country

THE BLACK DEATH of 1348–49, when half the population of Britain died, produced radical changes in the farming system of the country. It may itself have been in part due (although its direct cause was the flea-carried bubonic plague) to malnutrition in a country already overpopulated in relation to the food it could produce. It was mainly the laborer who died, because he was hungry and because he lived in hovels overrun by the rats which harbored the plague. The Black Death wiped out whole country communities. Land was untilled and villages deserted.

Because of the shortage of cultivators, there was a swing from arable farming and crop raising to sheep farming. It is reckoned that around that time the sheep population increased to 12,000,000 in England, and this produced a closer bond than had existed before between town and country, because wool was the source of common survival. It became so important that the Lord Chancellor, presiding over the House of Lords, sits on a woolsack to this day. Wool was the basis of an export trade which brought in staples, like corn, to eke out the diminished cereal production. And so it was, in a sense, the beginning of commercial England, of the era of the merchant princes.

This pastoralizing of England was, paradoxically, the forerunner of the Industrial Revolution. People forget that the Industrial Revolution did not begin with the invention of the steam engine but with the enclosures of the common lands on which the yeoman and commoners had the right to graze their sheep and cattle. The enclosure of these lands within the great estates is now recognized as a practice beneficial to the land, however harsh it may have been in its effects on the people. It enabled land which had gone out of cultivation following the

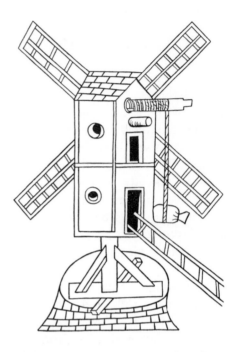

Post mill with auxiliary drive to drum by which sacks of grain could be lifted. From a fifteenth-century German manuscript.

Black Death to be brought under the plow again, and it restored proper land management in terms of drainage, fencing, rotation and conservation of pastures. It meant, however, dispossession of freemen and by the eighteenth century had produced a flow of the landless into the towns to be available as labor in factories; these were workshops of hired hands, even before the introduction of the spinning jenny, the mechanical loom and the steam engine, which later replaced the water wheel as the source of power.

With the development of the export trade and of the navy needed to protect it came the onslaughts on the great native oak forests. (A curious footnote to this is the fact that the shipbuilders determined the forest management in a way which is still evident in the English landscape today. They had to find their curved timbers in the shape of the limbs of the tree— while cutting the straight planks from the trunk. The variety of hull shapes could be obtained only if the branches were allowed to spread in certain ways. So trees were selectively cut to pro- duce this effect, and the dense oak forest which had defeated the Anglo-Saxon farmers was replaced by the coppices.) The other factor was the demand for iron, for cannon, chains and armor. As we have seen in other parts of the world, the need to get charcoal for ironmaking and for cement played havoc with the timberlands. Much of the deforestation of Britain was directly due to the iron-smelting industry. The southern wood- lands disappeared, and the iron industry of the Weald, in Kent, came to an end with the exhaustion of wood charcoal. Then the industry shifted to the Midlands and the coal seams of the Black Country of the ironworks.

Coal had been mined in Britain for centuries before it replaced charcoal in iron smelting. The first charter giving liberty to the town of Newcastle upon Tyne to dig coal was granted by Henry III in 1239, and in Scotland the Abbot of Dunfermline was granted a charter in 1291. The first man to smelt iron ore successfully with coke (in which the harmful sulphur has been removed from the coal) was Abraham Darby in 1709. With coke the iron became more liquid in the smelting process than it had done with charcoal, and it was thus possible to make lighter castings. Around 1750 coke-produced pig iron had achieved the quality which the forge masters were prepared to accept. This is a significant date because ironmaking had encouraged the ex- tension of coal mining and coke iron. A new, abundant source of fuel was available for the steam engines.

The stage was thus set for the first Industrial Revolution. The landless were available as factory workers. Mass-produced iron changed metalworkers from blacksmiths into machine makers. Mass-produced coal was abundant as fuel. And James Watt was about to invent the steam engine.

26 Out of the Past into the Present

THAT INVENTION we can count as the end of the past and the beginning of the present. Our contemporary scientific and technological civilization is no older than the United States of America, the political foundation of which coincided with the advent of the steam engine.

The machines were now able to produce surplus wealth on a scale never possible in previous history. From the material prosperity which resulted, men obtained the means and in-

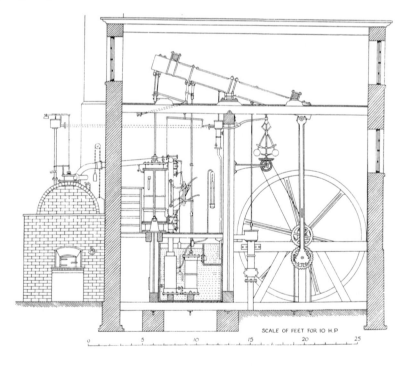

Watt's Double Acting Rotative Steam Engine (1784)

centives which have made possible the marvels of the mid-twentieth century. What we see today is the acceleration of a process which has been going on continuously for two hundred years. Industry provided the demands and set the pace for science. (For example, at the end of the eighteenth century, when factories made the mass-production textiles possible, the millowners would have been balked if they had had to rely on sun bleaching of their fabrics. This was the challenge to the chemists to produce the bleaches.) It was the new industrialists, like Watt, Boulton and Wedgwood, who reinvigorated the Royal Society of London. It was a British industrialist, James Smithson, who endowed the Smithsonian Institution in the United States, which he had never visited. The industrialists, with their new wealth, backed the curious enterprise of Benjamin Thompson, the American "colonist" who became Count Rumford and established the Royal Institution. He promoted the idea of "an establishment for feeding the poor and giving them useful employment . . . connected with an institution for bringing forward into general use new inventions and improvements, particularly such as relate to the management of heat and the saving of fuel and to various other mechanical contrivances, by which domestic comfort and economy may be promoted." But it also included the "teaching by regular courses of philosophic lectures and experiments." Thus it provided the laboratory and lecturing facilities for Sir Humphry Davy and for Faraday. In terms of the latter, the Steam Revolution thus promoted the Electrical Revolution.

Industry stimulated science. Science set the pace for industry. In 1840 a new word entered the dictionary—"scientist." The "man of science" who had hitherto been indulging his curiosity about natural phenomena now became a vocational "-ist." Science was no longer just a part of learning; it had become an end in itself. The degree to which this specialization progressed can be measured by the fact that in 1870 there were only six teaching laboratories in England but by 1900 there were over a thousand; "scientists" were coming off the production line.

The nineteenth century might well be summed up as the age in which the machine took over the functions of muscle.

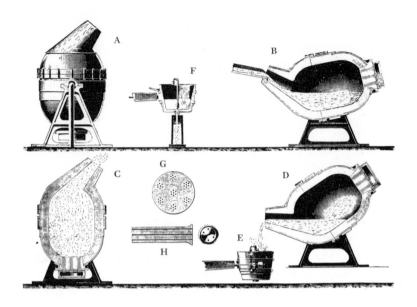

The first form of Bessemer's movable converter (1860). A *The converter before charging begins.* B *Molten iron being poured into the converter.* C *Position during blow.* D, E, F *Tipping into ladle.* G, H *Bottom and* tuyères *through which air passes.*

The first half of the twentieth century was the period in which machines began to take over the functions of the human senses as well. Electronics have given to industry devices which are more sensitive, more accurate and, indeed, more reliable than those senses of sight, hearing and touch which first differentiated our tree ancestors from the groundling beasts and the development of which produced the convolutions of the brain of thinking Man. The photoelectric cell, for its predetermined purposes, is more precise and constant than the human eye. The microphone can be refined to, and beyond, the faculty of human hearing. Electronic devices can control and manipulate massive machine tools with a precision, where necessary, of a millionth of an inch— far beyond the "feel" of the most skilled craftsman. The electronic computor includes a "memory" more infallible than

MEDIEVAL ALCHEMY   *Stradamus print of "The Alchemist's Laboratory"*

MODERN CHEMISTRY   *Texas Company refinery at Port Arthur, Texas*
[Wide World]

Man's, can do calculations hundreds of thousands of times faster than any mathematician, and without human frailty or compunction will exercise Man-given judgments or even, in the highly advanced types, make value judgments of its own.

27 *Man Shrinks His World*

MAN HAS encompassed his world with artificial satellites, has reached out for the moon and, beyond it, for the sun. He has reduced his planet to dimensions which can be encircled once an hour by a machine of his own creation. In the course of a single day every place on earth will pass under such a satellite in its orbit.

There may be escape routes to other planets, but for mankind in general those circling satellites should be a reminder of the small world on which the multiplying millions have got to contrive to exist. They should be a reminder to us of the totality of our present civilization.

Ever since *Homo sapiens* first began to master his environment, his species has survived and multiplied because it has been possible to extend the local limits of capacity. In the past those limits were extended either by technological means such as irrigation or by expansion through empire or emigration, as when the new continents were opened up in the nineteenth century. Now the local limits are global limits. Man has to become, by ingenuity and wisdom, the master of his environment on a world scale.

Knowledge, which is what science is, is not wisdom. Wisdom is knowledge tempered by judgment, and judgment is the awareness of past experience—and, most important, of past mistakes. That is why this book has given so much attention to past civilizations before it faces the challenges and opportunities of our present civilization.

PART
SEVEN

A Pause for Thought

"True science teaches us to doubt, and, in ignorance, to refrain."

—CLAUDE BERNARD

1 Radioactive Rain

IMAGINE THE GENIE of Aladdin's lamp being ordered to escort a raindrop from the middle of the Pacific to the sources of the Nile.

He would catch it as it fell into the ocean.

It would elude him by turning into water vapor in the palm of his hand and by escaping into a cloud.

He would hang on the skirts of that cloud as it scurried over the Rocky Mountains;

Dive after the raindrop again as it fell into the headwaters of the Mississippi;

Swim after it down the river to the Gulf of Mexico;

See it evaporate again in the tropical heat of the Caribbean to be carried by the climatic currents to the mountains of Ethiopia;

And he would go plunging with it into Lake Tana, to follow its journey down the Blue Nile.

That is not, nowadays, a nursery story. It is scientifically possible to pursue a raindrop in this way and to learn from it the hidden mysteries of our climate.

The "genie" is tritium—triple hydrogen—a radioisotope. Tritium is needed to produce, and is released by, H-bomb explosions. Those explosions are the result of a process like that by which the sun produces the rays of energy on which all life on earth depends. In the sun, with billions of years in which to do the job, the process is complicated, but it consists of building up hydrogen atoms into helium atoms and releasing a lot of spare energy. ("Spare" means a thousand times more energy than comes from the splitting of atoms in the fission bomb.) It needs four hydrogen nuclei to make one of helium. Tritium is triple hydrogen, which

291

means that only one more atom has to be flash-welded to make helium and the resulting explosion. But lots of waste tritium goes up into the stratosphere and circulates around the earth. Because, like ordinary hydrogen, it combines with oxygen to make water vapor (H_2O) and thus form into rain, the tritium comes back readily to earth.

In the blizzard snows of the Arctic and Antarctic, the geyser springs of Colorado, the rains of Chicago, the Thames water of London, the cisterns of Switzerland and the sources of the Nile, this radioactive hydrogen has been found. The traces are minute and harmless but measurable and far greater than can be explained by natural tritium, which is created by cosmic rays from outer space colliding with the elements in the air. The increased tritium is man-made, released by the hydrogen-bomb explosions in the Pacific and Soviet Asia, and it has been used by the scientists to gain knowledge about the world's weather and about the movements of air and ocean currents.

They have been able to track the movement of ocean water over the American continent. The rain clouds formed by the evaporation of the Pacific are precipitated by the mountains. About a third of the water in the Upper Mississippi Valley comes from the ocean rain. The other two thirds are from water evaporated from the land surface. This was shown by tritium evidence. Following through the process, they found that the water returned to the oceans as river water or as moisture in the air masses moving from the land to fall as rain over the sea. Thus water from the Pacific was carefully checked across the United States and into the Atlantic.

Another surprising discovery was made in the hot geysers of Colorado which were supposed to be jets from primeval springs: they were found to contain H-bomb tritium from the remote Pacific. This showed that the geysers were, in part at least, supplied by rain water seeping down into the springs, to be boiled up and ejected.

It was also found possible, with the aid of tritium, to measure the age of water, to tell, for example, whether springs were regularly replenished with rain and at what intervals. This was important in desert conditions where heartbreaks have happened when wells which had seemed promising have given out after a few months or years. The explanation has been that water was coming from geological pockets. It was "fossil" or "plutonic" water which was sealed off in the formation of the earth's crust. The source, in that case, is no more than a water bottle which, once emptied, cannot be refilled.

2 *Radioactive Plants*

WONDERFUL! But there is another side of the story. What is true of tritium is true also of more dangerous radioactive by-products of the H-bomb explosion—radioisotopes such as radiostrontium and radiocesium which are harmful and even lethal to life and which are carried by the same or similar climatic movements.

The risks of another bomb-made isotope—radiocarbon—were at first minimized by the experts because it is what is called a beta emitter. That means that it ejects electrons from its nucleus and those electrons are not particularly dangerous to human beings.

It has been mentioned in this book (p. 78) how radiocarbon could be used to help us date more accurately archeological finds and so establish the dates of prehistory. This is possible because radiocarbon exists in nature and, like ordinary carbon, combines in all organic life. It has what the scientists call a "half life" of 5,000 years. That means that half the original atoms will have split and decayed in that time and half of the remainder will decay in the following 5,000 years, and so on. From the various proportions the periods of time can thus be measured up to 30,000 years.

293

But man-made radiocarbon also combines in the chemistry of all living things. Neutrons, atomic particles from the H-bomb, cause the nitrogen in the atmosphere to change into radiocarbon. This will combine in the algae of the sea and the plants of the land and will enter into the food cycle, on which life depends. It may not be visibly harmful to human beings or to the higher organisms, but scientific concern has been expressed, rather belatedly, now, as to its effects on the more sensitive microorganisms and cellular plants. Even beta emissions might radically change or kill the benevolent organisms which are part of the food cycle of animals and men.

3 *Radioactive People*

SCIENTISTS, of course, know a lot about the physical chain reaction which causes the explosion in the A-bomb and acts as the detonator in the H-bomb, but very little indeed is known about the biological chain reaction which radioactivity may produce. It is known that radiostrontium, which never existed in nature, is present today in the bones of Atom Age children probably everywhere in the world. Radiostrontium imitates calcium and enters into the bone-building process. It escapes from the H-bomb as a gas, to become particles of radiostrontium, and is stored in the stratosphere, moving with the climatic currents and coming back in rain. It has a half life of nearly twenty-five years. Among milk-drinking populations the strontium passes through the cow. It gets originally into the soil and then into the plants which the cow eats, but it is in part retained by the cow so that the quantities passed on in milk are reduced. This is not true among populations which get their food direct from the soil, like the rice eaters of the Orient, and the United Nations investigators found that the amount of radiostrontium absorbed into the bones of Oriental children was six times as high as the proportions in Occidental children. The clinical consequences are debatable; it is not known how many cases of leukemia or bone cancer may be attributable now and in the future to this intake of radiostrontium —but everyone is agreed that any radiation beyond that which already exists in nature can be harmful, shortening life even when it does not produce deadly diseases.

4 *Radioactive Chickens Home to Roost*

SINCE JULY 16, 1945, when the first atomic bomb was exploded at Alamogordo in New Mexico, entirely new factors have been introduced by Man into his environment—factors capable of affecting the balance of nature in ways still imperfectly understood.

In this book we have been looking at the achievements and mistakes of the ancients. From now on we will be examining the possible achievements and mistakes of the moderns. And we have to remember that we are no longer dealing with small localities, like the land between the Euphrates and the Tigris, but with a whole planet round which a piece of man-made hardware can circle once an hour. Our mistakes, like our achievements, can be written large on a world scale.

The camera eye of an artificial satellite scanning the globe, rotating once a day within its orbit, can see no "curtains" or frontiers. There are no frontiers in the terms we are now discussing. When atomic experts are not sure of the hazards involved, they push the hazards as far away as they possibly can. New Mexico and Nevada, whose deserts were big enough for the atom bomb, were not big enough for the H-bomb. So American tests had to be carried out on distant islands in the Pacific. So, too, with the British; they pushed the hazards away to Christmas Island in the South Pacific. So, too, with the Russians; they carried out their tests in remote parts beyond the Urals. And the French in the Sahara. The fallout of radioactive sewage which was supposed to be safely disposed of in some remote place was found to be "banding" in the jet streams circulating around the Northern Hemisphere and to be coming down, like radioactive chickens coming home to roost, on the very countries who had initiated it—and also on neighbors who had had no part in it.

5 *Radioactive Burial Grounds*

THIS DOES NOT APPLY only to fallout. It applies to radioactive waste, both from military atom factories and from the reactor stations, engaged in peaceful uses. In the fission process, in which energy is released by the splitting of atoms (but not in the fusion process, in which the H-energy for industrial uses will be released by the building up of atoms), there is bound to be radioactive waste. Some of that waste is relatively harmless, but some of it is distinctly dangerous. There are long-lived radioactive by-products which remain dangerous for years, decades, centuries and even millenniums. (Plutonium has a half life of 24,000 years.) Their disposal is a major public-health problem.

Others are short-lived and virtually harmless. Even they have to be treated with such scrupulousness that at Harwell, for instance, the effluent which is discharged into the Thames has a lower radioactivity than the natural waters of the river itself.

Others, again relatively harmless, are regarded as fit to be discharged into the sea. At Windscale, the atom factory in Cumberland, the pipelines for this second type of effluent run two and a half miles out into the Irish Sea, where wastes can be dispersed and diluted by the currents. Nevertheless, continual studies have to be made of the organic life in the Irish Sea before the Ministries of Health and Fisheries can be reassured. Here very few signs of radioactive "pickup" have been found except in the case of seaweed, which is slightly more radioactive than normal.

There are even more dangerous products which are a costly headache. Not only are they radioactive, but the radioactivity generates heat, and therefore any atomic "coffins" have to contain and withstand this heat and they have to be interred in "burial grounds" (the official term) where they can remain undisturbed for an indefinite period of time. In fourteen years the United States accumulated 65,000,000 gallons of radioactive elements, stored in more than 100 indestructible steel tanks. Those cost more than $162,000,000. By A.D. 2000 the amount of waste from peaceful uses will be so great as to require, on the present system, over 1,000 acres per year of "burial grounds," even if they use the most compact methods of disposal, such as fusing the fission products in glass.

As the chairman of the "hazards session" at the second Geneva Conference on the Peaceful Uses of Atomic Energy said: "The tombs of radioactive waste are becoming as elaborate and as expensive as those of the mummies of the Pharaohs."

6 Biological Chain Reaction

THERE SEEM to be few ways of avoiding this burial system. It is true that much of the radioactive waste, in terms of its separate elements, is valuable as radioisotopes for research in industry, medicine, agriculture, etc., and in medical treatment. That may be some consolation to the economists but scarcely to the health-hazards experts, because it means that instead of being safely buried, the radioactivity will be distributed in small units all around the world, and unless the elements are handled by responsible experts under international safeguards, the risks may be increased rather than reduced. Under wise international control this last anxiety might be removed.

An alternative which has been heavily canvassed is to dump the materials, embedded in concrete or in durable containers, into "trenches" in the oceans. In the drowned landscape beneath the seas there are great valleys, by comparison with which the Grand Canyon of Colorado, a mile deep and two hundred miles long, is not so very grand. Nineteen ocean "trenches" are over four and a half miles deep, and some are thousands of miles long. These seemed to be likely places. It was assumed that they were troughs of stagnant water. There, so the argument went, the dangerous elements in their concrete or metal coffins would lie undisturbed until their radioactivity was spent.

I remember the consternation which was caused at the first Geneva Conference when this suggestion was challenged. An American oceanographer asked one of the experts where in the Atlantic this might be done and, on being told, indignantly pointed out that through that particular canyon ran an undersea river with a fierce, fast current which might batter the containers and release the activity. The Russians on that occasion also entered a caveat about the glib assumption that the interchange between the bottom waters of such "trenches" and the surface was a slow one—slow enough to give the assurance that, no matter how long-lived, the elements would not be brought back in dangerous form to the surface.

In the three years between the two United Nations conferences (1955 and 1958) the Russian ship *Vityaz* carried out oceanographic surveys of twelve of the nineteen "trenches." A detailed account was given to the second conference of the findings in the Tonga Trench, which extends southward for nearly 700 miles from the Samoa Islands to the Kermadec Islands. The expedition found that, by comparison with the findings of the Danish *Galatea* expedition in 1952, the deep-water temperature had risen. It was found that, even at the greatest depth, a change of water takes place in as brief a period as five years. The distribution of oxygen and phosphates and the presence of living organisms consuming oxygen at every depth showed that the water was actively mixing, horizontally and vertically. That meant that the dangerous materials with long-lived radioactivity would be liable to break loose and escape upward into the upper layers of water. There the marine life would become radioactively infected and form a biological chain reaction which would end up in the food of human beings.

This warning was reinforced at the conference by Dr. B. H. Ketchum, of the Woods Hole Oceanographic Institution. He showed that there was a kind of biological elevator in the sea which would bring radioactive material from the deeps to the surface. Sea plants and organisms concentrate fission products, assimilating them from the water, in which they may be in dilute proportions, and storing them. Thus the plankton in the Bikini test area of the Pacific had 470 times more radioactivity than the water itself. Living organisms could pick up, concentrate and transfer the radioactivity from the contaminated layers of the ocean to the uncontaminated. Dead organisms would sink toward the bottom, and the fission products, bound up in their skeletons, would increase the radioactivity in the depths. Thus there would be an upward and downward biological movement of radioactivity apart from the physical mixing of the upper and lower waters. This drastically changed the picture which assumed that the transfer between the deeps and the surface would take more than 300 years.

7 Radiation Knows No Frontiers

THEN, quite apart from the bombs, there are the air-borne risks. Those were demonstrated, fortunately without serious harm, by the "burnout" of the British reactor at the Windscale plutonium factory. In 1957 one of the reactors, which had been operating since 1950, "misbehaved." The reactor was air-cooled. The air from the atmosphere was drawn through filters to remove impurities which might become radioactive and was then blown through the reactor core. The exhaust air was passed through a bank of filters mounted at the top of a stack 410 feet high. These filters trapped the larger particles from the damaged reactor, but finer particles and gases escaped.

The measures taken as a result of the accident are now the textbook lesson for public-health authorities everywhere. They included making an exact record of the meteorological conditions and of the findings of the "flying squads" of radiation experts who toured the area, examining the herbage, the soil, the water and milk. The milk revealed the presence of radioactive iodine, and the supplies from farms over an area of 200 square miles were banned. Vegetables, eggs, meat and drinking water were monitored, but no contamination was found which could constitute a hazard. Adults and children were clinically examined to discover if any radio-iodine had been ingested and had found its way to the thyroid gland. No results were found to cause dismay. The survey was extended to southern Scotland, Yorkshire, Lancashire, Westmorland and North Wales, and samples of milk were collected from districts hundreds of miles away. Traces were found in harmless proportions, but they showed how widespread the possible effects could be.

This experience, however harmless in the circumstances, underlined the demand by the Netherlands Royal Academy of Sciences for international measures to control the radiation risks. The spokesman of the Academy, Professor J. H. de Boer, emphasized the demonstrable truth that radiation knows no frontiers. The hazards are particularly serious in areas of dense population and industrial activity, such as western Europe. He pointed out that the siting of reactors might be a risk to neighboring countries and there must be international agreement about their location. He cited "stationary sources of danger"—all types of reactors, fuel-reprocessing plants, stores of radioactive wastes, and industries increasingly using radioisotopes. He also cited "mobile sources"—atom-driven ships and possibly atom-propelled aircraft and the transport of radioactive materials by sea, air and land. The radio-active material might cross territorial frontiers in the atmosphere, the waters of the oceans, rivers, canals, etc., and by actual transport.

All this emphasizes the fact that our Atomic Age civilization is global in its risks as well as in its opportunities and that, in bearing in mind the lessons of the past, we must be aware of our limited knowledge in the present and take care that we are not, in ignorance, prejudicing the future. We may be appalled by the inroads of the deserts resulting from past mistakes, but they are minor compared with Man's new capacities to change his environment for ill as well as for good.

8 *Peanut Politics*

IN THE YEARS immediately after the Second World War Britain was desperately short of fats, as well as the bread to go with them. Ernest Bevin was the Foreign Secretary and he dared to turn this domestic shortage, this kitchen politics, into foreign affairs. He went and faced an audience of housewives in Lancashire, where fish-and-chips shops are as commonplace as hamburger and hot-dog stands are in the United States. There the "Frying Tonight" signs had long been the consolation of any family trying to eke out its rations with fish and chips wrapped to take home. Bevin told them:

"You complain because you can't get fish suppers in Lancashire. Why can't you get fish suppers? Your Lancashire trawlers are bringing in the fish and there's plenty of potatoes. But the fish fryers can't fry. And why can't they fry? Because there's trouble in Indonesia; because there's a lot of bother in Burma; and because we haven't got things straightened out with Siam. And, because of all that, India can't get rice from these countries. And because India has to grow food for its own people we can't get ground-nuts from India. And because we can't get groundnuts from India the Lancashire fish fryers can't get the oil and you can't get your fish and chips."

Peanut politics, thus graphically accepted by the Foreign Secretary, were to play a very big part in British affairs and figure largely on the map of Africa.

In giving his picture of world interdependence on ground-nuts, the Foreign Secretary might have gone even further back. The groundnut had a humble history. It started off, like so many other staple foodstuffs, in South America. It was taken from there to the East and to the West, to Africa and to India, by Portuguese explorers. The slave ships from West Africa took the peanut back to the United States where it became a popular crop, and a simple delicacy, among the slaves in Carolina. During the Civil War the soldiers of the Northern armies acquired a taste for salted peanuts and took groundnuts back to the North, where they became, eventually, the staple food of the ball-game crowds.

The human body cannot function without fats and edible oils. The Eskimos, without plants, have no direct access to carbohydrates, but they survive very well (when they can get them) on meat protein and fats. The explorer Stefansson tried an Arctic experiment of living on nothing but meat. That was all right as long as it included the fat, but when he ate nothing but the lean he became violently ill.

In the *lean*, after-war years the British—50,000,000 people on an island, depending for half their food on foreign countries—were becoming incipient Stefanssons. His early symptoms had included irritability, and the British people, reduced to one third of the normal consumption of oils and fats, were becoming personally and politically restive. Where were the fats to come from?

An executive of the United Africa Company was pondering this problem as he flew over Tanganyika en route for Dar es Salaam. As he looked down he saw what he thought was the answer—great empty stretches of deserted scrubland with red soil. Only 6,500,000 acres, 3 per cent of the territory, were under cultivation. In his brief stopover at Dar es Salaam his "instinct" was confirmed by those who knew the country. He returned to London with a scheme which was too big even for Unilever, the parent company of United Africa, to handle. He put the suggestion up to a harassed Minister of Food, who immediately sent out a three-man mission on a quick (too quick) reconnaissance of the territory. They hacked their way through the bush into the scrub, sampled the red soil, found it peanut-worthy, took the advice of the settlers, glanced at the rainfall charts, and put forward a scheme for transforming 3,000,000 acres of Tanganyika into margarine for the British housewife.

Remember, this was 1946. We had just come out of a war in which to the engineer nothing was too big or impossible. "Pluto," the oil pipeline, had been strung across the Channel for the Normandy landings. "Mulberry" and "Gooseberry," the portable quays, had created ports on open beaches, and machines by the hundreds of thousands had poured into Europe. The postwar food emergency had the urgency of battle. What might have been called "Operation Fish-and-Chips" was launched. It was estimated to cost £23,000,000 and the expense was authorized by Parliament. The rest is acrimonious history. By the critics of the Government of that day the Groundnut Scheme can be written off as a costly failure. I do not agree. I think that all the millions that went into it were a useful, if unintended, contribution to mutual aid and

303

U.N. technical assistance—as a warning of the things you cannot do to nature and get away with. (Incidentally, a substantial part of the scheme was ultimately salvaged and worked well.)

9 *Bulldozing Nature*

BASICALLY the trouble was that the Groundnut Scheme had been regarded as a job for engineers—a military operation inspired by the unproductive and destructive efforts of war and directed in the actual onslaught by military minds. Nothing like enough field work had been done by people who knew the willfulness of nature. Even the local meteorology had not been studied sufficiently, or the availability of ground water; nor was the nature of the soils sufficiently understood. Of course, soil surveys were made and the samples, which were taken in the dry season, showed that this was "good" soil; it had the right consistency and characteristics. But as events proved, it also had the fickleness of tropical soils. Came the rains and the soil caked because of its clay content. Came the equatorial sun and the soil dried out so hard that the crops were imprisoned in it. No one had realized the abrasive quality of the soil, which ruined plowshares and wrecked implements.

Used tractors, salt-rusted on the beaches of the Philippines, and converted Sherman tanks from recent battlefields were sent in to bash down the forests and tear up the scrub. The engineers, who had made airfields anywhere, any time, during the war had foreseen no difficulties in bulldozing nature. They did not know the African scrub! It was not just a case of hoeing weeds on a large scale. The roots could not be pulled up; they had to be cut in advance, and the soil, in conspiracy with the scrub, blunted the shears. And when they did get the roots up they had loosened the soil which the roots had held together. Behind the relentless machinery came mocking clouds of dust—the soil which was supposed to grow groundnuts—and gulley erosion in the tracks of the tractors.

There was a reasonable excuse for everything that went wrong; on a small scale it would have been a matter for adjustment; on a large scale it was a chronic crisis.

10 *Jeeps and Juju*

THEN THERE WERE the people. The staff were responsible experts, but they were experts in their own field. They were the volunteers of a civilian expeditionary force. At one time the labor force totaled 2,000 men and women from Britain and 30,000 Africans. In the main, the tribal Africans were being brought into the White Man's mechanical world for the first time. It was relatively easy to train them to handle machines; indeed, in the end the Africans, more familiar with the terrain and the peculiarities of the scrub, became better at handling the machines than the white drivers. Maintenance, however, was another matter, although again the Africans eventually proved themselves extremely efficient mechanics. (The fact that an African's ears were dragged down to his shoulders by heavy rings in the lobes did not make him any less capable at a lathe.) There were labor troubles of a very different kind from those which contractors usually encounter, because the local tribes had their juju and their superstitions.

One young district engineer was confronted by a sit-down strike when a baobab tree was jarred. This is an enormous tree of the African savanna land, sometimes twenty feet in diameter. The fat trunks of the baobabs are crowned by branches that look like roots; indeed, the local lore is that once the gods were angry with the baobab trees and buried them head downward. From bitter experience, after trying to uproot these trees, the scrub clearers learned to go around them. But one day a bulldozer collided with one of them and jerked a skull out of its trunk. This was an ill omen and the African squads quit work; the spirit of an ancestor had been disturbed.

The young engineer acted quickly. He called a council of the elders. "It is true," he said, "that we have disturbed the skull of the Unknown One. But let us gain from this misfortune. Let the skull of the Unknown One be placed on my right hand in council and let it whisper wisdom in my ears." And it was so. The skull took part in the council, and its advice to the engineer was that the tribesmen should go back to work. Heeding their ancestor, they did so.

11 *The Lesson of the Bees*

MISGIVINGS WERE felt quite early about monoculture—dependency on groundnuts as the only crop. So someone had the bright and right idea of introducing another oil crop—sunflowers. Those would have the advantage of allowing the soil to recover from the groundnuts, of letting the insects and microorganisms get to work, breaking up and helping to fertilize the soil. But sunflowers have to be pollinated by bees. There had been plenty of bees in the wild wilderness. They had been the plague of the scrub clearers who had found themselves being viciously attacked by the swarms whose hives they had destroyed. But they had been destroyed in the thoroughness of the scrub clearance. The result was a fantastic episode in which bee experts were rushed out from Britain to see what could be done to restore the bee population. In the end, British and Italian bees were exported to Tanganyika to be the maidservants of the sunflowers!

Not all the area was tsetse-ridden, but much of the wide expanses of empty land which the executive had seen from the plane was empty because it was held in fief by the tsetse fly. (That fly has kept 4,000,000 square miles of Africa as a wilderness, because neither man nor beast can live with it.) Here was a challenge and, as the land was sprayed and cleared of scrub and forest, the tsetses, which cannot survive away from leaf shadows, gradually disappeared. Soil over which the tsetse had stood sentry was open to exploitation. Much of it, once it was deprived of its forest cover, died.

Naturalists were belatedly called in, and they confronted the organizers of this 3,000,000-acre scheme with a disquieting report. They were called in as doctors to a sick land, and their diagnosis drastically changed the scope and character of the scheme.

Time and time again crops had withered from drought while heavy rains were falling only a dozen miles away. (One of the main areas had been placed on the wrong side of a range of hills which precipitated the rain.) There were local failures, too, which anyone approaching nature with the caution she deserves could have foreseen and avoided.

By 1954 the original 3,000,000 acres had been wisely restricted to 300,000 acres and the vast mechanized scheme had been tempered to a system of husbandry more easily reconciled with the nature of the soil and the people of Tanganyika.

"Push on regardless," the injunction of any thrustful combat commander, had not worked. Today, by co-operation with the people and with nature, by a combination of rotation cropping and conservation grazing, by the introduction of communications, water supplies and schools and hospitals, Tanganyika has benefited substantially from the "Groundnut Scheme." But it is never referred to nowadays as such by those who are the heirs to the "Dear Departed."

12 *Keeping the Balance*

THE GROUNDNUT SCHEME was a salutary lesson to those who think too big, who want to take short cuts and who do not proceed by pilot schemes which "feel their way" and "persuade" nature. The lesson has been well learned in one place in my experience.

When the Indian Government decided to clear 2,600 square miles of jungle (see p. 35) they called in first the World Health Organization to rid it of the malaria which had made it jungle and then the Food and Agriculture Organization to clear it. The F.A.O. sent into North India one of the engineers from the Tanganyika Groundnut Scheme. There he had done a remarkable job in hauling down tropical forests by harnessing great linked chains to heavy tractors. Two tractors would move through the jungle hauling between them the loop of chain and just dragging down the trees. He had at his disposal, in India, bulldozers, tree dozers and bush bashers—elephantine machines which the jungle could not resist. At his side, however, was one of the world's most eminent ecologists, who had written in the 1930s one of the earliest warnings about erosion and what happens when the balance of nature is upset. It was his job to see that the mistakes of the African scheme were not repeated, and it was he who resisted, in a country clamoring for food, the insistence that the whole area should be cleared. Instead, more than half the area was left as forest reserve, into which the wild beasts of the region could retreat and which would act as the forest cover to break the monsoon rains and absorb them, like a sponge, so that the underground springs would be replenished and the dangers of erosion and the desiccation of the soil prevented.

13 *Walking on Water*

In January 1958 the first oil to flow through the 112-mile pipeline began to pour into the storage tanks at the desert railhead of Touggourt. This was the oil from the Hassi Messaoud oil field. The report of this occasion in *The Times* added, "French airforce helicopters, parachute troops and camel corps men are patrolling the pipelines to prevent any attacks by insurgents."

For me this report had a special and personal interest. Eight years before, in a survey of the deserts for Unesco, I had caught up in the Sahara with an Oklahoma oil prospector. For over two years he had been traveling in the desert, in parts where no one believed there could possibly be oil. When people asked him where he expected to find oil in that forbidding region he used to wink at me. You see, his job was to find oil, not to talk about it! I doubt if anyone he met in the Sahara at that time ever believed that he was doing anything but wasting his time.

In those days (as recently as 1950) the Sahara was still to the French what the rolling main was to the British. One had great rollers of sand and the other great waves of water, but both were romantic in the traditions of their nations. (It is said that Winston Churchill never had any misgivings about the outcome of the desert war because to him the strategy and tactics were just fighting Nelson's sea battles all over again.) For the French the desert was the Foreign Legion, the White Fathers—the heroic desert priests, the wandering Bedouins, and the veiled Touaregs. And an area nearly as big as the United States under French dominion bulked large on the colored maps of the world.

There were ardent souls who, if they were not suspected of the *cafard* (Saharan madness), were disregarded as dreamers. They believed that in the Sahara there were not only mineral potentials but possibilities of agricultural development. At that time I saw the hopeful attempts at what was called "desert colonization." French agronomists and irrigation engineers were successfully recovering quite large areas of desert tracts, including the Wadi Guir, which once had been the great forest where Hannibal may have got his elephants (see p. 237). I saw, too, some of the potential and actual mistakes—like a great dam in the Atlas Mountains, a magnificent engineering achievement, which was gradually filling with silt because no effort had then been made to revegetate the catchment area, from the uncovered slopes of which the soil was being scoured off into the reservoir.

There were a few odd people in the Sahara then, scientists, men and women, who really believed that it could be transformed. There was the Frenchman who alarmed me by saying to me as we trudged shin-deep through the burning sands of Grand Erg, the Great Sand Sea: "We are walking on water." I eyed him with some alarm—an obvious case of the *cafard!* Then he explained.

He maintained that in the dunes and under the dunes there was water. In the night the dew condensed on the dunes and enough of it soaked through the sand sufficiently quickly and deeply to escape evaporation in the heat of the day. But his main contention was that under the Sahara was a great "freshwater sea" fed by intake from the rains of the Atlas. This "Albienne Nappe" had long been regarded as a geological legend, but in 1950 a tube well was sunk at a place called Zelfana and a 300-foot "piezo-pressure" had been obtained. This artesian source was creating a man-made oasis in the heart of the desert.

14 *Saharan Eldorado*

ANOTHER OCCASION which made me suspect my own susceptibility to *cafard* was one morning when I was driving over the desert south of Colomb Béchar. There before my eyes was a mirage of an Arab, swathed in veils and with his *burnous* flying, cycling over the desert on a bicycle. To convince myself that I was not imagining things I followed him and he led me to a coal mine in the Sahara. I would not have been surprised if I had been better informed, since this mine at Kenadsa had been functioning with Bedouin labor for quite a while and its coal had brought me into the desert on the railway line which runs from Algiers to Colomb Béchar, the military and administrative center of the northern Sahara and now the center of the first desert "industrial complex." The coal mine produces 300,000 tons a year. Just south of the town lie deposits of high-grade iron ore, with 60 per cent iron content; 150 miles west are other and more substantial iron-ore fields.

But the richest deposits of iron ore lie at Gara-Djebilet, eighty miles southeast of Tindouf. There the reserves are estimated at 5,000,000,000 tons. In Mauretania the deposits so far found are estimated at 100,000,000 tons. And in the Saharan rocks have been found lead, copper, zinc, chromium, manganese and tungsten. In the mountains of the Hoggar, the region of the veiled Touaregs, uranium, the atom-fission fuel, has been found.

The oil strikes, however, are what really excited the French. Four firms were granted concessions to prospect and explore for oil. Two of them, the Compagnie des Pétroles de l'Algérie and the Compagnie de Recherches et d'Exploitation des Pétrole du Sahara, had the backing of Royal Dutch Shell. The rest of the capital was put up by French finance houses and the government. The first encouraging "showings" were at Edjele, near the Libyan border. As a start, twelve wells were bored and oil was found at a depth of 1,350 feet. Further north oil also gushed at Hassi Messaoud, 400 miles south of Algiers. Natural gas hissed at In Salah. There is no reason to think—and some winks I remember might confirm my suspicions—that these are the only places where oil will be found.

A ceaseless airlift of passenger planes carrying technicians and of freight planes carrying machinery followed those discoveries. Geologists and prospectors by the thousands started swarming all over the desert. The Sahara began to assume the significance of El Dorado or Klondike. Frenchmen lined up all night, waiting for the sale of Saharan bonds to open. Quite suddenly the whole picture of the empty desert changed from romance to purpose.

15 *Desert Colonization*

IF THE SAHARA were what our inadequate classroom atlases suggest it is, just an empty space, one might be as optimistic as some of the French experts. But, in their enthusiasm to exploit the natural resources, they tend to ignore completely the human problems. Or, if they think of the human problems, it is in terms of White settlement. They will talk of "industrial oases," with Le Corbusier skyscrapers on stilts towering above the dust storms. They will invoke science and technology as evidence that solar energy could be harnessed to produce air conditioning and refrigeration. They certainly could create a man-made environment, insulated from the blistering heat of the Sahara and producing the amenities of Paris in the desert. All this is feasible and, indeed, commendable as a basis for civilized living for those who are developing the desert.

It is not, however, the only type of human problem in the desert. There are the wandering tribes who are almost entirely ignored in the desert blueprints. Numerically they might almost be disregarded. After all, the experts say, there are about 1,500,-000 tribesmen in this area almost the size of the United States. That is not a very happy comparison, because that was about the number of Red Indians roaming the plains when the Palefaces discovered that Indian land was desirable and that the tribal territories covered rich ores and richer oil. The story of that struggle is not a pleasant one. It could be repeated in the Sahara.

It is wishful thinking to say, as some of the experts do, that the new way of life will bypass the old and that there will be an acquiescent coexistence between the industrialists and the nomads. This assumes that each will give the other a wide berth—because there is plenty of space for both. But in fact there is a traditional conflict of interest. This was obvious even in the immediate postwar years when the French became exercised about the problems of North Africa, culminating in the independence of Tunisia and Morocco and the bitter and expensive struggle in Algeria. The concern was less with the desert proper than with the Europeanized belts of the north, but even at that time the human problems of the desert were beginning to impinge. There was a tendency for individual nomads to break away from their tribes to drift into the cities and ports and to become rather shiftless laborers. There was also a tendency for the tribes to move north, with the consequent risk of upsetting settled cultivation. This led to a technically enlightened policy of "desert colonization."

The able engineers and agronomists of France began to create man-made oases, to sink wells to depths which the nomads themselves had never reached and to distribute the water in concrete canals and conduits which reduced one of the risks of desert irrigation, the salination of the soil owing to the high evaporation of spread water and the aggregation of the salts in the soil as a result. There was also exciting large-scale experiment in wadi cultivation. Those wadis are the short-lived rivers which come down in spate and spread themselves and their silt over the desert, to soak in and evaporate quickly. The silt dries out into a sort of crazy paving of sun-baked tiles, which desiccate and are blown away as wind-carried soil. This dust is fertile.

Those wadis are the cereal lands of the desert tribes. They may wander with their camels and herds, pasturing them on the scant vegetation, but seasonally they return to the wadis to plow and to plant their desert barley immediately after the spates and return later to do the harvesting. Their methods of cultivation are primitive and their crops are poor.

It was obvious to the French agricultural experts that by modern methods these wadis could be much more extensively and intensively cultivated and that the scruffy barley could be replaced by better barley and, indeed, by wheat. It meant mechanization —heavy tractors, light tractors, disc plows and machines capable of breaking the hard topsoil and cracking subsoil so that the spate waters could sink deeper into the ground and escape evaporation. It meant also agricultural experimental stations in each locality to breed and select the best types of plants which would give the highest yield in any particular area.

With proper management it could mean secondary crops as well—cash crops, such as poppies for pharmaceutical exports and cotton for local wear. It meant also a system of collective cultivation by which the tribes would agree to pool their patrimonial lands and to accept a kind of tithe system: if the land were prepared for them by mechanized methods, a fraction of the produce would be retained by the French Société; if the experts also did the sowing, that would mean another fraction; if the harvesting were done for them, that would mean another fraction; and if the threshing were done by machines instead of winnowing, yet another fraction. So if the entire job was done by the Société, their share of the produce would be the equivalent of the renting of the tribal lands. All this was very intelligent and a sensible approach not only to desert reclamation but also to providing an adequate grain supply for the desert tribes and, beyond their needs, a surplus for export.

Yet it was evident that the nomads were truculently suspicious even of those well-meant intentions. This might seem quite unreasonable because the benefits would appear to be obvious, but as was explained to me by a wise Frenchman, the well-meant intentions could only be misunderstood. Why, the nomads would say, should the French be so generous? There must be a catch in it. The only catch was that the French were trying to prevent the drift of the nomads by making their livelihood more secure in the desert. When I wrote about this at the time, describing quite objectively the intelligent technical measures which were being taken, I had indignant letters from North African Arabs protesting that this was a device "to keep the Bedouin in the desert." The glib reply could have been that there is only one problem more difficult than keeping the Bedouin in the desert and that is getting the Bedouin out of the desert. Indeed, there was nothing inconsistent between the French aims and the Bedouins' desire. But the direct action and the paternalism of the French had roused suspicion and resistance.

16 *Allah's Land*

How MUCH MORE, therefore, will the industrialization processes be misunderstood? That the Saharan Bedouin, like the Eskimos, will eventually accept a technological civilization cannot be gainsaid, but the short-term resistances to change will be aggravated if they are ignored.

If, as we have done in this book, we look back on the age-old struggle between the nomad and the settler, we might guess what will happen if that way of life is altered by compulsion. There are the deep-rooted resentments of tradition, which in the desert have acquired the sanctions of religion. There are desert property rights which are imperfectly understood. For instance, I have raised with French experts the question of tribal lands, which in the vast expanse of the desert are apparently only vaguely demarcated, and was told that these lands would be respected "as far as possible." They knew that the lands of a tribe were separated by distance into the seasonal pastures and crop lands, but I wondered whether, even if they respected these areas as "reservations," it was realized that the nomadic "corridors" between these areas were also regarded as tribal rights of way and that pipelines or installations which straddled them would lead to serious complications.

I had an insight into these difficulties in the Sahara. We were crossing a tract which was neither rock nor gravel nor sand, but

reasonable savanna land. I asked the Frenchman who was with me why this potentially useful tract had not been developed for pasture or cultivation. He replied, "Because it is Allah's Land." This was the Moslem equivalent of "God's Acre," land gifted to Allah and hallowed as such. Various tribes had ceded this land to Allah and used it as common pasture. The Frenchman explained that since there was no temporal authority in Islam, like the Ecclesiastical Commissioners of the Vatican, which would act as the legal trustees of such property, any attempts by the alien or the infidel to obtain property rights would be a religious outrage.

"You see," he said ruefully, "we have not yet found a lawyer who can argue directly with Allah!"

In 1960 I returned to the Sahara to see what the investment of £500,000,000 could do in the way of desert recovery. By that time fifty oil wells had been drilled at Hassi Messouad, and the limits of the oil field still had not been reached. A twenty-four-inch pipeline was already carrying the oil 400 miles to Bougie on the Mediterranean coast. Another pipeline was already planned, so that by 1963 the shipped output of the field would be 14,500,-000 tons. Yet this was only one of five known oil fields. The second in importance and accessibility was at Edjeleh, near the Libyan border. This would involve a pipeline through independent Tunisia.

Then there was Hassi R'Mel, near Ghardaïa, where the reserves of natural gas were so enormous that there was talk, in 1960, of building a pipeline to the Mediterranean, under the sea to Spain, and through Spain to France, Italy and West Germany and across the Channel to Great Britain. I traveled 1,200 miles to the southwest to Fort Gouraud, on the Tropic of Cancer and the border of Mauretania and the Spanish Río de Oro. Here was a two-hundred-mile-long mountain range containing iron. Some of the mountains were almost solid iron—ore of nearly 70 per cent iron content. While the bulldozers were tearing roadways up the steep

A PILLAR OF FIRE BY DAY   *Torches of flaming gas from the Saharan oil field*
[Peter Collins]

317

mountainsides, camel trains were jingling their way across the high plains, which were black from horizon to horizon with the screes of iron ore. While the engineers were installing the most modern mining and handling equipment, the blue-turbaned tribesmen were digging pits, as they had done for countless centuries, to chisel out tombstone slabs of salt which the camels would carry from Timbuctoo and Chad. Two ways of life separated by thousands of years were visible there, side by side.

The mining company, with capital from France, Britain, Italy and Germany, was granted the concession by the "Islamic Republic of Mauretania," a member of the French community—a country as big as France but with a population of 600,000. The World Bank "put up a stake" of £21,000,000. The project involved massive mechanization to blast, chute, scoop and load those mountains onto trains capable of hauling 20,000 tons a day across the desert. This railway had to make a detour around the border of Spanish Río de Oro, down an escarpment 1,000 feet high and across the dune land to the coast 400 miles away. A new harbor was being built at Port Etienne. There, and at Fort Gouraud, two townships of at least 5,000 people were to be built with air-conditioned homes, schools, hospitals, social centers, etc. One of the conditions of the concession was that within ten years the Mauretanians (in the Fort Gouraud district two warrior tribes) were to be educated and trained to the point at which they would be capable of taking over the running of the mines themselves. To emphasize the contrast between the two ways of life—between the salt chiseling and the mechanized mining—we calculated what it would mean if instead of the railway camel trains were used to shift the iron ore. It would have meant 20,000,000 camels!

The oil and the iron are only two tokens of the mineral potentialities of a desert nearly as large as the United States. There are known deposits of coal, manganese, copper, phosphate, uranium and rare metals.

But one of the most impressive developments is the exploitation of the Albienne Nappe, the fresh-water "sea" under the Sahara. Wells, without which the oil and mineral resources could not be adequately developed, have been sunk. At Hassi Messouad there are two swimming pools, drawn from the Nappe, abundant water for the operations, and over 50,000 trees were planted in 1960 to fix the dunes, provide windbreaks and the greenery for a town which will eventually hold 30,000 people. Old oases were being extended by similar wells so that they could be the market gardens of the new developments. The wells were yielding about 90,000,-000 cubic meters of water a year. That is just about the known intake of the Nappe from its outcrop in the Atlas Mountains. There may be other annual sources of supply, but the hydrologists, for the time being, were insisting that the annual outtake should be restricted to the known intake—that, until more was known about the capacity of the Nappe, they should not draw on "water capital." But there was another exciting discovery. In the Tanezrouft, in what looked like the most hopeless gravel desert, it was found that there were at least 50,000,000 acres of fossil soil. This goes back some 7,000 years and contains—there in the heart of what is now arid desert—the pollens of lush Mediterranean vegetation. That soil is not dead; it is merely sleeping. Water could bring it to life again, and the water is there underneath in the Albienne Nappe. One can imagine "hothouse" prairies in the middle of the Sahara!

17 *Well Warned*

As a FOOTNOTE to these new developments in the Sahara it is well to recall the experience of California. A hundred years ago the Gold Rush took people into the Central Valley of California. This was a relatively arid region. The first irrigation was by means of stream diversions. Then surface wells were dug to supply water for domestic and stock-watering uses and subsequently for crops. Then artesian sources were discovered. Such wells began to give out as intensive cultivation increased. So mechanical pumps were applied to suck up the lower ground water. The prosperity of the region abounded, and the snatch and grab for water went on until the water table had fallen so low that the pumps were sucking up the brine of San Francisco Bay. The day was to come when the hydrological situation of this region was to be regarded as a "national emergency."

Those are three examples of the problems which, despite all our science and technology has to offer, are written large in warnings:

i. Nuclear risks can affect the balance of nature on a global scale.

ii. Overambitious schemes can upset the balance of nature on a regional scale as in Tanganyika.

iii. The quest for mineral resources, as in the Sahara, is replete with difficulties of human ecology.

We can reproach the ancients with the mistakes which they made largely out of ignorance, but it will be unforgivable if we exaggerate those mistakes, knowing (as we do) the things we do not know.

PART
EIGHT

Flood Tide

"*Piers for use on beaches: They must float up and down with the tide. The anchor problem must be mastered. . . . Let me have the best solution worked out. Don't argue the matter. The difficulties will argue for themselves. . . .*"
—SIR WINSTON CHURCHILL'S instructions for the Normandy landings

1 $E = mc^2$, or $C = B{:}E$?

MAN'S GREATEST ACHIEVEMENT, since his mastery of fire, was the release of atomic energy, with its fulfillment of Einstein's equation, $E{=}mc^2$ (energy equals mass multiplied by the square of the speed of light; in other words, energy can be turned into matter or matter into energy). We know the dangers, as well as the opportunities, with which that equation is fraught. But there is another equation just as portentous—$C{=}B{:}E$.

"C" stands for the *carrying capacity* of any area of land and the ability of that land to provide food, drink, and shelter for the creatures who live on it.

"B" means *biotic potential*, or the ability of the land to produce plants, for shelter, for clothing and, especially, for feeding. Only plants are able to use the sun's energy to synthesize, from the air, the water and the soil, foods in the forms on which animals can exist, and provide human sustenance.

"E" stands for *environmental resistance*, or the limitations that any environment places on biotic potential. These limitations may be climate, or terrain, or the spread of cities, or man-made erosion.

The *carrying capacity* depends on the balance between the other two factors.

This formula can be applied to any area of land, from a back yard to the entire surface of the planet, and can include the oceans, since their plant life, and sea creatures, can be most important to Man's survival.

Carrying capacity will be improved by increasing the *biotic potential* or by reducing the *environmental resistance* or preferably both. Or the equilibrium can be maintained by restricting the population which the area is expected to support.

323

In simple formulation: if too many animals are put out to graze on ranges of low *biotic potential*, e.g., sparse vegetation, and high *environmental resistance*, e.g., sparse rainfall, the land will be overgrazed, the plant life will be exhausted (and the *biotic potential* thus reduced), the soil will be eroded (and the *environmental resistance* thus increased), and the ranges will not then have the *carrying capacity* for their existing population or even for a reduced population.

The whole history of *Homo sapiens* has been a struggle with this equation. When primitive Man first made a club to kill a beast, and used a flint to cut off its skin so that he could wear it for warmth, he was overcoming *environmental resistance* to his own species; he could migrate climatically to areas of greater *carrying capacity*. When he first gathered seeds and tilled the ground, he was increasing the *biotic potential,* and when he irrigated the soil he was increasing the *carrying capacity* of the areas which had been arid. Vice versa, he reduced the carrying capacity of vast areas by overcultivation, overgrazing, destroying forests and having the soil scoured off by the rains or blown away by the winds.

In Britain farms listed in the *Domesday Book* have a higher *biotic potential* today than they had in Anglo-Saxon times, although they have been cultivated for 900 years. The rice terraces of Luzon in the Philippines are still highly productive, although they have been in use for 4,000 years. So, given good husbandry, *biotic potential* can be enhanced, not diminished. On the other hand, if a city like London is allowed to sprawl over the richest soils of Middlesex, Essex, Surrey and Kent, the *biotic potential* is irretrievably buried under bricks and asphalt. If the prairie grasslands of the Middle West are broken by the plow and, year after year, wheat is grown and the nourishment sucked out of the soil to be shipped as grain and lost as sewage into the North Sea, then *environmental resistance* remorselessly takes charge and dust bowls are created. When forests are cut down (one American newspaper consumes, as newsprint, the annual growth of a forest the size of Shropshire or Wiltshire) the rains, which were once filtered by the vegetation into the underground springs, rush off the naked mountainsides, carrying the soil with them. The beds of rivers are raised by the silt, and the lowland farms are drowned by the floods and smothered by the detritus.

To the natural *environmental resistance,* Man has added his own. The effluents of his chimneys and sewers, the wastes from his mines, factories, distilleries and chemical plants, reduce the sunlight, poison the atmosphere and the rivers, and corrupt the soil. And now there are the added hazards of radioactivity spread by climatic factors and the problems of disposal of radioactive waste.

We are liable to forget that the "populations" which the world supports are not only those of the human species or the animals adapted to our convenience. There is a rival world of birds, insects and microorganisms and the creatures we call "pests." A lump of earth no bigger than a football could contain more organisms than there are people on this earth. Thus we are competing for the *biotic potential.*

2 *Winged Stomachs*

TAKE THE CASE OF THE LOCUST: When the east winds of Egypt brought the locusts and "they covered the face of the whole earth so that the land was darkened," the plague may have seemed an act of God to the Israelites, but Man was largely responsible for the visitation. It was the price which was being paid for the cultivation of the Nile Valley.

What is called the "desert locust" is not a typical insect of the open desert or of the arid grasslands which occur in marginal desert areas. In fact, the natural requirements of the locusts do not suggest a high degree of adaptation to desert conditions. The

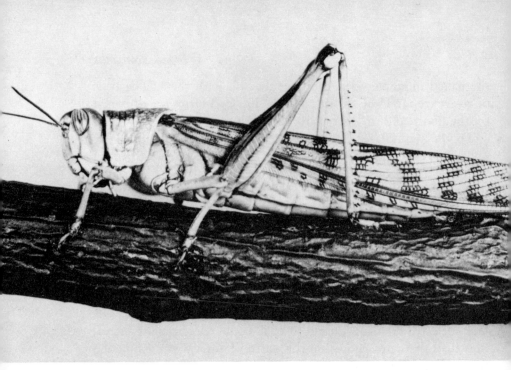

WINGED STOMACH *All-devouring female desert locust* [Shell Photographic Unit, London]

female locust lays her eggs in sand, but not dry sand. The eggs have to have a very high degree of humidity. When the young locusts hatch, they must have sufficient green food, usually tender plants which spring up after a shower of rain. The adults can survive in dry conditions but, for their sexual maturation, they require succulent green food and humid air. Thus they develop in "ecological islands"—sand dunes on coastal plains, belts along the beds of seasonal rivers and around springs.

Their migrations are related to weather factors; they need the winds to carry them on their flights, but major swarm movements take place toward zones of convergent air masses, which are associated with rain. The locusts and the rains usually come together.

Thus cultivation is an important factor in the development of plagues of locusts. An irrigation scheme in the Aden Protectorate has, in recent years, turned it into a locust breeding ground. Similarly, along the plains of the Red Sea, in Eritrea, Saudi Arabia and the Yemen, cultivation has bred the desert locusts. One major swarm, in 1952, seemed to have come out of the naked desert, but its source was finally traced to a remote area in the Fezzan, in Libya, where alfalfa was being cultivated in a wadi bed. Here is an irony of nature: that cultivation promotes the locust which destroys what is cultivated.

The locust menace is increased by the sporadic cultivation of marginal desert land—such as that of the nomads of the Arabian Desert. The Bedouins may lose their poor crops to the young, hopping locusts, but, when the insects take wing, they may destroy the food of millions, perhaps 2,000 miles away. While settled cultivators have learned by bitter experience, and by famine conditions, what locusts can mean, the desert nomads have by no means the same attitude. Indeed, international efforts to overcome the locusts have on many occasions been frustrated by the refusal of the nomads to co-operate, to report the existence of hopper swarms, to kill them on the ground with poison bait, or to allow the locust fighters access to the localities. The reason is that the Bedouins regard the locusts not as a destroyer of food but as a source of food. Locusts to them are a delicacy, as shrimps

WINGED ATTACK *Aircraft spraying insecticides to destroy locust swarms* [Shell Photographic Unit]

might be to others; they roast them or dry them and grind them into flour, to make locust bread. Locust fighters have had to go into Arabia with bags of specially minted Maria Theresa dollars to buy the rights to kill the locusts!

The plague of the Pharaohs is still with us on a scale more menacing even than in Biblical times because the desperately needed food of millions is involved. The "strategic" range of the locusts is so great that a swarm originating in East Africa will devastate southern Russia or Iran or Pakistan. They know no boundaries, and no country in the locust regions of the world can feel safe from them. Therefore they must be fought on an international scale; given a "Grand Alliance" and constant vigilance, the menace can be averted. This was dramatically demonstrated during the Second World War when the locusts were held completely in check by the Allies. The campaign was organized on a military scale. Great Britain and the United States furnished supervisors, trained technicians and 1,000 troops, who did the field work, with 500 vehicles to patrol the region and to rush to any threatened spot. The Soviet Union devised specially equipped aircraft for the spraying of the breeding grounds. All the governments of the Middle East fully co-operated, and all swarms were held in check.

Again, in the spring of 1951 similar joint action saved Iran from what threatened to be the worst locust plague in eighty years. The insects were breeding over an area of some 2,000 square miles in a remote part of the country. Within ten days the United States had supplied aircraft and new and more powerful insecticides, and most of the locusts never left the ground.

Unfortunately, with the deterioration of the political situation in the Middle East in recent years, the task of the Food and Agriculture Organization of the United Nations, which took over locust control, was made more difficult. Never was nationalism so insensate as in this matter. For £1,000,000 the F.A.O. could effectively control the desert locusts, but the national expenditures totaled ten times as much as that. Even that figure is a fraction of what the destruction of food costs when the locusts break loose.

Locust fighting is not just laying bait or spraying clouds of locusts from the air; it is also the research into the lives and habits and behavior of this insect which is, apart from Man in war, the most thorough living engine of destruction. A locust is merely a winged stomach with a jaw. A locust eats its own weight of food every day, which in the case of a swarm means thousands of tons per day.

3 *Beneath the Dinner Table*

IN THE UNITED STATES, even with its highly advanced argricultural services, 10 per cent of all food crops are devoured by Man's rivals before they are harvested. The percentage in other less scientifically equipped countries is far higher. Insects are consuming, in the fields, food sufficient to maintain ten times that annual increase in population which is worrying everyone.

In 1946 the world was faced with famine. A conference, called by Sir John Boyd Orr, the Director-General of F.A.O., was held in Washington. We were confronted by a shortage of grain and grain equivalent which could have meant the sacrifice of 75,000,000 people. "Grain equivalent" included rice, the staple food of 75 per cent of the Asian people. There was a shortage of 12,500,000 tons of rice. But that shortage, the result of the ravages of war, was equal to the amount of rice annually destroyed *in store* by pests. Much more was destroyed in the fields. Indeed, the appalling Indian rice famine of 1943 was mainly caused by a fungus disease which, in critical areas, led to the loss of over 90 per cent of the crops. The frequent attacks of the gallfly on growing rice can destroy a whole harvest. This fly affects young plants in India only between September 14 and October 15, and the

Large-scale plowing in the Dakotas (circa 1880)

answer found by the scientists is to breed strains which can grow earlier and avoid the gallfly, which, once its occupation has gone, disappears. Another rice pest, the borer grub, attacks rice at two stages. It kills young plants, but those which it attacks in later stages lose their grain ears. The borer likes strains which are mildly scented. So the scientists have bred varieties which aromatically repel them.

(Incidentally, there was no famine in 1946. The grim facts with which we were dealing were true, but twenty-three nations met in Washington and agreed to self-denying ordinances by which they restricted their consumption and spread the shortages, or at least the available supplies, and all mankind benefited.)

The Food and Agriculture Organization has studied what happens to the rice and bread grains of the world while they are waiting to be prepared for human consumption and has disclosed figures which are certainly eye openers. Rats, insects and fungi destroy annually some 33,000,000 tons of essential foods. That is enough to feed the entire population of the United States for a year; alternatively it means, on a world scale, that one person in every fourteen in the world is liable to die yearly from starvation because he is deprived of that food by these predators.

It is also reckoned that millions of tons of foodstuffs are wasted in feeding the disease germs and parasites in the human body. A gross example is, of course, the intestinal worms which are universally prevalent among the people of the tropics. A peasant may work a third of his life just to feed his tapeworm. But it applies also to the innumerable germs which batten on the human victim and make it impossible for him to absorb the food which he eats or prevent him from producing food which he might eat.

4 *Winged Dagger*

THE MALARIAL MOSQUITO is a spectacular menace because, although it sucks only a tiny amount of blood, it has afflicted something like 300,000,000 people in the world and has killed annually about 3,000,000. Where malaria is endemic, that is, where it afflicts the majority of the population, it may not be a killer in the sense that malaria would suddenly cause death. It certainly shortens life and it cripples the population.

I have seen at first hand what malaria means in most parts of the world. It is definitely one of the principal causes of the shortages of food in tropical countries. The malarial season very often coincides with the transplanting of the rice or its harvesting, or both. Two out of every three of the peasants who might have been working on the land at those critical periods have been sick of the fever. The result has been poor crops through inadequate husbandry. In other parts, as in the north of Thailand, the malarial season has coincided with what might have been a second growing season. The peasants, without undue food shortages to themselves, have settled for a single crop, although they might have produced two and might have provided a surplus for export to other hungry peoples.

In East Pakistan, where unfortunately they have had two malarial seasons, malarial control and the virtual banishment of the
mosquito have meant that the crops from the existing acreages—
without extension of cultivation—have been increased in some
crops by over 50 per cent. So malarial control could, in United
Nations terms, be genuinely regarded as a form of "Technical
Assistance," that is, a means of increasing economic output. And,
through the World Health Organization and the United Nations
Children's Fund, malaria-control schemes were vigorously demonstrated throughout the tropical world.

5 Evolution Before Our Eyes

THEN THERE WAS A MOMENT which I shall not readily forget, in
October 1954, when a disquieting report was received at the
World Health Organization in Geneva. It came from Dr. Peter
Issaris, the leader of the malaria team in Indonesia. The consternation which was caused was like that which would occur in a military high command if its Intelligence Corps reported that enemy
forces, in bulletproof uniforms, had penetrated the defenses and
were operating behind the lines—and an enemy which had been
considered finally defeated. That was, in fact, what the report
meant.

In a campaign in which the lives of millions of human beings
and the health of hundreds of millions of human beings were involved the appearance of a malaria mosquito invulnerable to
counterattack was a justifiable cause for alarm. The mosquito, in
this case, was the *Anopheles sundaicus*, the malarial mosquito of
Java, but presently the same reports were being received from
other regions as well, proving that the mosquito was showing resistance to insecticides.

Up till then everything had been going well in malarial control. Although there had been evidence that the houseflies in Italy and the typhus-carrying lice in Korea had begun to develop a resistance to D.D.T., there had been hopes that the mosquito had not the same capacity for resistance. The result was profoundly disturbing because it became plain presently that the mosquitoes which were D.D.T. resistant were not just occasional ones which had escaped, or individually resisted, D.D.T. or had even acquired, like arsenic eaters developing an immunity to the poison, a habit of D.D.T.

What was happening, in fact, was evolution before our very eyes. It was found that a fractional percentage of all mosquitoes had a genetic, or hereditary, resistance to the poisons which killed their kin. While the vast majority of mosquitoes were killed, that percentage survived, and when they "intermarried" they bred a type of mosquito which had a natural resistance to the poisons. At first the disposition was to pooh-pooh the development and to suggest that it could be overcome by simply switching the insecticides—that while D.D.T. might fail, other chemicals might succeed. This was only partially true. At the most it gave a respite, but presently the mosquitoes were found to be resistant even to the alternatives. Once this was apparent, the medical alarm became real because, in regions where malaria had been controlled, the natural human resistances to the deadly effects of the disease had been reduced and if the malaria was reintroduced afresh into these regions, it would tear through the tropics like a forest fire.

This led to the World Health Organization's proposals to substitute for malaria *control* malaria *eradication*. This means something quite different. In malaria control, the idea is to reduce the insect population—the mosquitoes, the bite of which transfers malaria from one human being to another—until the numbers are insignificant. But "eradication" means getting rid not of the mosquitoes but of the malaria itself. This is perfectly feasible, because after about three years, if there is no reinfection, the parasites of malaria disappear from the human blood. It was reckoned that the time it would take for the few insecticide-resistant mosquitoes to multiply and replace those that had been eliminated

333

would be about five to seven years. If, in that interval, the parasites could be removed from the human being, the reassertion of the mosquito, although unpleasant in terms of biting, would not convey the disease; the mosquito has to suck the malaria parasite from a human victim and transfer it to another human victim in order to spread the disease.

The strategy of the W.H.O. campaign, therefore, was to press on with the insecticides to reduce, by killing off the non-resistant types, the mosquito population and, therefore, the spread of the disease. Thoroughly prosecuted, this would mean that the number of active cases would be reduced to clinical proportions—that is, that individual cases could be treated and cured with modern antimalarial drugs. Combined with actual treatment, there could be a prophylactic campaign: there are drugs which, taken regularly, will prevent people from having the disease. Since, however, this is a regimen which few uninstructed people are capable of following, one device was to introduce these drugs into the common salt which the tropical peoples would be using. In this way it was hoped that before the emergence of the insecticide-resistant mosquitoes in force, the disease would be removed from the blood of the human patients and, therefore, could not be spread.

This was perfectly feasible, but national shortsightedness interfered with a great international project. The countries with the financial means to support this campaign were, by and large, those countries which had already got rid of malaria. The support, however, of the Malaria Eradication Fund and of W.H.O. was quite inadequate. Some countries afflicted with malaria began, with the assistance of W.H.O. and the U.N. Children's Fund, to undertake eradication on a systematic scale. Mexico, for example, organized its campaign as though it was a military operation —including generals, transport officers and an operational High Command. With hundreds of motor vehicles carrying the spray teams over the countries, with malarial cavalry mounted on horses and mules climbing into the High Sierras and penetrating into the jungles, the Mexicans began thoroughly to remove malaria. But the surrounding countries, impoverished, it is true, were not so thorough. They pleaded that malaria was only one of their urgent concerns and that it was too ambitious for their limited resources. That was quite true. But it merely emphasized the fact that this was an international commitment and not a national one; if the malaria of these countries spread over the frontiers, the Mexican efforts would be completely wasted.

6 Radioactive Mosquitoes

PEOPLE DO NOT USUALLY ASSOCIATE mosquitoes with the Frozen North, but old Arctic hands will tell a tenderfoot, "Skeeters! They are so big we skewer them on spigots and roast 'em!"

That is an exaggeration, but they are certainly "man-eaters." Fortunately they do not, like the anopheles mosquitoes of the tropics, transmit malaria; but when the muskeg swamps unfreeze in the Arctic summer, the insects swarm in such vast numbers that the settlers' lives become unbearable. Indeed, it can be said that the mosquitoes, like the warble flies of the north, are a bigger obstacle to the development of the Arctic regions than the cold or the long night.

If, as will be proposed later in this book, the Arctic and sub-Arctic regions are to be made part of our habitable world, something will have to be done about these hostile and voracious insects. But apart from devising ways of destroying them, it is important to know how they fit into the ecology of the region, and, for both reasons, scientists are hard at work studying their habits. Ingenious methods have been devised to keep track of the swarms and to learn more about the individual mosquitoes. One of these devices enlists the help of nuclear energy. Dr. Dale W. Jenkins, of the U.S. National Research Council, described at the first

U.N. Peaceful Uses of Atomic Energy Conference at Geneva (1955) how it had been possible to "tag" the mosquitoes.

It is known that the mosquitoes drink the nectar of Arctic poppies (again, people do not usually associate flowers with the Frozen North). The scientists feed the poppies with an artificial fertilizer containing radioactive phosphorus. In the Arctic poppy, the phosphorus finds its way into the nectar. The mosquitoes, flower feeders, sip this nectar. Thus they pick up the radioactive elements, and from there on they are marked. They carry in their bodies a "radio transmitter," and scientists with detecting instruments can follow them wherever they go and so find out vital information concerning their habits—information that will lead to their effective control. By moistening the pupae of black flies with radioactive liquid, the scientists were also able to study the habits of this other northern pest.

All over the world the use of the by-products of atomic energy, the radioisotopes, is making it possible to study not only the behavior of insects but of microorganisms, including viruses, and thus to know better this rival world of living things which are not only Man's competitors but in many cases his indispensable allies.

7 *Disease-Carrying Snails*

ANOTHER EXAMPLE OF A DISEASE which ignores frontiers and which not only cripples or kills individuals but also beggars nations is bilharziasis. This is a disease which is carried by snails. The water snail, which is its vector, release parasites into water, and they penetrate through the skin into the blood system of people working barefoot in irrigation systems or bathing in the rivers. This disease is particularly rife in Egypt, but it spread through the

Middle East and through most of the continent of Africa. Apart from shortening life and making the victims miserable, the disease prevents the peasants from working and reduces their energy in the processes of producing food. An example of its serious economic impact is provided by Israel. Here half the country is thirsty desert. To irrigate that desert and make possible the settlement of thousands of food producers, the Israelis, at enormous expense, laid down a pipe system from the north to Beersheba, in the desert of the Negev. The engineers finished the job, but it was found that there was bilharziasis, introduced by soldiers on leave from Egypt during the Second World War, in the waters of the north. It would have been disastrous for bilharziasis to have been spread into the south, and the project had to be held up for a year while the snails and their disease were eliminated.

8 The Valley of the Blind

In GHANA one of the hopes of the infant sovereign state was the Volta Scheme, which was to harness the great river and to produce electricity and irrigation waters. But in the headwaters of the Volta River was the "Valley of the Blind." There, as in northern Nigeria and parts of East Africa, breeds the Simulium fly. This fly, which breeds in the shrubs along the streams, transmits by its bite a parasite. This parasite completes its life cycle in the blood stream of humans, and by a cruel dispensation of nature at one stage of its development it impinges on the human eye and produces blindness. In the "Valley of the Blind" most of the people were so afflicted. There was every possibility that this fly, and its consequences, might be carried by the Volta Scheme into other parts of Ghana, hitherto immune. One of the factors to be taken into account in the development of an engineering project was, therefore, the getting rid of the risks of the Simulium.

9 *The Rival World*

OF ALL THE MYRIADS of species of insects and organisms in the "rival world" only a small fraction are, in fact, hostile to Man—although, as we have seen, the ravages of those are immense. Animals, insects and organisms are regarded as pests or pestilences only when they are to the disadvantage of the human species. They have their own preoccupations. In the struggle of nature they batten upon each other and act as predators, controlling, in competition with each other, the overdevelopment of particular types.

Often we are ungrateful. We forget, for example, that the black rat, which spread the bubonic plague and gave rise to the Great Plague of London, was eliminated (and with it the disease) by the fortuitous introduction into Britain, and into Europe, of the alien brown rat. The brown rat exterminated the black rat and multiplied to become a pest itself.

When microorganisms cause food to rot we call it "putrefaction," but when they break up sugars and produce alcohol we call it "fermentation." We blame organisms for causing disease or for destroying our food, but we forget that the living processes would be quite impossible without microorganisms. We are appalled at the thought of harboring germs in our body, but our digestive processes could not be completed without them. The stomach is nearly always free from bacteria because its acid destroys most of them, but the intestines have an increasing number of germs—the large intestine swarms with them. Most of them serve a useful purpose in the process of digestion and disposal of food, and physiologists have sometimes to remind doctors who are prodigal in their use of germ-killing antibiotics that they may be interfering with the beneficial processes of nature.

We resent the fact that viruses produce diseases, like the swollen-shoot disease of the cocoa plant, but we forget those other organisms which produce the nodules on the roots of plants which are indispensable to the intake of nitrogen from the soil. Plants and trees are dependent on insect life and on bacteria to enable them to absorb their food, and our crops and our forests could not exist without the co-operation of the germs in the soil.

Sometimes I visit that part of London which is known as "London Fields." I remind myself that at this very spot were once the Plague pits of London into which the tumbrels tipped the dead and with them the Plague germs. Some 70,000 people died in that Plague and were disposed of in pits. How could all this malignancy be swallowed up by the soil? The answer is now so abundantly plain that one wonders, in retrospect, why we did not discover penicillin until the middle of the twentieth century. The answer, of course, is antibiotics. Those are the microorganisms which destroy the pathogenic germs of disease. Penicillin itself came from a fungus, *Penicillium notatum*, a mold which grows on hyssop, but most of the other antibiotics, streptomycin, chloromycetin, aureomycin, gramicidin, and many others, however, have come from the soil.

10 *Tsetse Sentinel*

MANY YEARS AGO I was lecturing on malaria and how to get rid of mosquitoes. A black-skinned Haussa from that coast of Africa which used to be called "The White Man's Grave" got up and said, "In my country we call the mosquito our sentry—it keeps the White Man out." In the same sense, as has already been mentioned, the tsetse fly has garrisoned an area of Africa as big as the United States against the depredations not only of the White Man but of the whole human species and its domesticated animals. Professor J. Phillips (who was belatedly called in, as a naturalist, to salvage the Groundnut Scheme of Tanganyika) accepts the view that the fly has protected most of the continent against the ravages of erosion and desiccation.

In a symposium on the "Biology of Deserts" he said:

"Where the tsetse fly exists on a large scale its attempted removal and the efforts to introduce livestock to fly-free areas must be accompanied by a policy and practice of herd control and pasture management, supply of water points, conservation farming and informed and firm administrative direction of the local people. Particularly disastrous is the consequence of the uncontrolled continuance of the widespread purchasing of wives by means of thriftless livestock—the status of a man being judged not by the quality of his stock but by the number. . . . In the absence of measures providing for the conservation of country hitherto under tsetse fly, overstocking would readily produce a far worse curse than the fly. It would lead to soil destruction and erosion."

11 The Sacred Cow

IT IS THE LACK of this kind of thinking which has caused destruction of widespread areas of the world and led to well-intentioned schemes for development going sadly astray. For instance, in the southern Sudan, where the true desert merges into savanna land which could be quite usefully developed (if common sense prevailed), the administrators, wanting very properly to benefit their people, opened up water holes. The result, in instance after instance, was that the tribes converged on these water holes in excessive numbers. They herded their scruffy cattle, which, as Professor Phillips pointed out, are thriftless, useful neither for milk nor for meat, but merely as an evidence of wealth. They came for the water, but presently the herds had trampled the area around, eaten all the herbage and reduced the localities to desert. This type of excessive grazing by useless cattle has also extended the Kalahari Desert, south of the Equator.

Reference to the thriftless money cattle of Africa recalls the problem of the Sacred Cow of India. In India there are as many cattle as there are people. They are sacred and cannot be killed. They eat more food than the human population, whose lack of food is a cause of chronic concern. The cattle give no meat and very little milk. A vast proportion of the cows are diseased, and they spread disease. It is revolting to the outside observer to see poor, decrepit beasts dying miserably of old age or disease and yet no one putting them out of their misery. It is absurd to see them blocking pavements or lying across the tramlines or holding up whole streams of traffic in busy cities but still having to be left to exercise their "free will." Thoughtful leaders in India are well aware of the gravity of this problem, but their difficulties were not eased by Gandhi, whom we think of as a man of great wisdom, but who said, "I yield to no one in my worship of the Sacred Cow!" The Food and Agriculture Organization, while treading warily amid the religious prejudices of the Indians, have gone in to help. Experts have at least done something. It is permissible for the hides of dead cattle to be taken and tanned, but the leather has been practically useless, because by the time the skinners have got to the cattle the hides have already been decaying or been full of blowholes. F.A.O. experts suggested the setting up of reserves where the aged cows could be "pensioned off." Attached to these compounds, known as *gosadans*, are skilled flayers, whose job it is to get at the animals as soon as they can after death, while there is still hope of salvaging the hides. As a result, the quality of the hides and of the leather has enormously improved, to the economic advantage of the villagers.

The experts have also introduced better breeding methods—

the "sacredness" does not extend to noninterference with these—so that at least the milk supply can be improved, but the problem, as a whole, remains intractable and perverse in a country whose hungry population is increasing at the rate of over 5,000,-000 a year.

The purpose of these examples—and hundreds more which could be quoted—is to remind us that no matter how grandiose our ideas may be about the conversion of nature to our purpose, short cuts are often the long way around. Measures which seem self-evidently useful to the experts, or experiences which have been successful in one part of the world, can themselves mean delays in development or cause irrevocable damage. The best advice that can be offered to any expert going out to underdeveloped countries is: know what you are changing before you start to change it.

PART NINE

How Many People?

"The passion between the sexes has appeared in
every age to be so nearly the same, that it may
always be considered in algebraic language, as
a given quantity."
                        —*An Essay on Population* by
                        THOMAS R. MALTHUS, 1798

1 Standing Room Only

IN THE COURSE OF 200,000 YEARS *Homo sapiens* multiplied to reach the figure of 2,500,000,000. It will take only thirty years to add another 2,000,000,000. The figures today are twice as high as they were a century ago. By the year A.D. 2000—just forty years off—the figures will be twice, maybe three times, as high as they are now.

To show how grotesque the present rate of population increase is, the United Nations experts, in their report, *The Future Growth of World Population,* projected their calculations 600 years ahead. Six hundred years is not long in the time scale which we have been using in this book. But in that relatively short space of time, if things go on as they are (and, of course, they cannot), there will be then "Standing Room Only" on the face of this planet.

Taking the whole land surface, including regions at present uninhabitable, each person would only have one square meter of land to live on.

This picture of people clinging to the planet like a swarm of bees is scarcely less alarming than the inescapable prospects of the immediate future—"inescapable" because, short of a universal catastrophe, the minimum figures of the United Nations experts are irreversible in the next thirty years. Death control will continue to operate, with the humanitarian services of the world bringing relief from disease and enabling people to live longer than the pathetic span of thirty years which is the lot of the peoples of most of the underdeveloped world. And no advocates of birth control are optimistic enough to believe that, even if wisdom did

345

prevail, the trends could be materially altered in the space of one generation.

As the official United Nations report said:

More disturbing than the projected figure of a population mounting to 6,000 or 7,000 million by the turn of the century is the fact that it will probably be attained that soon. The year A.D. 2000 is no further in the future than the year 1914 is in the past. Not only technical achievement but progress in international co-operation and organization will have to be more effective than during the past 43 years if the expected numbers of mankind are to be accommodated to the minimum conditions required for human dignity.

The estimates produced by the Population Branch of the United Nations' Bureau of Social Affairs do not tally with those previously calculated in 1951 and 1954. The upward revision has been necessary because, whereas in the past the figures of the Chinese population had been just guesswork ("about 463 million"), the first completed census (1953) disclosed that in Red China there were 600 million people. So the experts had to think again, and the result was that the lowest estimate for 1980 became 3,850 million instead of the 2,976 million of the 1951 estimates. That means that the world has to provide board and lodging for nearly 1,000 million people who were not foreseen ten years ago.

2 The Demographic Revolution

IN THE LIFETIME of the younger politicians of today the Demographic Revolution, which takes no account of political ideologies, will have completely changed the pattern of world politics. Whereas at the beginning of this century there was one European to every two Asians, by the end of this century the ratio will have become one to four. (The term "European" includes the entire Soviet Union.) Latin America will have increased its population tenfold in the twentieth century, and the remaining continents will have increased fourfold.

The existing trends give the experts no consolation; there is no prospect of an abatement in this flood of population. The measures of death control will keep more people alive. Birth control in countries of high fertility is not likely to produce a decrease very soon and, in most countries of comparatively low fertility, no further decrease appears to be imminent. Even if the family-planning campaigns of the governments of India and China were effective and if, though it is unlikely, Latin America with its Catholic traditions were to practice birth control, the figure for the next twenty-five years could be less bad but not substantially better than the worst misgivings. In only one country, Japan, has there been any dramatic reversal of trends; there the birth rate per thousand dropped from 34.3 in 1947 to 20.1 in 1954.

More somber even than the total figure for the world is the distribution. At present the prosperous, technologically advanced countries contain slightly more than one third of the world's population. By the end of the century these countries will account for only a quarter or even one fifth. Obviously, unless human ingenuity and technical co-operation is better applied than at present, the gulf between the prosperous and the impoverished countries will widen at the very time when the political consciousness and insistence of the peoples of the underdeveloped countries will grow. Against this picture the most ambitious programs of "mutual aid" so far carried out have been merely tinkering with the problem, and nothing less than economic development on a scale far greater than anything so far contemplated can modify the social and political upheavals inherent in this Demographic Revolution.

The population quandary is obvious. The biggest factor in the changing picture is the decline in mortality which has been made possible by cheap and effective disease control. The exception is in a few areas which are remote from centers of administration and are at the moment inaccessible to life-saving devices. At the one end, more infants are being saved to live, to marry and to procreate. At the other end, in the advanced countries, people are living longer and the span has reached over seventy years—double the life expectation of an Indian baby. It is neither politically practical nor morally conceivable that the people in the underdeveloped countries should be denied the amenities of modern medical progress. To discriminate against the people of such countries is tantamount to selective genocide. The experts of the United Nations did not hesitate to demand "new rationalized attitudes toward procreation" and said that the basic research into the physiology of reproduction could find measures of birth limitation suitable for mass use. They said, "We are swimming against the tide of evolution, but having discovered how to increase the flood, we have not also, through biological science, the means of arresting it."

Unfortunately the science of agriculture has not made the same advances as the science of medicine. There is no agricultural equivalent to malaria control or the cheap-drug treatment of tropical diseases. In 1958, for the first time since the Second World War, the global production of food changed for the worse, but even allowing for that recession, which was grim in itself, it was nevertheless true that the per capita figures for calories were abreast of the increased world population. Unfortunately, however, it is not a question of per capita but of per stomachs, and although there is global availability, there is local and regional hunger in those very countries which are multiplying fastest. The generally satisfactory world figures include the undistributed surpluses of the Western Hemisphere and reflect the gratifying results of the fast recovery of the war-ravaged farms of Europe. Farm technology can increase abundance, but the impoverished, fecund peoples of the underdeveloped countries cannot afford the implements, the seeds, or the fertilizers, nor sufficiently quickly can they acquire the know-how.

3 Beyond the Climatic Frontiers

As THE REPORT of the United Nations population experts points out, the population which the world could maintain might be as high as 16,000,000,000—and even that estimate might, in view of the scientific progress, be revised upward. Certainly the present figures and even the pessimistic future ones are far short of what the earth could sustain if this were a rational, co-operative world.

The climatic frontiers—the hot deserts and the Arctic wastes and the neglected high-altitude areas—can now be advanced by the plant breeders, who can select and adapt crops to previously impossible conditions. There are the vast unused vegetable resources of the sea; and, in terms of fish, we are practically still at the cave-man stage—we are hunting our fish instead of husbanding them.

The limits of numerical survival, however, do not depend on technological progress alone. The intensive use of resources for the benefit of all mankind depends on a specialization of human activities and, as far as the future is concerned, on a much greater degree of social organization than we have so far achieved as a world community. (Here we might remind ourselves of the remarkable achievements of the Inca civilization.) It also requires individual discipline and restraint—things which human beings can scarcely tolerate beyond a certain point. It means that it is impossible to contemplate a future in which we continue to exploit and to exhaust the soil and the mineral resources of the earth. This would be a Belshazzar's Feast at which we have ignored the plain writing on the wall.

The United Nations report said: "The growth of population during the next 25 years, therefore, has an importance which transcends all social and economic considerations. It is the very heart of the problem of our existence."

Indeed it is, unless we want to share the death wish of the lemmings, which, when they multiply beyond their subsistence, drown themselves in an orgy of mass destruction.

The ledger-reckoning of population is the sum to which this whole book had been adding up—since the first successful attempts of *Homo sapiens* to maintain the survival of his species and to reproduce himself as a thinking creature in competition with the rest of life on earth. What has been discussed, in the length and depth of history, has been the emergence of successive civilizations, developing in certain regions and, in some cases, coalescing. But now there is only one locality, the globe itself, and one civilization, the totality of mankind.

Around that globe, like the sentries of a prison wall, march the man-made earth satellites, to remind us that, apart from a few escapees to the moon or the other planets, the members of the human race are prisoners on this planet. There is no escape from the earth's crust and the resources of soil and minerals which it contains, and there is no escape either from the common liabilities to mankind. A few years ago it was possible for one to ignore, even if one had to deplore, the human catastrophes of famine and pestilence. They always seemed to be a long way away—until the bread lines of the Hungry Thirties brought them nearer home. Today every country is no more than a few hours' distance from any other country. Half a century ago a famine costing millions of lives in China or in India might have produced prayers in churches and public subscriptions, but it was not a conscience crisis. In 1959 the death of a hundred people from hunger in the Maldive Islands, those lonely atolls in the Indian Ocean, could provoke large headlines in Britain and indignant editorials demanding action. Conversely, a louse brushed off the rags of a beggar in an Eastern bazaar could be in London or New York a few hours later, with all its threat of typhus and pestilence.

The world, in terms of the material needs and hazards of mankind, has become a single community. It is not only that the advanced countries are sympathetically aware or politically concerned about the needs of less fortunate countries. The less fortunate countries are fully aware that hunger and diseases are not just the "will of God." They no longer fatalistically accept them as their inescapable lot. Emergent nationalism is one of the symptoms of this new awareness, and, as is abundantly plain from the ideological stresses in the world, the economics of necessity and of welfare are fully recognized even by illiterate people. Whatever the patriotic impulses of freedom, by which they deliver themselves from the rule of alien people, the Third Freedom—Freedom from Want—is the most insistent. And woe betide any government which fails in measurable time to meet the material demands of the people.

4 *How Bold a Program?*

THE "BOLD NEW PROGRAM" which President Truman offered in his Point Four, promising economic and technical aid to the underdeveloped countries, was a noble gesture. But, without diminishing the generosity of the act, it is nevertheless true to say that it was an admission of the facts of our shrunken world and of the material, as well as the political, relationship of the United States to the rest of the world. This was a recognition that, in the long run, the Western world would not be able to secure either the sources of raw materials or the markets needed to keep its industries in operation unless it could make effective the raw material resources and the enormous consuming power of what has been called "the underdeveloped areas."

Since the underdeveloped countries no longer regarded their role merely as primary producer countries, as suppliers of materials for the more advanced countries, it was obvious that their industrial development and general raising of the standard of life was an inescapable condition of securing the supplies on which the industrialized countries had come to depend. The world, in terms of food and materials, had become one.

This fact was not easily accepted by the countries which had secured an industrial pre-eminence. Even when the idea of White Men's empires had become *démodé* and the idea of either political or commercial imperialism had become "bad taste," there was still a sense that the advanced nations—the "white" nations—had secured their pre-eminence by some God-given dispensation. Somehow we felt that only peoples with special or innate abilities could have created and taken advantage of the Industrial Revolution and that the backward nations, lacking these abilities, had been left behind.

But what are the facts? As we have seen, Man, the toolmaking animal, developed his skills and his intellectual capacity in widely differentiated parts of the world. Civilization, which for the purposes of this book can be taken as meaning Man's mastery of his environment and the extension of the amenities of life, developed independently, from the Indus and among the Incas. Yet the Eskimo can step quite nonchalantly out of the Stone Age into the Atomic Age and master mechanical skills; and yet the aboriginals of Australia, the most primitive of all our modern primitives, can whittle a boomerang for which the aerodynamicists have no satisfactory mathematical explanation.

5 A Warning to Temperate-Zone Man

WE, OF EUROPEAN ORIGIN, may regard ourselves as the heirs of Graeco-Roman culture and of Judaic-Christian religion, but these themselves were the heirs of much older traditions. With humility we, who boast of our scientific and technological civilization, might remind ourselves that while our forefathers were running around naked, painted with woad, highly advanced civilizations were flourishing in the countries we now call "underdeveloped." The material civilization, of which we enjoy the advantages and boast the supremacy, is, after all, in time scale, no older than the United States. While the colonists there were asserting their independence, the Steam Age was originating with James Watt in Britain. With it came the machines of mass production and the commercial surpluses which they produced.

The first Industrial Revolution thus began in Britain, spread to Europe, to America, to the Soviet Union and to Japan. Geographically, therefore, the Industrial Revolution "belonged" to the North-Temperate-Zone Man. No wonder Temperate-Zone Man is inclined to preen himself! Has he not, in a brief two hundred years, achieved a mastery over nature and an industrial prosperity which has set him above, and apart from, all the others?

Let us, however, consider the facts objectively. The break-through to industrial prosperity which began with the steam engine depended on cheap, accessible fuel—fossil fuels (coal, oil and natural gas) which nature had stored away millions of years ago. Industry was anchored to geological deposits. Where fuel was cheap and ready-to-hand, factories created wealth, which could pay for education, endow research and provide capital for the new industries which burgeoned from such research. With this chain reaction of prosperity and this feedback of knowledge endowed by capital, the break-through became a runaway. In Asia nearly 70 per cent of all energy is still muscle power, human or animal; in the United States only 4 per cent is so derived. The average Western worker, with a finger flick of a switch, can have at his service the power equivalent of a hundred human slaves.

But consider the map. We might notice a fact which should temper the pride of Temperate-Zone Man. The power on which his exultant prosperity has been based came from fossil fuels. But nine tenths of the world's known coal reserves and four fifths of the world's oil reserves lie north of latitude 20° north, just south of the Tropic of Cancer. Most of the so-called "underdeveloped" countries lie south of that line, and the inescapable fact is that, with the best will, they could not have had any share in a fossil-fuel Industrial Revolution, except as the providers of food and raw materials, which they were.

By geography and geology, and without any reference to any innate abilities which they might have manifested if they had been given the opportunity, the peoples of these countries were barred from the first Industrial Revolution and its fruits.

Only those who have seen the nature of poverty in these countries can possibly measure the consequences. A typical scene in a tropical country is that of a bullock team raising water from a well. To the chanting of the drivers, the bullocks trudge backward and forward under the relentless sun, lowering buckets into the well, hoisting the water and tipping it into the watercourses to irrigate the thirsty soil from which both men and beasts get their food.

Those peasants are poor, desperately poor, yet they use the most expensive power in the world—muscle power. Bullocks have to be bought, tended and fed, yet, even with the meager food and

Modern saqiya *(wheel of pots) turned by a camel*

pitiful earnings of the men who drive them, the energy equivalent which they produce costs twenty times as much per unit as the energy output of Britain's Calder Hall Atomic Energy Station.

A great many people in the world are poor because they, of necessity, use calories in their most expensive form as food and energy in the most uneconomical way of muscle power. Although we may glorify muscle effort—and, indeed, laud it in the performances of athletes—it is deplorably inefficient. The advance from the steam engine to atomic power, from the pulley belt to automation, has represented the emancipation of Man from muscle slavery.

Fully to grasp the difference between muscle power and mechanical power one has to think of a transatlantic liner. If that liner were a trireme, with slaves pulling on the galley oars, it would need 3,500,000 slaves to row it in five days from Southampton to New York.

The paradox of power is that those who are power-deficient are power-extravagant. When we go around the house switching off lights to keep the electricity bill down, we might think of the Indian villager burning cow dung to cook his food for his muscle power. Because he burns that dung, instead of using it as manure, his soil is undernourished, his crops are undernourished, and he is undernourished.

6 *The Misery-Go-Round*

THIS IS THE MISERY-GO-ROUND of poverty: because the peasant is poor he is undernourished; because he is undernourished he underproduces; because he underproduces he is poor, and because he is sick, poor and hungry, he is ignorant. But that is a very different thing from saying he is unintelligent. And because of poverty, these people are condemned to live like animals, and they breed like animals.

One way of modifying that grim demographic picture is to raise the standard of living. This is an economic fact which has a biological validity: as the standard of living rises, the family unit becomes smaller. In Western countries this has been attributed to "keeping up with the Joneses"—if you want an automobile, you can't afford another baby! But it is not as simple as that. For instance, in the Ganges Delta region of India a survey showed that a peasant with ten acres (a big holding in the delta) was likely to have a family of what one might call "Western" average (three to four), while his neighbors with half an acre or less would be having ten to fifteen children. The first would be as illiterate as the other, but somehow his relative prosperity influenced the size of his family.

How to interrupt this misery-go-round, *la ronde* of poverty? If people are sick, they cannot grow food; if they cannot grow food, malnutrition exposes them to disease. So one obvious point is to start by getting rid of disease. But if you get rid of disease, children survive to marry and to multiply, people live longer, and there are many more mouths to feed. With disease-free human energy, peasants can produce more food, but presently there is a surplus of hands; there is underemployment on the land—too many people trying to subsist on the fractionated, patrimonial soil.

The practical answer is to drain the surplus labor off the land into industry, to persuade the peasants to combine their holdings into units more amenable to modern methods, so that they can increase their products beyond their subsistence and have surpluses with which to feed those transferred to industry.

This, as will be seen, is a sophisticated form of the pattern on which, from earliest times, communities have developed—the peasant increasing his yields to support the craftsmen and, ultimately, sustain the complex superstructure of society.

But how can it apply in countries which are already overpopulated? Which raises immediately the question of what we mean by "overpopulated." India is "overpopulated" but in terms, not of density per square mile, but of yields. And yields are a matter of methods. As Dudley Stamp, already quoted (p. 277), has pointed out, England, with a population of a million and a half, was already "overpopulated" at the time of the Norman Conquest, in the sense that all the land which was responsive to the methods of the time was already farmed and people were pushing, precariously, into marginal lands.

The natural increase in the United States (through rise in the birth rate and diminishing of the death rate) is higher than that of the Asian Indians or Indonesians. The population is increasing at about 3,000,000 a year in the U.S. as compared with 5,000,000 in India, although the existing population there is nearly double the American one. But whereas in India nearly 70 per cent are employed on the land, only 18.5 per cent are so employed in the U.S. (and only 5 per cent in Britain). The high standard of living in the Western Hemisphere is due to the fact that the burden of the increase is borne not by the subsistence efforts of peasants but by the industrial productivity which, in a sense, has transferred itself to the soil. By mechanization and improved farm technology the U.S. farmer can support in food about forty people *away* from the land. And, furthermore, the farm industry produces such an excess beyond the needs of the United States that the Government has to spend billions of dollars in "price-support" schemes for the farmer to prevent him from swamping the open market.

7 *The Price of Progress*

THAT IS WHAT CAN BE DONE when a country is industrially prosperous, but what happens when there is chronic poverty? Where do you start? The peasant in India is poor (less than $150 a year average income), so that anything to improve his cultivation—better implements, better seeds, better fertilizer—is beyond his means. In the Indian Government's plans an annual increase of 700,000 tons of cereal is needed to meet that increase of 5,000,-000 extra mouths a year.

The various ways of getting it would be (1) to purchase it from abroad at a cost of $1,000,000,000 a year; (2) to purchase enough fertilizer to raise the additional crop, at a cost of $300,-000,000 with the delays of delivery and distribution; (3) to import a new fertilizer plant each year, which would cost $200,000,-000 and would take five years to get working; (4) to build an engineering plant capable of making the equipment for the fertilizer plant, which would cost $30,000,000 and would have to be planned ten years ahead of need.

To a country like India or China, "lifting itself by its own bootstraps," the last course is the only possible one (while people go hungry in the meantime). Alternatively, help might come from outside. Leaving sentiment out of it, and looking at it in a tight-lipped business way, consider it from the point of view of a successfully industrialized country: the grain is in the silos of the Western Hemisphere and there is a $300,000,000 deal to be done. Or equipment manufacturers might want to collect that $200,000,000 a year for new fertilizer plants. Or engineering firms might be prepared to build the workshops to produce the fertilizer plants. Or they might say, "To blazes with it! That puts the Asians in competition with us." In that case, if help is refused, the Asians would have to go ahead and do it all from scratch. Human misery had to be added to the final reckoning. And that reckoning, politically and economically, will do the advanced countries no good.

"But," some will say, "look at all the money that has been poured into the underdeveloped countries—U.S. Mutual Aid, U.N. Technical Assistance and loans from the International Bank, the British Colonial Development and Welfare Funds, the Colombo Plan . . ." All right, look at them! In 1959 commodity prices slumped. The advanced countries could buy their raw materials far more cheaply from the producer countries. The British balance of trade and gold reserves improved enormously. The Prime Minister could say, "You've never had it so good!"

The Secretary-General of the United Nations, Dr. Dag Hammarskjöld, however, pointed out what this prosperity meant in reverse—in the underdeveloped countries:

A fall of only 5 per cent in the average of their export prices is approximately equivalent to the entire inflow of capital which they receive not only from the International Bank loans but from all other public and private loans and government grants.

The price of some staple primary products had dropped by from 10 to 47 per cent!

Thus, ten years after President Truman's "bold new program" the gap between the prosperous countries and the impoverished countries was not closing but widening—"Unto every one that hath shall be given."

Yet the facts of our shrunken world remained inescapable. New nations were emerging with an insistent awareness that disease and hunger were not "the will of the gods" but at the discretion of Man and a test for their governments. The 4,000,000,000 people of 1980 were only twenty-one years off. And so were the predictions of the Paley Report.

8 No Country Is Self-Sufficient

THIS REPORT of the findings of the U.S. President's Material Policy Commission, presided over by Mr. William Paley, was published in five volumes in 1952 and dealt with the problem of prospective mineral supplies to meet the demands of the United States. In 1950 the U.S.A. was using about half the world's supply of minerals and was increasing its demand by about 3 per cent per annum. In that year the United States consumed 2,700 million tons of materials of all kinds—metallic ores, nonmetallic minerals, agricultural materials, constructional materials and fuels. That represented 36,000 lbs. for every man, woman and child in the country. With less than 10 per cent of the "Free World" population and only 8 per cent of its area, it consumed more than half of the world's supply of petroleum, rubber, iron ore, manganese and zinc. Of the hundred mineral materials used in American industry, the country which had once been regarded as wholly self-sufficient was finding only one third entirely at home, another third partly at home and partly abroad, and the remaining third entirely abroad. In the nature of new materials needed for atomics and electronics, that last fraction becomes very much magnified.

The major recommendation of the U.S. Commission was:

The over-all objective of a national materials policy for the United States should be to ensure an adequate and dependable flow of materials at the lowest cost consistent with national security and with the welfare of friendly nations.

How much more true is this recommendation of Britain which Mr. Aneurin Bevan once described as "a lump of coal entirely surrounded by fish"? Fifty per cent of Britain's food and, excluding coal, practically all the raw materials of its industries have to be imported—"at the lowest cost consistent with the welfare of friendly nations." Or of keeping nations friendly by ensuring their welfare?

What the Paley Report illustrates is that the world is inescapably one, as far as raw materials are concerned, and that no country, however big, can now be self-sufficient. Even the United States, which in fifty years took more minerals out of the American continent than had been mined from the entire earth's crust since Neolithic Man, must look to the development of the underdeveloped countries for the maintenance of its standards of living.

PART
TEN

The Future

"For Man there is no rest and no ending—he
must go on—conquest beyond conquest. This
little planet, Earth, its winds and ways and all
the laws of mind and matter that restrain him.
Then the planets about him. And at last out
across immensity to the stars. And when he has
conquered all the deeps of space and all the
mysteries of time—still he will be beginning."

From the film scenario of *Things to Come*
by H. G. WELLS

1 Summit Conference, A.D. 2061

THE TIME *is a century ahead. The place is Alert, on the northern coast of Ellesmere Island, in the Arctic. The Nuclear War has not happened. The occasion is the winter session of the World Assembly, in which delegates from all the regional federations are taking part. The following is a dispatch, date-lined February 15, 2061.*

Premier Ehagoetok, of Ellesmere Province, has reminded the delegates that they are within 400 miles of the North Pole.

"You may not have noticed the North Pole itself," he said, "but that was where your retro-rockets started braking for the landing here."

Recalling the quaint folklore of a century ago, he has pointed out that Alert was then called "Santa Claus's home town" because it was the most northerly inhabited place on earth. "Inhabited" was then almost an exaggeration, because the population had consisted of only eight weathermen. They, however, had not been the first settlers.

"Nowadays, when we neither boast nor excuse our ancestry," said the Premier, "I hesitate to point out that my own people, the Eskimos, of the Thule and Dorset cultures, had been here and in adjoining Peary Land, in Greenland, centuries before them."

As a matter of history, the Premier continued to explain, Robert Peary, 150 years ago, had started for the North Pole on his sea-ice journey from the neighborhood of Alert. And almost a century ago the first to-the-moon-and-back rocket expedition had returned here. (Delegates would be able to visit the crater, for the annual wreath-laying service.)

363

The weather station had "put Alert on the map," but its world importance and its growth as a city had really begun when Dumbbell Bay had been transformed into an ice-free lagoon for submarine freighters.

"Dumbbell Bay is now called 'Rutherford Basin,'" the Premier explained, "after Lord Rutherford, the Father of the Atom. The name is appropriate because, of course, the submarine ships are nuclear propelled and because it is kept unfrozen by the heat from Alert's nuclear reactors. Personally I prefer the Eskimo name for the ice-free basin—*Aglu*, which means 'Seal's breathing hole'—because just as a seal keeps a ventilating shaft through the ice, we keep a 'breathing hole' for the underwater freighters, tankers and liners.

"As a respite from your labors, I would advise you to take the excursion, which we have arranged, on the Trans-Polar Ferry. You can make the round trip to Siberia and back in a weekend. That may seem slow going in these days of passenger-carrying rockets which bring New Zealand within an hour's distance of Alert. But we Polar peoples are very proud of our underseas scenery, and you will see why when the submarine floodlights pick out the undersea alps as you sail between their peaks. . . ."

Dr. Okoboyko, of the United States of Africa, this year's President of the World Assembly, congratulated Alert for the enterprise which had made it, at least for the duration of the sessions, the capital of the political world. Like Premier Ehagoetok, he hesitated to invoke the past of his people in an assembly concerned with the future of all peoples, but it pleased him to remember that it was here, on the north coast of Ellesmere, that a Negro, Matt Henson, had set out with Peary for the Pole. In those heroic days who would have foreseen that the frozen Arctic would have become not only part of the habitable world but that the long night of the Arctic winter would be turned into perpetual day . . . ?

The President's reference is to the man-made "sunlight" in which the delegates have arrived and which is visible all over the Northern Hemisphere. Rockets have been fired into space and, in the vacuum just beyond the earth's atmosphere, sodium has been released. The effect, on a celestial scale, is like that of the sodium lamps which once illuminated the highways, because the ionizing radiations, passing through the suspended and finely dispersed sodium gas, have filled the vacuum of the sky with a bright yellow light. This sky glow lights up the Arctic darkness more prosaically but as brightly as nature's own pyrotechnics, the Aurora Borealis. Nowhere in the world is this lighting as effective as it is here in the Arctic where the white snows reflect it like burnished gold.

The ionized layer serves another purpose for the Assembly. This man-made mirror in the sky reflects the television waves and enables the proceedings to be seen all over the world, because, apart from the "scatter" over the Northern Hemisphere, the transmissions are relayed by similar sky reflectors to the rest of the globe.

What has most impressed the visiting delegates is Alert itself, a city of 50,000 people, where the tall apartment buildings and the luxury hotels are able to house the thousands of visitors—the delegates and secretariat of the World Assembly—without difficulty.

The town planning of Alert is typical of the layout of other Arctic cities. Whereas in Antarctica the continental capital, Amundsen City, has been constructed entirely underground, beneath the 10,000-foot icecap, the Canadian cities have remained aboveground, but with their inhabitants and their activities immune from the elements. This, a century ago, would have been regarded as a remarkable engineering feat, because of the problems of permafrost. It would have seemed impracticable then to have constructed a city of such massive buildings, the heating of which would have melted the permanently frozen subsoil and produced queer effects in the frozen bedrock. In the meantime, however, methods have been evolved by which effective insulation has ensured sound foundations and has prevented the type of subsidence which, a century ago, compelled the moving of the town of Aklavik, at the mouth of the Mackenzie River.

Someone has called Alert the "Arctic Stonehenge." Like that famous temple of the Druids on Salisbury Plain, it is in the form of a great circle. At the circumference are twenty-story-high buildings which are apartments, hotels and offices. They are like Stonehenge's "standing stones," monolithic and symmetrical in design and in height. The top stories of the buildings are linked by enclosed bridges just as the "standing stones" were joined by lintels, laid horizontally on the verticals. From directly overhead one gets the impression of a rim of a wheel. Actually this elevated "rim" provides a circular runway on which vertical-lift aircraft descend. On landing they are automatically lowered into their "garages" in the interior of the "rim." Inside this circular corridor, 200 feet above the ground, is a moving roadway which takes people from one block of buildings to another. The buildings are also linked to each other at various levels and are joined to the City Center, from which the corridor streets radiate like the spokes of a wheel.

The City Center is half a mile in diameter, enclosed in a dome which is as high as that of St. Paul's Cathedral, but rising from the ground like a giant igloo. In principle the dome is like an enormous vacuum flask. It consists of an inner and an outer shell, with an insulating space between. Since it is made of transparent plastic, unaffected by heat or by cold, the sky above is visible and the effect, when there is no sodium sunlight, is like that of a giant planetarium.

Inside this dome, with its controlled "climate," are the gardens, where any plant can grow, the sports arenas, the "open-air" theater, the football stadium, the swimming baths, and the ice-hockey rink. Here (although there are neighborhood shopping centers in the buildings on the perimeter) is the market and, dead center, the "Pearson Forum" where the Assembly is being held and which, on this world occasion, has just been named by the President as a tribute to the first Canadian to win the Nobel Peace Prize. The City Center is suffused in artificial sunlight, not just from the sodium sky glow but from discreet ultraviolet radiation which gives the people of Alert that healthy tan which might have been acquired on a tropical beach.

On the outskirts of Alert, and linked to it by an enclosed corridor roadway, is the rocket airport. Here rocket liners, remote-controlled, can land with pin-point accuracy. Air "lanes," as constant as the lines of longitude, have been bringing in the delegates' rocket liners on safe schedule. Automatically a radar "trigger," operating at a height and distance electronically calculated to the rocket speed, applies the rocket brakes, the retro-rockets acting in reverse to the propelling motors. This man-proof system is guaranteed, without mishap and in any weather conditions, to land the rocket airliner gently in the middle of the airport. The base is ten miles from the City Center but less than four minutes' distance in time. The roadway in an all-weather corridor is ballroom-smooth, and the wheelless cars float over it on a cushion of air. The automatic motors which propel the cars also compress the air which is ejected on the underside, as jets, providing an air cushion on which, without the friction of wheels, vehicles can attain a speed of over 500 miles an hour.

The delegates, who held their last World Assembly at Hassi-Messaoud, which a century ago was the oil "boom" town of the Sahara and is now the administrative capital of the North African region, take climatically immune cities for granted. Indeed, today there are many Canadians who have forgotten their northward expansion and even the political ructions which compelled the removal of their capital from Ottawa to the shores of Baker Lake. There had been a threat of secession by the young provinces north of 60° latitude, unless the Government would move nearer to the geographic center of Canada. With the economic wealth involved in the former Northwest Territories and the Arctic Archipelago, this was a serious threat which prevailed, in spite of the opposition of Old Canada and the Prairie Provinces. The district of Chesterfield had accordingly been made a Dominion enclave in the Keewatin Province which, with its Atomic Age minerals, had become one of the wealthiest regions of the world.

The attempt to unfreeze Hudson Bay by thermonuclear energy has also been conveniently forgotten. This ambitious project, and expensive failure, was not merely an attempt to unlock the bay from its ice prison and to keep it open for shipping all the year round, but to modify the climate of the north and midwest. The "modification" had temporarily happened but with serious results, not in Canada but in Europe. That was the occasion when the World Meteorological Organization had had to apply sanctions: unless the interference with the European weather was stopped, the W.M.O. threatened Canada with a "weather blockade"—the precipitation of the rain-bearing Pacific clouds before they reached British Columbia.

So the North had come to terms with its natural climate. The old, forbidding ideas about the Frozen North had disappeared, and the so-called "Frozen Frontier" had been opened up as dramatically in the twentieth century as the western frontiers had been pushed back in the nineteenth century. The "covered wagons" of the northward migration had been the "flying box-cars," the aircraft which could steeplechase over impossible terrain and accomplish in hours journeys which, by land trek, would have taken weeks and even months. Aircraft, too, had revealed the prodigious wealth of minerals hidden under forests, lakes, barrens and ice of the Canadian Shield. Geological scouts in helicopters had gone ahead of the ground prospectors.

The winning of such wealth for the Atomic Age (including not only the fissile fuels, like uranium and thorium, but metals indispensable to fusion reactors as well) had made atomic reactors economic even in the early days. Here was wealth buried in places remote from the roads and railheads of surface transport—places as isolated as islands in the sea or oases in the desert. Thus they had been created "industrial oases," accessible only by air. The components of the reactors and the generators had been flown in (in the same way as on the DEW Line operations [Distant Early Warning], which in the 1950s had strung radar-defense stations across the Arctic), men, materials and complete settlements debouched by aircraft. These atomic stations did not need continuous supply by pipeline or by rail, which coal or oil installations would have needed; once constructed and "critical," the reactor fuel could be replenished by air so infrequently that the stations

368

were virtually self-sufficient. With abundant heat and power from the atom, ores could be mined, milled and refined on the spot and reduced to bulk so small (yet so valuable) that the output could be handled by aircraft. With abundant heat and power, communities could be created with all the amenities of the cities of the South. Mining camps were no longer just bunkhouses and mess halls, poker games and itinerant miners, working their contracted shifts and heading south again. They became towns and eventually cities, where families grew up and went to school, unaware of any "bright lights" except those of their native north.

One of the ironies of the North was that atomic energy was used to keep the "Frozen North" frozen. The handicap to air movement had been the freeze-up and the breakup. In the winter aircraft, on skis or even on wheels, could land on the thick ice of the lakes or sea or the hard-bound land strips; in the summer there were the abundant lakes and rivers where they could land on pontoons. But in the in-betweens, flying was hampered until there was surplus energy enough to keep the airfields frozen by refrigeration pipes, as had been possible with indoor ice rinks. The same applied to roads.

Behind the miners went the farmers—yes, the farmers—although in those days, a century ago, it had seemed impossible that crops would grow in such inhospitable climate. The climate did not radically change, but the plants did. By intensive selection, using atomic radiation and chemical mutagens to speed up plant variations and make possible in five years what would have taken fifty by conventional botany, the plant breeders produced types of grain, root crops and vegetables which could be adapted to the conditions of the farthest north.

They created types which could escape the frosts and grow to maturity in the long days, but short season, of the Arctic and sub-Arctic summer. They devised crops to suit the soils of the converted muskeg and conditioned into soil the sands of the glaciated pre-Cambrian Shield. They planted trees far north of what had been the limits of the timber line.

The first great agricultural advance had been up the alluvial valleys of the Liard and the Mackenzie to the vast delta which is now so productive that it is called "the Arctic Nile." But wherever townships grew, even in apparently hopeless places, crops followed—though in some places they resembled merely cottage gardens or intensive market gardening. The other thing was the breeding of a type of Arctic dairy cow as tough as the moose, as far as climate was concerned, and as lavish as the Friesian in terms of milk.

One of the visits which has been arranged for the delegates to the World Assembly concerned, as always, with the perennial problem of a multiplying population is to the great fish ranch of Kane Basin. This was not the first, but it is now one of the most efficient sea farms in the world. It was created by the simple device of passing electric currents across the northern and southern limits of the straits which separate Ellesmere from Greenland and electrically fencing in the fish. Here there was some help from the change of climate which was becoming noticeable even a century ago when, in the 1950s, the fish were already moving up the west coast of Greenland. The use of fertilizers in the enclosed basin increased the phytoplankton and thus the zooplankton, and the fish multiplied. In 2061 the fishing yields are even greater, because the nuclear reactors which supply the power for the Kane Basin fish factories have provided heating for the fish nurseries and a further tempering of the cold sea. The harvest of the sea fish in the Kane Basin is now as big as that of fresh-water fish from Great Bear Lake, the biggest inland fish ranch in the world.

Frobisher Bay, now the capital of Baffin Province, was the first of the domed cities of the Arctic because it was the eastern base of the defense system. It showed that the architects had sense enough to learn from the Eskimo. After all, the domed igloo had proved itself a pretty effective form of architecture!

The importance of Alert dates from the opening up of the polar oil fields and the mining of the great coal deposits of Ellesmere Island. The existence of the oil fields had been first suspected from the aerial photographs taken by the Royal Canadian Air

Force on their northern patrols and mapping surveys after the Second World War. Those showed on many of the polar islands what looked suspiciously like salt domes, the enormous surface "bubbles" of rock which often indicate the existence of oil. But what use was oil locked up in the permanent ice of the Arctic? The coming of the submarine tankers changed all that: Meighen and the Ringnes Islands were not more inaccessible than the Persian Gulf.

Then, beneath the glacier-filled valleys and nunataks, those peaks like knapped flints, was discovered a wealth of metal ores on Ellesmere which turned Eureka, farther south, into an industrial city and Alert into a prosperous provincial capital, 400 miles from the North Pole.

Writing this behind the storm-proofed windows of a nineteenth-story apartment, I can look northward toward the Pole over a snow-covered landscape, glittering like gold under the sodium sky glow and shimmering as the winds whip the snow crystals into what once sounded so menacing as "blizzard."

I am high above the whirling surface snow which has buried the corridor roads, the spokes of Alert's wheel, and I am looking into the glowing dome of the City Center as though it were a crystal ball.

What I am seeing in the crystal however, is not the future but the past—the weathermen of a century ago, just eight of them making unseen friends by "ham" radio in a world from which they were cut off, and, deeper in the past, Peary, struggling through a blizzard such as that now swirling down below and on which I look down with Olympic detachment. And I echo the words which the President used at today's opening of the World Assembly on this February 15, 2061:

Here in Alert we have proof that the Arctic is part of our habitable world, of that world which has become so small, in terms of time and distance, that we, in tropical Africa, are your near neighbors. But it is a world which has become so small that we must cherish its surface as we would a garden and treasure its resources as we would our household possessions. Today we have lit a beacon in the Arctic night, the torch of Man's achievements.

2 Top of the World, A.D. 1961

THIS REPORT on the Summit Conference of 2061 may read like a fantasy, but it is less of a prediction than a projection. Everything in it is scientifically and technologically feasible in the light of mid-twentieth-century knowledge and experience. The voyages of the *Nautilus* and the *Skate*, the United States atomic submarines, have already made traffic under the ice completely practicable. Plans for nuclear-powered submarine tankers and freighters were already on the drawing boards in 1959, and ice-free ports ("seal's breathing holes") are already an engineering proposition, using not nuclear heat but compressed air to prevent the ice from forming. The plans for the domed city of Frobisher, in Baffin Land, are already under way. The economics of "packaged" reactors are already self-evident—the essential need of settlements in the Arctic, including the radar stations and military bases, for heat and power, and it costs one gallon of aviation fuel to fly in two gallons of crude oil. Thus the comparative economics of nuclear and conventional fuels are not as between electricity generated from cheap coal and oil but are related to the cost of transportation. The proposition of an "industrial oasis" has already been demonstrated by the El Dorado Mine, on Lake Athabaska, where the uranium was mined, milled, and refined and flown out, as casks of sodium uraninate, by ordinary scheduled airlines.

The construction of DEW Line, the chain of radar stations across the Far North, did not so much unlock the doors of the Arctic as burst them wide open. The impact has been dramatic.

One day I flew with a team to King William's Land, where, using as a pin-point the cairn beneath which were bodies from Sir John Franklin's ill-fated expedition of 1847, we landed on a frozen bay. We cut through seven feet of ice to examine and test it for structure and stresses. We sent a signal, guaranteeing the ice as safe for landing, to Edmonton, six hours' flying distance away. Presently a Globemaster freight plane landed, and from its nose dropped a ramp down which trundled tractors, bulldozers and sledge trucks. Simultaneously the belly of the aircraft was opened and electric hoists descended, laden with whole prefabricated buildings in flat sections. Those were swung clear and more cargo, including cookhouse equipment, was unloaded from the hold. Such an operation, from touch-down to take-off, took only twenty-five minutes. In that time a whole construction camp could be off-loaded on a polar island where a few hours before the only inhabitants had been polar bears.

3 *Polar Oil Field*

AFTER ANOTHER MISSION in which I took part in the Arctic, our aircraft landed at an island base to refuel for our return journey to the south. The summer breakup had set in, and from then on heavy aircraft would not be able to land. Ours, officially, was the last flight in or out.

On landing, the captain gave an instruction that the fire extinguishers were to be tested. That meant shaking the carbon-dioxide cylinders to make sure they were filled. A not-too-bright member of the crew misunderstood the instructions and "tested" by pulling the master switch, which is used when an aircraft is completely on fire. As a result the aircraft and its engines were smothered in fire-extinguishing foam.

The prospects were grim. The chances of another aircraft coming in to relieve us were remote. The alternative was to dismantle the engines and clean them. And by that time the ground might be unsuitable for take-off.

373

Arctic flyers are philosophic—they have to be—and the crew and I returned to our hut while the mechanics tackled the engine. That night (and "night" was a relative term, because it was the period of twenty-four hours' daylight) we were debating who would eat whom first—we or the polar bears! Then we heard the noise of a plane and we rushed out to find a Dakota circling around, preparing to land.

By a curious coincidence, the kind that was always happening to me in the Arctic, out of that plane stepped four friends of mine. They were scientists from the Dominion Geological Survey. For the same reasons as concerned us, they were rushing to complete, before the breakup, the supply stage of Operation Franklin. This was the 1955 geological survey, organized like a military campaign, to reconnoiter the polar islands north of the Canadian mainland. The aircraft, which had so unexpectedly arrived, was building up supply bases for the summer operations. These were to be conducted by footslogging geologists, supported by helicopters. The helicopters had also been brought in by freight plane.

The mishap to our plane turned out to be a piece of good fortune for me because I was able to join Operation Franklin and to fly on sorties to islands which I had never hoped to visit, including some which no one had ever visited before. But it also meant that I was in at the beginning of a discovery which a few years later was to rock the stock exchanges—the discovery of a great polar oil field.

The Royal Canadian Air Force on their military patrols had taken photomaps and had recorded curious formations in the scatter of islands which lies west of Ellesmere. From the cockpit of an aircraft those looked like volcanic craters surrounded by a ring of jagged peaks, but when the geologists in Ottawa saw the photographs, they guessed that they were eroded salt domes. Salt domes, in southern U.S.A., Mexico and Persia, are identified with oil. They closely resemble volcanoes, but the upthrust of lava is replaced by crystalline rock salt. There is a central vent—a circular "plug" of salt—cutting vertically through the other strata and sometimes reaching the surface, but in most cases the plug does not show on the surface and is overlaid by sedimentary rocks. These, in turn, become worn down into ragged peaks around the central "bubble." The inner formation is like an inverted bowl. Inside, if it is a continuing oil source, there will be natural gas immediately under the dome, then oil-bearing rocks (porous formations capable of holding oil), then water, and finally non-porous base. The oil thus trapped is unable, as in other conditions, to escape and vaporize on the surface.

Long before they knew about salt domes, oilmen knew that when an oil well exhausted itself they got a flow of brine. This supports the belief that oil began in the primeval seas. Millions of years ago nature began to prepare pump stations for twentieth-century cars. During the long periods of the Paleozoic, Mesozoic and Cenozoic ages the seas teemed with animal life. From time to time the earth's crust would shift; great plains would lower and the oceans would roll over them, or the sea bed would lift and become plains from which the water receded. During the time of submergence, layer after layer of mud, sand and lime-carrying plant and animal remains were deposited—sometimes miles thick. Buried far underground, the organic matter which had once been sea life was subjected to enormous heat and pressure—a gigantic geological autoclave which, in the alchemy of nature, converted the organic matter into mineral oil. So the rock salt of the "plug" and the gypsum which forms the "tent" of the dome were, like the oil itself, all part of the early sea bed.

On Operation Franklin they knew, pretty shrewdly, before they started, the sort of thing for which they were looking. At least eleven such domes had been identified on Meighen, Ellef Ringnes, Amund Ringnes, Axel Heiberg, and Melville islands. Subsequent ground surveys (which stopped short of drilling) confirmed their suspicions. These were true salt domes and they were associated with abundant petroliferous or bituminous rocks and with reservoir beds with impermeable caps—all signs that oil had been effectively trapped.

As we pored over maps and speculatively plotted the possible

The Drake Oil Well, Pennsylvania (1886)

configurations of the oil-bearing regions, a picture emerged which is probably more substantial than mere fantasy. It would fit in with the modern theory of the "wandering pole" (discussed on p. 170) and with the refurbished Wegener Theory of Continental Drift (p. 168). Seas, teeming with the kind of organic life needed for oil making, would have to have been warm seas, but if the land surface had "crept" and moved from near-tropical latitudes, that would be understandable. If we accept, too, the theory of Continental Drift, with that great raft of the Americas surging westward, the picture becomes exciting.

The Rockies, the Sierras and the Andes become the "bow wave," thrust up by the movement. Pressing behind them is the solid land mass of the hard-rock Pre-Cambrian Shield and the Innutian Mountains (of Greenland and Ellesmere), and squeezed in between is the sea with its bed being forced upward and its water being shed. If you look at the map, as we did, with those assump-

376

tions in mind, you can see the configurations of the oil-bearing region, stretching from the north of Ellesmere, through the oil-dome islands, down the Mackenzie to the oil field of Norman Wells (a few miles south of the Arctic Circle), down through the oil lands of Athabaska and Alberta, down through Oklahoma and Texas and the Mexican Gulf. A plausible picture!

The findings of Operation Franklin did not "hit the headlines" for another four years. The first reports were discreet, not because the experts had much doubt of the existence of oil (although drillings were still needed to confirm the nature and extent), but because the Canadians were canny. As long as those islands were remote wastes, nobody had given much thought to them. It had been tacitly assumed that, with deference to Danish Greenland and its territorial waters, the lines of longitude extending from the continental limits of Canada to the North Pole made all islands in the sector Canadian. But the "sector principle" has never been regarded as sound international law. (If it was, Britain would have to recognize the rights of Argentina and Chile to the Antarctic Islands, the Falklands and South Shetlands.) So sovereignty had to be established by right of occupation, and the Canadians proceeded to take the necessary steps of manning the islands.

4 *Polar Submarines*

THE OTHER REASON why Operation Franklin and its oil finds were not heavily canvassed at first was the fact that the oil was mainly on islands perpetually locked in the ice. There seemed to be no satisfactory way of getting it out to the southern markets. All this was changed when the *Nautilus* and the *Skate* navigated the Polar

THE FUTURE BENEATH THE SEA *The nuclear-powered submarine* Nautilus, *returning from her 5,000-mile voyage under the North Pole, forerunner of submerged circumnavigator* [Keystone Press, London]

Basin *under the ice*. They demonstrated the possibility of submarine tankers and freighters and (why not?) liners. From the designers' standpoint, the idea of such submarine ships was attractive, because they had to contend with only one element, water. There were none of the problems of wind resistance and waves which have tormented ships and their passengers since the first frail craft ventured on the bosom of the ocean. The designers could "think big"—in terms of 100,000 tons, it need be, and, with atomic power and swordfish-design lines, of speeds higher than those attainable on the surface.

378

Freezing the Arctic

The atomic-powered submarines, of course, could go on circumnavigating the globe below the surface for indefinite periods, but that was no special recommendation when it was a question of carrying freight. They would have to surface sometime to load and unload, but in the Arctic they would be roofed in by ice.

The muskrats and the seals had solved that problem ages before. When the ice begins to form, they choose a given spot and keep a breathing hole open by simply breaking and melting the ice regularly as it forms. Seals will maintain an *aglu*, or breathing hole, through seven feet of ice. (This the Eskimos know, and they watch the snow on the surface of the sea ice heaving as the seals come up to breathe; thus they can harpoon the hapless animals.) Ice-free lagoons could be created and maintained—in the first place, by using compressed air, and later, when the development of the oil (or other mineral) settlements justified them, by the heat from nuclear reactors.

The coincidence of the two factors—the recognition of the significance of Operation Franklin and realistic plans for atomic submarines and harborage—fluttered the markets in the spring of 1959.

(For the record: our aircraft was "de-extinguished," and both it and the Franklin planes made their getaway before the thaw could prevent them.)

5 Freezing the Arctic

JUST AS IMPORTANT as the physical transformation of the Arctic landscape by such developments was the psychological effect on the hundreds of newcomers to the Arctic. They discovered

379

their own misconceptions of the Arctic. Of course, there are blizzards, and anyone who fools around in a blizzard is asking for trouble. But these blizzards are like the "sand devils" of the desert; they are rarely snowstorms coming out of the sky but are ground snow, frosted into crystals, being whipped by the winds. Indeed, in many of the areas I have visited in the Arctic the precipitation is less than in parts of the Sahara Desert. There are "arid zones" in the Frozen North with less than four inches of rainfall equivalent (in the form of snow), but, of course, four inches of rain means forty inches of snow. The snow, during the winter, does not melt but can be air-borne as blizzards by the winds.

At a lonely weather station I asked an American weatherman why he had signed on for a third tour of duty in the Arctic. He said that the attraction for him was color photography! Color photography in the Arctic! In popular imagination it is just unrelieved white, but as people like the weathermen discover, the Arctic is rich in color. In the Arctic night, lasting six months, there is not just a black-out; there is the moon reflected by the white brilliance of the snow. There are the "moondogs," the paraselenae. (The real moon is surrounded by luminous rings due to ice crystals in the atmosphere, and in these rings appear mock moons, repeating the original across the sky.) But even when there is no moon the sky glow in the clear atmosphere makes the night visible. In addition, there are the pyrotechnics of the northern lights, flaunting their fantastic-colored draperies in a décor which no producer could ever imitate. In the summer there are the parhelia, the mock suns. These "sun-dogs" multiply the images of the sun in the sky as the paraselenae do the moon. When the snow leaves the Arctic islands, as it does in the summer except in sheltered canyons or on the ice plateau, the landscape becomes alive with color. There are Arctic poppies, red saxifrage, purple Arctic willow and the innumerable colored mosses and lichens. The Arctic flowers are all brightly hued— red, blue, orange and white. The sides of the hills in the Arctic summer are often completely covered with saxifrage. There are butterflies in the Arctic, and mosquitoes and tiny black spiders and beetles. There are 200 kinds of birds, including the snow owl and the gyrfalcon, one of the world's most beautiful birds.

"Colors!" said the weatherman enthusiastically. "Colors so beautiful that the color films can't do justice to them. They are very, very, very beautiful." And that from a man who had told me that what had brought him to the Arctic was the "hardship" pay, which he could not spend and which was to buy him a car or a house at the end of a year's tour of duty. He stayed for three years.

On my visit to Alert, 400 miles from the Pole, I walked around in a light pull-over and a pair of flannel trousers and became sunburned. On the shores of the Baffin Bay, Eskimo men and women go around naked to the waist, basking in the summer sun like the Samoans of the tropics. At the mouth of the Mackenzie River, where it runs into the Polar Sea, one can go surf bathing, with the atmospheric temperature at over 80°.

It took the White Man a long time to learn what the Eskimo had known for hundreds of years—that the best time to travel in the Arctic is in the winter when the rivers, the lakes and the sea are frozen and you could, if you wanted to, sledge uninterruptedly from Hudson Bay to the North Pole. The times of inconvenience are the freeze-up and the breakup, when the broken and melting ice makes travel, or air landings, difficult, if not impossible. Hence the suggestion that one way of using surplus nuclear power would be to keep the airstrips and access roads continuously frozen, by refrigerating them as one would do an ice rink.

6 Crops for the Arctic

AT THE BEGINNING of the twentieth century the provinces of Saskatchewan and Alberta were classified on the charts as unsuitable for grains. The climate was too dry. Today, of course, those provinces are rich in wheat-growing territories. And certainly then no land north of 55° latitude would have been considered likely grain-growing land. The climate has not changed in the meantime. What has happened is that the climate has been flouted by the plant breeders who have bred strains of grain like Thatcher and Saunders wheat and extended the frontiers of grain-growing westward and northward.

Similarly—and again this is not a prediction but a projection of work which I have seen going on—agriculture will be extended well north of the Arctic Circle. For instance, in Alaska, the forty-ninth state of the United States of America, nearly 900 families have "homesteaded" on a basis of commercial agriculture, although most of them have farmed on a part-time basis. Over 300 farms operate in the Matanuska Valley, just north of Anchorage. Even further north, around Fairbanks, near the sixty-fifth parallel, there are about sixty farms. Most Alaskan farms market vegetables and potatoes, but others have developed dairy farming and grain growing. A successful dairy farmer in Alaska can net about $4,850 a year, a potato farmer about $3,500 a year, and a poultry farmer about $4,000. It is true that most of Alaska by modern definition is "sub-Arctic" and inside the timber line crop production is mainly on sub-Arctic brown forest soils which need artificial fertilizers for proper cultivation, and imported fertilizers are expensive. The tundra soils of Alaska, underlain by permafrost at shallow depth, can support surprisingly thriving gardens when the surface layers thaw out.

In Canada there is the Mackenzie River Basin, the northern extension of the Great Central Plain of North America. There

382

are three main regions: the Mackenzie Lowlands, the Pre-Cambrian Shield to the east, and the Mackenzie Mountains to the west. Three features dominate it: the Mackenzie River, Great Slave Lake and Great Bear Lake. There are myriads of small lakes and extensive muskeg swamps which result from the poor natural drainage of the permanently frozen subsoils. The soil surveys of the region have not been exhaustive, but, for a start, one can assume a million good acres of soil in the valleys of the Mackenzie and Liard and in the region from Fort Smith to Great Slave. The fertility of the soil is good, and the application of fertilizers can get crops off to a quick start, to take advantage of summer daylight and of summer temperatures of as high as 97° at Fort Simpson or 93° at Aklavik, near the mouth of the Mackenzie. The million-acre figure for the Mackenzie region could be changed considerably if there was consistent settlement and proper forest management. The combination of conservation and clearance would improve the "air drainage" as well as the land drainage.

In the early days of Peace River, to the south, the settlers regularly lost their crops through frost until it began to look as though the region was too far north for agriculture. But as settlement progressed and the forests were intelligently cleared, the "air drainage" was such that the frost hazards were reduced and, as a result, the land drainage improved. Today Peace River, with 16,000,000 acres of cultivable land, has become an agricultural, grain-growing region. The recovery of muskeg swamps is comprehensible when one remembers that vegetation is an insulator. It prevents the sun's heat from penetrating and thawing out the frozen subsoil so that it remains rock-hard and impermeable to drainage. But once the black soil is exposed it absorbs heat, and, year by year, the heat penetrates deeper into the permafrost and the "bottom falls out of the muskeg."

(One should remind oneself that white snow reflects heat and that vegetation acts as an insulator, whereas black soil, or any blackness, absorbs heat. This principle was put into spectacular application by the Chinese in 1959 when, in the snow-capped Kilian Mountains of northwestern China, their scientists, with organized labor, began to melt the glaciers. The method was to spread coal dust or burned grass or wood and other dark-colored materials on the ice of the glaciers to increase the absorption of the sun's heat. By this process it was hoped, in the summer months, to melt about seven square miles of glaciers to provide enough water to irrigate 50,000 acres of farm land.)

When I told people that I had seen delphiniums chest-high growing a few miles from the Arctic Circle, they just did not believe me until I produced certified color photographs to prove it. This remarkable growth is due to the twenty-four hours of daylight. The excessive ration of sunlight, however, does not always encourage the best results. Tomatoes, for example, need about seven and a half hours' "sleep," and crops have to be adapted to the continuous light.

At the Dominion Agricultural Research Station at Fort Simpson I have seen experimental crops of such a variety that a list of them reads like a seed merchant's catalogue: spring wheat, barley, oats, Indian corn, potatoes, alfalfa, clover, timothy grass, asparagus, rhubarb, bush beans, broad beans, pole beans, beets, broccoli, Brussels sprouts, cabbage, carrots, cauliflower, celery, chard, cucumbers, lettuce, melons, parsnips, peas, spinach, rasp-berries, currants, and strawberries. And the flowers: cottage pinks, columbine, daisies, sweet william, peonies, delphiniums, lupines, poppies, lobelias, sweet alyssum, petunias, pansies, marigolds, snapdragon, asters, cornflowers, clarkia, sweet peas, nasturtiums, phlox, stock, and "youth-and-old-age."

7 Tailor-Made Plants

IT IS NOT MERELY a case of finding existing varieties which are suitable for, or can be accommodated to, Arctic conditions. It is possible by modern methods to create special varieties which will grow under the precise conditions which are to be tolerated. This "tailoring" of plants can be achieved by radiations, by using the by-products of atomic energy, by X rays, or by treating the seeds in atomic reactors. Another method is to use chemical "mutagens." The botanical scientists know the varieties for which they are looking and can spell out the specifications, which they could secure by normal selection methods and cultivation, but it might take anything up to fifty years to get the precise qualities which they desire. The new methods provide drastic short cuts.

The demands are exacting. For instance, at Aklavik at the mouth of the Mackenzie River, near the Arctic Sea, the average frost-free period is sixty-six days. Thatcher and Saunders wheats, the successful varieties of the Prairie Provinces, take ninety-four and ninety-one days to ripen and, in the best years, seventy-five days. So if there are to be grain crops in the Arctic, the period of maturing will have to be cut—because they are not looking for frost-*resisting* strains but merely frost-*cheating* strains. What are needed, therefore, are crops of all kinds which will be "gluttons" for sunlight, since they have to put up with the twenty-four hours' daylight of the Arctic summer—frost-cheating, high-yielding and, of course, good quality. By modern methods, either radiative or chemical, it is possible to cut the selection and breeding time of such varieties from fifty to five years.

The great possibilities of extending grain production into Arctic regions were emphasized by Professor A. Gustafsson of Sweden at the International Conference on Peaceful Uses of Atomic Energy. He pointed out that most agricultural species, even high-bred ones like wheat and barley and maize, are still "rather old-fashioned."

"Our crops are out-of-date," he said. "Barley is very much what it was 500,000 years ago. Now we can give the barley some of the qualities of the wheat and wheat some of the advantages of the barley. We can give the cereal the special characters which agriculture requires—stiffer straw, earliness, protein or oil content, baking quality, fiber strength, grain size, or malting properties." By atomic radiation the scientist can remake chromosomes of a plant and "modernize" it.

(Chromosomes are the portmanteaus in which nature packages the genes, the hereditary characteristics which are passed on from one generation to the next. Radiation can rearrange the packages.)

Radiation, however, is a blunderbuss method. It cannot give precision. Hundreds of seeds have to be irradiated with differing doses of radiation, and most of them will be completely useless, and the rest, time and time again, may not indicate the kind of qualities that are required. It means selecting the radiated seeds and trying to find from them the peculiar qualities for which one is looking. This is a laborious business, but in this way plant breeders can do in a few years what nature requires aeons of time to do and, in dealing with plants, they do not have to worry about harmful hereditary changes which would bring deformity or death to human beings and animals. For every beneficial change likely with radiation there are on the average 500 bad ones, but the plant breeder has no compunction about getting rid of the mutations which he does not want.

Professor Gustafsson later found what he regarded as a more precise and useful method. In place of, or in addition to, radiation, he used the chemical, ethylene imine. This chemical imitates the genetic effects of atomic radiation by attacking DNA (deoxyribonucleic acid). DNA is the basic chemical of life and is present in the genes. What was particularly encouraging about this work with ethylene imine was the evidence it gave in support of the belief that the time is not far off when it will be possible to separate chromosome rearrangements and genes changes from one another. From the knowledge experimentally gained it should be possible to direct the mutation process to produce by deliberate design the very kind of changes in plants which are wanted. For example, the Swedish workers were able to produce by irradiation a type of barley which came to maturity three weeks earlier than the mother strain. This would be within the time limit of the frost-free periods in the Arctic. Similarly by such methods it is possible to develop crops for low rainfall regions and for difficult and sparse soil.

There seems to be no question that it will be possible in

the very near future to extend crop growing farther north than the present climatic limits of agriculture. The question then is whether it is worth while. If we look at it in the large, of course, there are the world's needs, but in recent years the piling up of grain stocks in the silos of the Western Hemisphere has done little to encourage the extension of acreages of growing by farmers. This is a criticism of our whole method of distribution of food, since the grain in the silos does not get to the hungry bellies of other parts of the world; in a world of wisdom the opening up of the Arctic to grain production might be a very sensible measure.

Short of that, however, if the Arctic is to develop as a system of industrial oases, as has been suggested, then the need for crops suitable for the settlers is obvious. This does not necessarily imply the growing of grain for export. The arguments of distance apply here. But it does mean the development of market-gardening crops and feeding stuffs for the animals which would provide fresh milk, etc. This again seems to be entirely practical.

8 *People Take Root*

QUITE APART from the debate as to whether there should be broad-acre farming (cereals) or truck farming (vegetables), the extension of horticulture as well as agriculture into the Arctic is socially important. In the experience of the North, people who plant roots grow roots themselves—that is, they become settlers. One sees, over and over again, houses with gardens which have become "home." This has been borne out by the experience of Uranium City, the site on Lake Athabaska of the Eldorado Mine. There the miners were well paid and they had, as miners' camps go, excellent amenities. They contracted for a year, or 300 shifts of work. If they cared to work extra shifts they could complete

387

their contract in less than a year. This contract labor made the mining labor migratory, and the turnover was at first very high.

But that gradually changed as living conditions improved. Married men began to bring in their families. They were encouraged to build their own homes in Uranium City away from the mining site so that they might become part of a wider community. Gradually more and more of the miners settled their families at Uranium City—instead of supporting them in homes in the south. Two things helped to make them settle. One was the development of schools (once their children got established in school, the fathers thought twice about leaving), and they also began to make gardens out of the inhospitable soil, building them in terraces of rock and nursing them into growth. The latter was almost decisive. The "house" had become a "home."

9 *The Arctic Is Warmer*

ONE OF MY ASSIGNMENTS in the North was from the Food and Agriculture Organization, and it was to consider the effects of the gradual warming up of the Northern Hemisphere. Scientific observations, which are still going on, confirmed what was manifest from many sources of evidence—that the temperature is measurably rising and that changes are taking place. This is conspicuous in the movement north of the fishing grounds. In the past thirty years a noticeable change has occurred. In the 1920s the catch of cod off Greenland had been less than 350 tons a year, but by 1951 it had risen to 169,000 tons. The cod had pushed far up the Davis Strait into Baffin Bay. (Now the sea conditions are so favorable that the cod propagates in Greenland waters, without migrating, as previously, to the Icelandic spawning grounds.)

In thirty years the average air temperature in the winter at Spitzbergen and in Greenland has risen by about 10° centigrade, while the temperature of the sea has increased by about 3° centigrade. At the same time the Arctic ice has decreased in thickness, as was shown by the *Nautilus* on its cross-polar journey, and its front in the ocean has retreated farther north. By common consent of all the Arctic "old hands," this warming up has been significant both in the continental north and in the Arctic islands, and modern scientific measuresments indicate the same thing.

Thus new climatic factors come into any future appraisal of the North, not implying, of course, that we shall presently have an Arctic Mediterranean or Florida, but a climate sufficiently changed to make appreciable difference. It may be a short cycle, but indications are that it is the upcurve of a long cycle, reverting probably to the conditions of 1,000 years ago when Eric the Red's Greenland may have been really "green land" in parts. One of the factors which has, perhaps, contributed to the warming up of the Northern Hemisphere is the increase of carbon in the atmosphere as a result of the industrialization of the continents of Europe and America. This has provided a carbon blanket which, with the carbon dioxide from the growth encouraged in the sea by the changing conditions, has accelerated the rise in temperature.

The warming up may affect, among other things, the nature of the timberlands, and a question has been put to me to which I have still no adequate answer: "Will the dieback of certain timbers in the south be compensated by a northern extension of the tree line in the north?" That may happen gradually and naturally, but a direct challenge is now offered by the Danes who are breeding, in Denmark, trees that can be adapted to the conditions the deserts of the tropical regions by borrowing and adapting of Greenland. (Much has been, and can be, done to reafforest non-indigenous trees—trees from other parts of the world—and it might similarly be feasible to do so in the frigid deserts of the North.)

One of the problems which must never be underestimated in the development of the North is the point, already made, that in many parts arid conditions exist even in regions where snow might give the impression of abundant precipitation. Professor Hugh M. Raup, òf Harvard University, has suggested that the frost and short growing season in most of the Arctic and sub-Arctic are not as significant as the shortage of water.

10 *The Real Man and the White Man*

WITHOUT QUESTION, however, the northern frontier will be opened up. Changes will take place in areas which we now consider empty and inhospitable. For example, the Canadian North is peopled by less than 20,000 humans, of whom 10,000 or thereabouts are Eskimos. One thing that is manifest (at least, to me) is that the Eskimos can be a very big factor in the development of the Far North. After all, they have been there for over 4,000 years. They know more about the conditions of their own country than any White Man ever can learn. They are a highly intelligent people and, as has been reiterated, mechanically skillful. Indeed, this book opened with the question, "How many oil drums, boss?" And it would seem as though this race, with its latent ability, has been waiting all these millenniums just for oil drums, waiting for materials on which they could exercise their skills. The development of the Arctic and the sub-Arctic must be a genuine partnership between *Kabloona* (the White Man) and *Innuit* (the Real Man, as the Eskimo calls himself). The North, then, is a challenge and an opportunity.

11 The Deserts Come Back to Life

AN INTERNATIONAL PARTY, invited by the Israelis to the opening of the Beersheba Desert Research Station, sponsored by Unesco as part of its Arid Zone Program, had a salutary experience. Our hosts bypassed the laboratories and took us instead to the ruined city of Obde, deep in the Negev Desert. There, from a hill honey-combed with dwelling caves and catacombs and crowned by the broken pillars of public buildings, we could see the story of desert agriculture as the Nabataeans and the Byzantines had written it in the landscape, a story smudged by time but still legible to tutored eyes.

The diversion was deliberate. In a country where every spade-ful of soil is a spoonful of history and potsherds are as common-place as pebbles, they argue that experience is a substitute for experiment. Empirically, by trial and error, the ancients, in the course of centuries, made their mistakes and remedied them (or failed to do so) and arrived at methods of desert cultivation and conservation which have a relevance today. Mechanical shovels, bulldozers, tractors and disc plows can do in minutes what once took months. Steel and concrete can reproduce their dams of masoned stonework. Gelignite and pneumatic drills can hollow mountains in which they once chiseled their marvelous rock cis-terns. Laboratory tests can tell in a few hours facts about the nature of the soil which they learned by generations of observa-tion. Science and technology can overcome the handicaps and limitations which restricted them in their struggle with their en-vironment. But we must know what those handicaps and limita-tions were and whether wisdom did not make them pause before they made mistakes which we can repeat today.

(For example, in the Negev there was a plateau crusted with

desert "pavement," beneath which were depths of loess, wind-blown dust, which, given water and careful husbandry, can become useful soil. The desert pavement had acted as a lid and preserved it. Then when, a few years ago, Israel was desperate for grain, an army of settlers from the north moved in with columns of tractors and plows, broke the pavement, sowed barley and, by dry farming, reaped a rich harvest—for one season! Then the winds came and the dry loess began to drift and build up into a system of moving dunes. The impetuosity which had ignored the warning of soil conservationists meant laborious years of refixing the dunes and preparing the plateau for the coming of the irrigation waters which would make cultivation safe.)

So the Israelis send out their archeologists ahead of the scientists, not just to study architectural ruins, but classical botany and classical farm systems and to reconstruct them as "living museums," as Professor Michael Evenari, of the Hebrew University, has done at Obde. The results are impressive in their significance for desert recovery, not only in the Negev, but throughout the deserts of the Middle East and, by stimulating ideas, in the deserts of other parts of the world.

Archeological botanists have learned not only what plants were economically useful to the ancients but have also been able to work out, from their plant studies, a reliable index of the climatic conditions which existed at various periods. (For example, they can tell that the rainfall of Obde, 2,000 years ago, was not appreciably different—plus a few millimeters—from what it is today. Thus their ancient systems of conservation were coping with similar conditions and their experience can be repeated.) And while modern water-finding methods, gravimetry and seismography, can seek out well sources in the deserts, the botanists can find them more cheaply and perhaps more directly by studying the plants. Desert shrubs find their own sources of water, and if one knows their root systems, it is possible to predict the depths at which water can be reached. Moreover, it is possible to tell the nature of the water—whether it is likely to be fresh or brackish—from the nature of the plants, because some are more tolerant of salt than others.

Professor Evenari, flying to the port of Elatt on the Gulf of 'Aqaba, noticed, about twenty-five miles north of the town, clusters of growth in a curiously suggestive pattern. He recalled the Persian *qanaats* (horizontal wells with vertical shafts) which had never been regarded as a feature of Palestine. As it turned out, the desert sands had choked the shafts, but trees and shrubs had found them an easy way of reaching the underground water channels.

12 *If the Dew Be on the Fleece*

ANOTHER THING with which the Israelis are likely to impress visitors before they start showing them laboratory "gadgets" is their familiarity with the Bible, which is itself a remarkable scientific textbook. Without reverting to the disputed "dew mounds" (p. 257), it is worth while recalling the emphasis which the Old Testament places on dew. The first "dew meter" is to be found in the Book of Judges (6:37, 38):

"Behold," said Gideon, "I will put a fleece of wool upon the floor; and if the dew be on the fleece only and if it be dry upon all the earth beside, then I shall know that thou wilt save Israel by my hand, as thou has said."

And it was so: for he rose up early on the morrow, and thrust the fleece together, and wringed the dew out of the fleece, a bowl full of water.

That was quoted to me by Dr. S. Duvedevani, the Israeli dew expert, whom I first met on the desert survey which I made for Unesco in 1950, as proof of the importance of dew, which he had made his scientific lifework. His evidence, even then, was impressive, but it became more so later.

One of his discoveries was what one can call a "dew horizon" in the soil. This depends on the evaporation of moisture from the deeper soil and the condensation and seepage of the dew on the surface. The level at which the two can meet and provide a moist layer can be fairly constant, according to the contours of the ground and the nature of the soil. If the plants can be selected which will root down to that "horizon," they can be assured of a consistent supply of moisture. An account which I wrote of this brought an unexpected visitor to see me in London. He was an expert from Egypt who, because of the political situation, could not go to Israel to see Duvedevani and came to get more information from me. He had seen that this "horizon" might be a rational explanation of the cult of the watermelon—those gourds of moisture which grow in the seemingly arid desert. "Cult" is right, because, as he pointed out, there was a kind of ritual planting of the melon seeds. They dug down to a locally traditional depth and planted the seed. Might not this age-old near-superstition be a reaching down for the dew horizon?

Another discovery led to Duvedevani being given a Unesco fellowship to go to California, where Dr. F. W. Went had a laboratory in which the climatic conditions of any part of the world could be reproduced. Here, under controlled conditions, his field observations could be repeated. In man-made dew, with precise measurements, plant behavior could be studied. One of his observations in the Middle East had been that certain plants appeared to absorb dew, in quantity, through their leaves and exude the excess through their roots. (This was an unexpected inversion of "translocation," by which the sap rises and the moisture drunk in by the roots is, in excess, sweated out by the leaves.) In California plants were grown in test tubes, under dew conditions, and this phenomenon was precisely measured. The report of the seventh session of the Unesco Arid Zone Advisory Committee was to record that this behavior was true of a large number of economic plants such as tomatoes, sugar beets, peas, squash and mint. Some plants are natural "dew gluttons," habitually absorbing far more than they need and exuding the excess moisture into the soil. This suggested interesting possibilities. Not only could plants, such as these, be grown in desert dew, but they could be used as "wet nurses" for other plants growing adjacently.

13 Chemistry of Ecstasy

AT ONE UNESCO CONFERENCE I felt about Dr. Went (who gave Duvedevani his opportunity) the way that poets felt about Newton who, they said, had robbed the rainbow of its poetry by discovering the spectrum. To me, one of the unforgettable experiences of the desert was the magic of the ephemera. After a shower of rain, in regions which might not have had rain for ten or fifteen years, the desert would suddenly burst into a dazzling carpet of flowers, brilliant reds, blues and yellows. This flower burst was a mystery of nature. . . .

Until Dr. Went explained that the ecstasy of the desert was no more than a matter of chemical inhibitors. These are chemicals which prevent germination. In the case of the ephemera, nature has provided the seeds with chemical "mackintoshes," or rainproof sleeping bags. If there is a flurry of rain, insufficient to bring the seeds to maturity, some of the chemical may be washed off, but the seeds will regenerate the inhibitor and go to sleep again for a few more years; but, comes a real shower, with a fair chance of ripening, the chemical will be washed off and the seeds will germinate.

That is only one of the many mechanisms by which plants come to terms with the aridity of the deserts. On a flight over a desert one may see how, around a tree or shrub, there is no hint of any other plant life, and one will say, "But, of course, the shrub has taken up all the moisture and the other plants have died." That is not necessarily true. There are often living seeds around the shrub, but they are being prevented from germinating by a chemical exuded by the roots of the shrub. If, however, there is a heavy shower which will wash that chemical out of the soil, there will be enough water both to liberate the sleeping seeds and bring them to maturity.

This principle of the inhibitors (and there are many other

types) is manifestly important in revegetating the deserts—the precondition of their development. The chemists can identify the exact nature of those chemicals. For instance, on a visit to a British brewery research institute, I was shown how they had isolated an amino acid by paper chromatography. (This, in its simplest form, is like making a blob of watery ink on a piece of blotting paper and watching the pigments of the ink separating out in varicolored halos. Similarly subtle chemicals, like the amino acids of the living processes, can be separated because, in a solvent suffusing through filter paper, they travel at different rates.) The chemists were trying to interest me in this one because it was a chemical which had been "predicted" and, indeed, had been synthesized even before it was separated as "the real thing"; but what fascinated me were the facts about this chemical.

Many, many centuries ago men discovered that they could make fermented drinks by soaking barley seeds in water and causing the seeds to germinate and malt. The brewers had always assumed that the saturation caused the germination. Actually they had been soaking out and throwing away the inhibitor. Here it was—already synthesized and capable of being manufactured commercially.

Now, if the plant scientists could tell the biochemists just how much water a particular plant would need to make it mature, the seeds could be coated with the prescribed amount of the chemical. Seeds could be scattered over the deserts, if necessary, by aircraft and left to germinate when the proper rains came around.

That may sound a slow way of doing things, but there are many stages in reclaiming deserts. For example, if you want to cultivate a likely area, it will be necessary to anchor moving dunes some distance away—as a kind of defense system. This can be done by marking out patches five meters square, making trenches around them and planting rough grass, in stem. Then in the center of the patch some deep-rooting shrub or tree is planted. The grass seeds and the tree roots spread and the loose soil is gripped. Gradually the dune is covered with a patchwork quilt or, more aptly, with a tarpaulin of vegetation which straps the dunes down. But if the process of cultivation is to be extended, areas of desert much farther away must be gradually revegetated, and it is in this extension belt that the scattered seeding might be useful.

Conversely it is possible to remove the natural inhibitors by acid treatment, or by pre-exposure to light, and so seize the opportunities of sudden soil moisture. This method allowed a perennial grass of the north of Israel to be used in the Negev.

14 *Living with Salt*

ANOTHER DISCOVERY which will be valuable in coastal desert regions or where water is available but salty was made by Dr. H. Boyko. He and his wife found that they could grow esparto grass on dunes irrigated with 50 per cent of sea water. This, curiously enough, had the effect of washing surface salt out of the dunes, because the sluicing with sea water carried the salts down through the loose sand. The surface salt and the sea salt would, of course, gradually accumulate in the underground waters and increase subsoil salination. Thus such a scheme must always be strictly supervised by experts. But they, too, might learn something from the ancient Sumerians, who managed to keep the subsoil salts at bay by rotating crops of weeds which dried out the soil at their root depths and formed a dry barrier which prevented salt water from seeping upward.

Salination, that factor which has meant the abandoning of whole regions and leaving them as deserts, is one of the most truculent problems in desert recovery. Yet desalination (removing the salt) is no longer a scientific problem. It can be done—at a cost. If it is a question of drinking water, then settlers will meet the cost to slake their thirst; if it is a question of water for an industrial process, then the cost of desalting may be a reasonable economic charge; but, if it is a question of irrigation water for farming, then the methods have to be much cheaper than those which the scientists have so far achieved—because of the quantities of water needed by the arid soils, and also, in many cases, in order to leach out the salts in those soils.

Solar distillation has been tried. This means using the heat of the sun's rays to turn the water to steam which condenses on some cold surface as fresh water. The limitation here is the quantities which one can get for any given capital outlay on a solar distillery. And, anyway, distilled water is not satisfactory for irrigation.

There is a much more effective way. It involves passing the water through a battery of *polyelectrolyte* membranes. That means using special types of plastic films. Different salts have different electric charges inherent in their molecules, and the selected films have, in their molecules, the opposite of those charges. So by passing electricity through the water the different salts are "sorted out" and screened by the plastic filters, and usable water passes out. (Notice the word "usable," because all the salts do not have to be removed; some of them are harmless or even beneficial.)

Of course, the cost of using electricity has to be taken into account. Nevertheless, improvements in this method and the reduction of the cost of the end result are a likely answer to the desert farmer's problems.

A third method is refrigeration. If salt or brackish water is frozen, the salts are separated out and the resulting ice is fresh. But salt water has a very low freezing point, and the extraction of the heat can be expensive. Some experts, however, are optimistic about the use of solar heat for refrigeration of brackish waters —that paradox which surprises the uninformed when they discover that a blazing gas jet can keep the contents of their refrigerator frozen!

15 Harnessing the Sun

THIS USE of the blazing sun of the deserts to produce "coolth" is already in practical application. Houses in the desert are air-conditioned by solar methods.

And, of course, nothing could be more satisfactory than harnessing the sun as the energy source for desert purposes. I remember a French scientist, in the Sahara, pointing to the fierce sun and saying, "There is *our* nuclear reactor." And, of course, he was right. For billions of years the sun has been converting hydrogen into helium and, in the process, releasing the rays on which all life depends on earth. That is the fusion process—the harnessing of hydrogen energy which was first released by Man as the cataclysmic force of the H-bomb—which, once it is achieved, will mean power unlimited. Even short of that, the making of "baby suns" on earth, the real sun offers great possibilities for scientific ingenuity. Let us harness some of its energy which is so prodigally available.

There are many promising devices. Archimedes is supposed to have set the Roman fleet ablaze at Syracuse by using a burning glass, and (pp. 208–9) the Incas used concave mirrors to light dry tinder for their fire-and-smoke signals which could send messages to Cuzco over a distance of 2,000 miles in less than three hours. Many people have lit fires with reading glasses. Today, in the United States, great mirror reflectors can focus the sun and produce points of heat as intense as the fireball of an atom bomb; and in the Pyrenees and Algiers, giant mirror installations are used for smelting intractable ores.

The Russians, while developing vast hydroelectric stations, building fission reactors and experimenting with fusion reactors, took up solar energy seriously, not as an interesting ploy, but as a part of their power system. They considered it a means of producing electricity in places beyond the reach of transmission lines. One of their biggest schemes is in Armenia, near Mount Ararat. The installation consists of 1,293 large mirrors mounted on electrically driven bogeys traveling around twenty-three concentric railways tracks. This battery of mirrors forms the arc of the circle and follows the sun around the sky. The rays are focused on a boiler at the top of a tall mast, and the steam thus generated is used to power electric generators. The station is designed to have a capacity of 1,200 kilowatts to supply electricity for the surrounding farms and operate irrigation pumps.

As part of a Unesco program in Israel, Dr. Harry Tabor developed at the Beersheba Desert Research Station the world's first industrial plant operating on solar energy. Black surfaces absorb heat, but if you turn such a surface face upward to the sun, most of the heat is lost by convection—by escaping upward, like the heat from a radiator. Ingeniously Tabor used simple curved mirrors as the gatherers of the sun's rays. Over this, to capture the reflected rays, he placed black-surfaced collectors, above which were pipes in which water was heated into low-pressure steam. Notice that the pipes were *above* the black surfaces. This arrangement cut the emission heat losses by four fifths and made the system economically possible for steam raising at a Beersheba factory.

Dr. Tabor, at the international conference on Science in the Advancement of the New States, at the Weizmann Institute in 1960, excited the scientists with a description of experiments being carried out at the Dead Sea, east of Beersheba. The idea had occurred to Dr. Rudolf Bloch of the Dead Sea Potash Company. He suggested that instead of using vast expanses of mirrors, which would be prohibitively expensive (as well as clumsy), square kilometers of water should be used. On first consideration this does not sound very clever. We already have huge expanses of lakes and man-made dams, and the effect of the sun on them is to evaporate off water as steam, thus losing the heat which is generated. But Dr. Bloch's idea was very clever indeed. In a lake in Hungary there exists a natural phenomenon: the bottom waters are hotter than the top waters. If we think of a hot-water cistern we can see how "absurd" this is—because hot water rises to the top and cold water stays at the bottom. Cold water is denser than hot.

But temperature is not the only thing that decides the relative density of water. Salt content also does. At the Dead Sea the salt is so dense that a swimmer cannot sink in it. So (said Dr. Bloch) let us have a sun-trap in which the bottom waters will be very salty and covered by a surface of fresh, or merely less salty, water. The waters, being of different densities, would not mix (unless stirred) and the fresher water would act as a lid to prevent the heat of the bottom water being lost by convection.

A solar pool is a shallow basin with a flat, dark bottom. Black, or dark, surfaces absorb heat. This heat builds up temperatures in the dense brine. That heat does not escape into the atmosphere. But it could and would leak into the banks of the pond. So it has to be very big, a square kilometer in area. In the experimental ponds at the Dead Sea it has been found that while the surface water may be only tepid, the salt water, an arm's length below, would scald the skin off a hand.

The heat generated in this way in a pool a square kilometer in extent could be converted into electricity and the installed capacity (as power engineers say) would be twelve times as great as the most efficient atomic-power station so far devised, at a price that would compare with the most optimistic estimates made by the British for their civil atomic-power stations. When Dr. Tabor described this project, Dr. Alvin Weinberg, Director of the Oak Ridge Nuclear Research Laboratory, in Tennessee, said, "This is the most important news I have heard at this conference." And the conference, including the world's eminent physicists as well as politicians of Afro-Asian countries, had been hearing about fusion power, breeder reactors and all the other possibilities of the second half of the twentieth century.

Another solar-energy device consists of silicon wafers embodied in a "solar photovoltaic battery." When the sun shines on the silicon, the battery converts 8 to 14 per cent of the sun's energy received into electricity.

In India the "Nehru Stove" has been developed. This is a simple concave mirror of polished aluminum which focuses the sun onto an oven. (It is like an inverted umbrella with the oven at the tip of the handle.) With this it would be possible to cook a meal for a whole family, but at £5 the cost of the stove is beyond the means of the Indian peasant, whose average income is less than £30 a year. Yet a contrivance as simple as this might well revolutionize the feeding of India's 400,000,000 people. For most of them their only fuel is cow dung, which, if it were plowed into the soil instead of burned, could regenerate the undernourished ground. It should not be beyond the wit and economics of Man to make such a stove more cheaply (perhaps out of plastics sprayed with a mirror surface) and make it available to the peasants of India.

The trouble is, very often, that those who think of development so often think of great engineering works—dams and the like. Yet the "break-through" is often much more elementary. For instance, in Afghanistan the Government appealed to the Food and Agricultural Organization to save the country from a grave situation. At that time the only product which could earn foreign currency was karakul, Persian lamb, but the flocks were in peril. There was disease, but, also, some 40 per cent of the flocks died during the winter from hunger. The veterinarians could provide the answer for the disease, but the other problem was winter fodder. This was solved quite simply. The F.A.O. experts introduced hoes and encouraged their use in the production of root crops, but they also introduced scythes. The Afghans only had a primitive sickle, but experts from Switzerland and Austria showed them how they could scythe the hay on the mountainside and store it for winter forage. They also taught the Afghan blacksmiths how to make scythes and encouraged their adoption by organizing competitions. (This latter was a minor mistake because the Afghan chiefs, who love competitions, treated scything as a sport for the well-to-do, and it took some time to convince those who had to do the work that it was a practical necessity.) The other circumstance was malaria clearance. The World Health Organization went into Afghanistan and cleared a malarial region, between the Hindu Kush and the Oxus River, which had been abandoned for centuries. It became a cotton-growing region, providing Afghanistan with a second export but also with cotton-oil cake for the winter feeding of the sheep.

16 *Desert Do-It-Yourself*

ONE OF THE EXPONENTS of the elementary approach to desert problems was Mr. E. W. Golding, a British expert on rural electrification and wind power, who was sent out to various parts of the world by Unesco. While others were thinking of nuclear power, multi-purpose projects, etc., Golding advocated "Robinson Crusoe" methods—making do with what was available—wind power, for instance. Sails could be made from rush mats; on well-chosen sites they could generate 3,000 watts. With storage batteries they could supply light and a small amount of domestic energy. More ambitious co-operative ventures might have 8 kilowatts or as much as 50 kilowatts with alternating-current generators when the speed was high and direct current for battery charging during low wind-speed periods. The cost per kilowatt-hour would vary according to the wind miles per hour from less than half a cent to five cents per unit. He showed how, in some regions, organic wastes such as brushwood, sisal waste, sugar-cane waste, husks, cobs, straw, coconut shells and animal waste could be burned in small steam-power plants, or fed into a producer to provide producer gas, or fermented to produce methane to be used as domestic fuel or to drive internal-combustion engines.

Nevertheless, the challenge of the deserts with their possibility of increasing the food supplies not only for the local inhabitants but for global needs calls for capital investment far beyond the means of localities or, indeed, of governments. As we have seen in the study of the past civilizations, the peasantry could only extend their cultivation so far and then had to rely on public utilities, personified by the overlord, who could build major irrigation canals. Similarly today the reclamation on the development of deserts requires the indulgence of those who can afford the heavy capital investments and who can make engineering resources available.

17 *The Subterranean Nile*

NEARLY A THIRD of the land surface of the earth is hot, dry desert. That definition would include the hopeless, rocky deserts of the sun-enameled *hammada*, the gravel desert, or *serir*, and the granulated sand desert. But it also includes great areas of desiccated alluvial soil and wind-blown loess, as well as semi-arid steppe land. As a rough approximation one might say that a ninth of the vast desert region could be developed, revegetated and cultivated, if only water were available for irrigation.

Modern knowledge of hydrology suggests that nine tenths of all the water of the land surface (as distinct from the oceans) is underground, at depth. That means that all the great lakes stored in aquifers, underground porous rocks, sands and gravel, like the Albienne Nappe (p. 310) or the grandiose subterranean tributary of the Nile.

The latter is an underground river about 560 miles long, starting some eighty miles south of Luxor and entering the Mediterranean on the west side of the Nile delta about seventy miles north of Cairo. According to Mohamed El Sayed Ayoub, one-time Inspector-General for Nile Control, the mean width of the subterranean river is six and a half miles wide and the strata of sand and gravel in which it flows is from 500 to 1,500 feet in depth, with a capacity which is six times the annual flow of the Nile—that great river with all the water of Lake Tana and Victoria Nyanza behind it. To call it a "river" may sound like an exaggeration, since its flow movement is about thirty feet a year. Nevertheless, about 4,000,000,000 cubic meters flow into the delta unused, despite the fact that the water feeds upward into the Nile itself and some 1,400,000,000 cubic meters finds its way into irrigation.

One imaginative scheme which has never been properly considered is to build a subterranean dam at the mouth of the underground Nile and thus force more of the water up into the river and raise the water table so that many of the Egyptian depressions might become extensive oases.

18 *Water Is Politics*

THE WORLD WAS REMINDED that water is politics when the crisis occurred over the High Aswan Dam, the great barrage on the Nile which was to create a reservoir stretching 500 miles south. At first the International Bank acquiesced, and then politics stepped in and the support of the bank and the United States was withdrawn. This "loss of face," and the need to redeem it, was one of the reasons why Colonel Nasser seized the Suez Canal, the act which led to British and French military intervention. Later the Russians promised Nasser help in pursuing the High Aswan scheme.

There were technical and cultural, as well as political, objections to the High Aswan project, including the "drowning" of the Nubian temples. But, without debating the merits of the case, the circumstances were a reminder that Egypt is a "water hostage." It has to import all its water from outside its boundaries. The sources of the Nile are in Abyssinia and Uganda, and even the great oases of Egypt depend on the rains of French Equatorial Africa feeding the Nubian sandstone layer which supplies the springs of the oases. Similarly one is entitled to regard the "Kashmir problem," in spite of its political and religious overtones, as a hydrological one. In Kashmir there are the sources of five great rivers on which both India (partly) and West Pakistan (entirely) depend. On the borders of Israel there are the "incidents," which are a continual reminder of the struggle for the waters of the Jordan, between Israel and her Arab neighbors. And, since we are plumbing beneath the surface politics, we might consider the flight of the Dalai Lama from Tibet as another instance of "water politics." In that forbidding country is the watershed of the rivers of continental China. But in Tibet also there is the largest concentration of usable water power in the world.

19 *Mile-High Cataract*

PROFESSOR HANS THIRRING, the Austrian scientist, described at the World Power Congress in 1956 a scheme to harness this power. The nub of the project is a hairpin bend on the Tsangpo River, which flows into the Brahmaputra. Between each end of that hairpin the drop is a mile and a quarter. The proposal was to short-cut the bend by a tunnel ten miles long. Through this would pour to a generating station the world's greatest cataract—dropping a mile and a quarter. He estimated that the capacity might be as high as 330,000,000,000 kilowatt-hours per year. This figure—the output of one station—was a quarter of all the electrical energy then produced in the world. (The project for a ten-mile tunnel is not a forbidding one, when one considers that the Aluminium Company of Canada drove a tunnel that long through the Rockies to get power for the aluminum works at Kitimat in British Columbia.) Thirring was proposing a consortium of Tibet, China, India and Pakistan to share the project and with international help to find the $8,400,000,000 which he estimated the undertaking would cost. The Chinese got there first.

20 *Taming the Yellow River*

AT THAT SAME World Power Congress we heard the first description by Chinese engineers of the gigantic schemes for the Yellow River. This river flows for 3,000 miles and throughout history has wreaked havoc; one flood in 1938 dispossessed 12,500,-

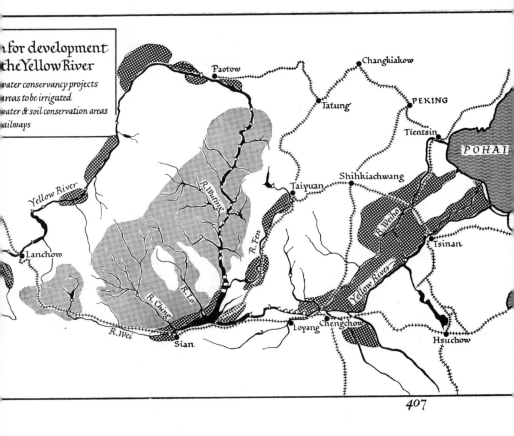

ooo people and cost 890,000 lives. The engineers told how, with technical assistance from the U.S.S.R., this river is to be harnessed, to control the floods, provide irrigation for 20,000,000 acres, improve navigation and produce 110,000,000,000 kilowatt-hours per year—ten times the total electricity generated in all China in 1954. There are to be forty-six dams, although the first five are to be completed by 1967. The Yellow River is the muddiest river in the entire world, but the engineering works are to be preceded or accompanied by vast soil conservancy and reafforestation schemes to stop erosion and prevent the silting up of the dams.

TVA (Tennessee Valley Authority) has become synonymous with such great multi-purpose enterprises. Its scheme controlled the floodwaters of seven American states, restrained their perennial havoc, built up irrigation systems and produced a vast hydroelectric potential—and incidentally helped to make possible the atom bomb, because TVA provided the electricity for the Oak Ridge plant, which produced the uranium 235. It was also an example to the whole world of how reafforestation and engineering could combine to undo the havoc of Man and harness the forces of nature.

21 Turning the Siberian Rivers

IN RUSSIA even greater schemes were undertaken. Ship canals were constructed from north to south across European Russia. Two dams at Kuibisheva and Stalingrad each had a hydroelectric output greater than America's Grand Coulee. But transportation and electricity were only part of the purpose.

A million square miles of the Soviet Union's steppe are desert,

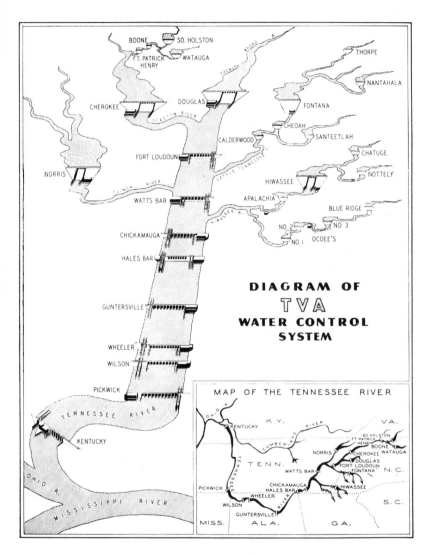

DIAGRAM OF

TVA

**WATER CONTROL
SYSTEM**

MAP OF THE TENNESSEE RIVER

and three quarters of a million of these form the Central Asian Desert. Rainfall between two and fifteen inches can occur in spring and autumn, but in the summer the dry winds, often with hurricane force, sweep from the Asian deserts into the European Ukraine. A fifteen-year afforestation scheme was started in 1948.

409

This included the planting of great windbreaks—3,300 miles of major tree line. This tree planting was accompanied by vast irrigation schemes—the most spectacular being in Turkmen.

Reference has been made in this book to the civilizations which grew up along the Oxus, now called the Amu Darya. Five thousand years ago there were cities in what are now desert areas, and there is abundant archeological proof of past irrigation systems. (And the interesting fact is that they used plant drainage, like the Sumerians.) At one time a branch of the Amu Darya flowed across Turkmen to the Caspian Sea, and the great oases, like Tashkent, with its population of 1,300,000, are proof of the fertility of the desert.

The process of recovering this desert has included the building of a dam across the Amu Darya near its delta to the Aral Sea. This can divert nearly 50 per cent of the flow into a 700-mile canal across Turkmen to Krasnovodsk on the Caspian Sea. Another 746 miles of branch canals are designed to irrigate about 5,000 square miles of desert, and the middle section of the canal is designed to flush-flood about 27,000 square miles of desert for periods of one to three months, to increase the pastures for horses, cattle and sheep. The predicted yields of the irrigation schemes are, in millions of tons: wheat, 8; sugar beet, 6; cotton, 3; and rice, ½. In addition there would be pastures for 2,000,000 head of cattle and 9,000,000 head of sheep. This, apart from the industrial crops, represents the food of 100,000,000 people.

An even more spectacular Russian scheme is the so-called "Davidov Plan" for diverting the rivers Ob and Yenisei. Those great Siberian rivers carry an enormous volume of water into the Arctic. The project depends upon the Turgai Gate, at a point about 51° 35' north and 65° 30' east, fifteen miles northwest of the town of Turgai. This "gate" is the turnstile, as it were, of the watershed between the Arctic Ocean and the Aral Sea. By building a dam 258 feet in height at Bielogorie (61° 8' north, 68° 30' east) near the confluence of the rivers Ob and Irtish, and by blasting a deep-cut canal through the Turgai Gate, the waters of the Ob could be sent a distance of over 1,000 miles into Lake Aral and from there to the Caspian Sea. By damming the Yenisei where it crosses the 60th Parallel and by linking one of its tributaries to

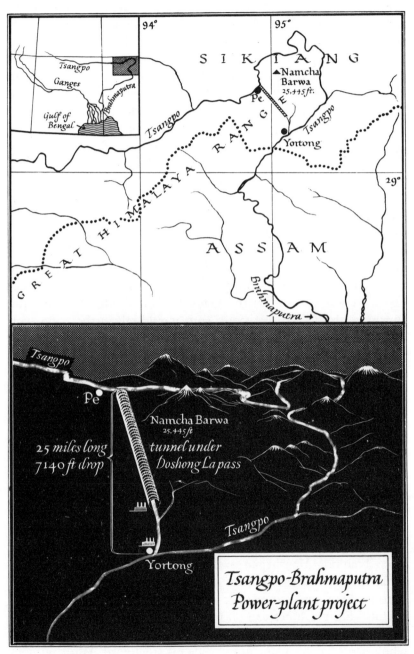

Tsangpo-Brahmaputra
Power-plant project

one of the Ob's, water from the Yenisei could also be diverted along this route. The effect will be to create a great man-made inland sea, as big as Great Britain, behind the Bielogorie Dam, linked by navigable canals to the Arctic Ocean and the Caspian Sea. When it is completed it will be possible to go by ship from the Mediterranean through the Dardanelles to the Black Sea and the Ozov Sea, up the lower Don, through the Don-Volga Canal and the lower Volga to the Caspian Sea, from there through the Turkmenian Canal to Lake Aral, up through the Turgai Gate Canal to the man-made sea and down the lower Ob to the Arctic. It will mean reclaiming over 60,000,000 acres of fertile land by irrigation, providing food for another 100,000,000 people. The hydroelectric output from the scheme will be equal to four fifths of the present total hydroelectric production of the United States.

Some indication of the amount of work involved in this scheme can be got from the fact that the cutting of the Turgai Gate Canal—just one part of the project—will mean shifting 23,500,-000,000 cubic yards of earth. A modern land dredge can shift 400 square yards of earth per hour, so it would take a thousand such machines, working day and night, seven years to make the cutting.

22 Shared Knowledge Can Reclaim Deserts

THE IMAGINATION need not boggle at such vast projects. Ever since Thinking Man began to think he has contrived the survival of his species by the modification of his environment. Twentieth-century Man can command the resources of his mechanical ingenuity. His machines can do in minutes what muscle slaves took months to do. He can share collective knowledge and treat the whole world as his plant nursery or his stockyard. With wisdom (and bitter experience has taught that it is rash indiscriminately to introduce plants and animals into an unfamiliar ecology) he can borrow the plants or the animals of other parts of the world and—but only with wisdom—adapt them to his local needs. One classical example of this was the invaluable introduction into other arid areas of the Australian eucalyptus, the roots of which reach down to find the water table. As a kind of reverse lease-lend, the introduction of "subterranean clover" has meant untold millions to the sheepmen of southern Australia.

One of the most worth-while enterprises of the postwar world has been the work of the Unesco Arid Zone Committee, which at very limited cost has brought together experts, and their experience, from all parts of the world, to share, or to initiate, researches which can make the great naked places of the earth, the deserts, habitable by Man and productive for his needs.

23 *Life at High Altitudes*

APART, HOWEVER, from the hot deserts and the cold deserts (of the Arctic and sub-Arctic), more and more attention is being paid to the problems of the high altitudes and the wet tropics. After all, the Incas, as we have seen (p. 211), were able to cultivate the Andes up to heights as high as 17,000 feet. There are at least 12,000,000 people in the world living in the rarefied atmospheres at 10,000 feet, or higher, above sea level. True, they are a special breed physiologically adapted to heights at which people accustomed to lower altitudes would be subject to "mountain sickness." There is, however, no reason why mountain areas and high plateaus should be "written off" as uninhabitable or unproductive, which is the attitude adopted by many geographers. It will always be a case of "the higher, the fewer," but "fewer" is relative.

Far below such heights there are neglected uplands. We have seen how populations tended to settle and expand on the alluvial plains and riversides. That is still true of most areas of the world. In southeast Asia there are supposed to be dense populations. Actually countries like Burma and even India are far less densely populated, in relation to their area, than western Europe. The reason is that close settlement is invariably in the valleys, while the settlers of the uplands are thinly spread. The irony is that the river peoples are the victims of the floods which, if controlled, would provide the water for the thirsty uplands. Therefore, among the "multi-purposes" of great dams, to control floods and "win" elec-tricity, ought to be included the irrigation of the uplands.

Such irrigation is completely feasible, as one can see from the age-old systems of the Chinese and the Javanese, by which they carry canals along the mountain ridges to form the infant cata-racts which tumble into the rice terraces and finish up flush-flood-ing the paddy fields of the plateaus.

24 *The Tropics—with Trepidation*

VAST AREAS of the tropical world are still unproductive, in terms of Man's needs. The area of Africa held in fief by the tsetse fly is as big as the United States. The malarial jungles of India cover soil which could feed tens of millions, and the deep hinterlands of Latin America, the Amazon and Orinoco forests, are still virtu-ally inaccessible.

But, as has already been consistently stressed, we must not brashly assume that such areas can be indiscriminately exploited.

It is not just sentiment which should make us pause and feel anxious about the destruction of wildlife in Africa or feel alarmed when lumbermen get loose in the forests. Nor must we lightly dismiss the tsetse fly which has so far protected virgin territory from rape. Wildlife, forest trees, the tsetse fly and even germs are part of that ecology, the balance of nature, which we must fully understand before we interfere with it.

Tropical soils are sensitive soils. I have seen a forest tract which was turned into a desiccated desert in seven years, because the forest had been cut down and banana plantations planted in military row. The forest growth had derived its nourishment from the deciduous leaves and rotting vegetation on the surface of the soil. The matted branches had broken the force of the torrential rain and had shaded the soil from the fierce sun. When the plantation was established, the natural compost disappeared; the soil was roasted by the sun and scoured off by the rains and finally blown away by the winds. The banana trees had sucked the nutriment from the soil, but the leaves had not been an adequate umbrella or parasol.

On the other hand, in Thailand I saw what forest management could do to preserve the forest complex, at the same time getting teak and still allowing areas for cultivation. In that teak jungle the forest dwellers had practiced shifting cultivation. Their practice was to cut down a tract of jungle and set fire to it. The ash fertilized the soil and gave them at most two years of rice. Then the monsoon rains would scour the tract and they would move on. To their traditional depravations had been added the ruthless modern cutting of the teak for export. The results one could see in the Mekong River, the waters of which had the consistency of liquid chocolate, heavy with the soil eroded from these forests.

Then a Forest Conservation Service was established. Trees were selectively cut, so that the balance of the forest was maintained, and an arrangement was made, quite amicably, with the jungle peasants. They were told which part of the forest they might clear and burn, in order to grow their rice, but before they moved on to their next strip, they were paid to plant teak saplings supplied by the state nursery.

25 The Wide-Open Spaces

OF THE LAND SURFACE of the globe only 10 per cent is cultivated in any way, and much of this is rough grazing, hardly better than desert or moorland. Only 6½ per cent is intensively cultivated. This is not a fixed proportion, naturally determined; it simply reminds us, once again, that farming capacity depends on the methods, and knowledge, at any given period of time. (Remember that at the time of the Norman invasion Britain was already "overpopulated," although the figure was only 1½ million, because all the land which was usefully productive by the methods then available was already being cultivated.) Hitherto there has appeared to be no chance of getting a reasonable return from any land that was either too hot, too cold, too dry, too wet, too rugged, or generally inaccessible.

So we are entitled to look at the world afresh in terms of modern science and agricultural technology. We can assume that, given the "directive" and the resources, the plant breeders could now "tailor-make" crops to meet conditions which have hitherto been intractable; that the soil experts could condition dust and clays into soil and make up the chemical deficiencies which have made some soils unproductive; and that with canning, deep-freezing and radiation-preserving, the food technologists will enable us to distribute produce from and to any part of the world.

Moreover, the yields of the land which has been cultivated so far have, in the light of our modern laboratory knowledge, been largely wasted. This is not just the question of wastage (p. 329) through pests in the fields and in storage. All those thousands of years Man and his animals have been growing domesticated plants for food or fodder, but they have eaten only those parts which were palatable or digestible and rejected the rest. Now we ought to be able to breed more specific chemical products. For instance, we can grow plants, or treat plants, so that they can yield the

416

types of protein which the human body needs, without it being first "processed" through the milk glands or the beefsteaks of animals. Only one thirtieth of the food value of the fodder consumed by an animal is available in the milk or meat. Or, as a British industrial development has shown, it is possible to extract from grass, or coarse plants, protein in forms which the body is capable of digesting and assimilating. This could be an immeasurable contribution to the needs of the hungry millions—provided that the supplies were cheap enough and accessible.

26 *Sea Ranching*

THEN THERE are the great waste resources of the sea. In terms of getting our food supplies from the sea, we remain at the stage of our Paleolithic forefathers, the cave-men hunters. We have domesticated the land animals, but we still hunt the sea creatures. Why should we not have sea farms and sea ranches? It has been demonstrated that, using sea lakes or fjords, it is possible to fence in fish and, fertilizing the water as we fertilize the land, to increase the algae, the sea vegetation, and the plankton, so that the fish will multiply and fatten. We can selectively breed such "domesticated" fish to suit our requirements.

As we suggested in that "projection" of the Arctic of A.D. 2061, straits, like Kane Basin, might be fenced in to become submarine range lands and we could have a submerged sea-Texas.

Apart from the sea creatures, there is the sea vegetation which is virtually unused. There are the jungles of seaweed which can provide edible food. When I was young, on the east coast of Scotland the fisherwomen, with their creels on their backs, used to go from door to door, calling, "Hey! Caller dulse and tangle!" They were selling seaweed, fresh gathered and succulent. One could buy a fistful for a halfpenny. Years later I had an expensive dish in a "posh" restaurant and discovered that it was carrageen, which is the Irish version of my old "Caller dulse and tangle." Extracts of seaweed, algenates, are used in ice cream and other comestibles and also provide fibers for weaving.

But the phytoplankton and the zooplankton, the microscopic vegetable and animal life of the sea, could be a rich source of food if we could learn how to collect and process them. In the food cycle of the sea the miscroscopic algae are eaten by the microcrustacea, which are éaten by the larger crustacea, which are eaten by the smaller fish, which are eaten by the larger fish, which are eaten by us. That is an elaborate and inefficient process. The whale, a mammal like ourselves, can have a length of sixty feet and a girth of thirty to forty feet, a mass of bone, flesh and blubber. To build that great body it just swims along with its mouth open, collecting the plankton and ejecting water. In this way it gets all the food and nourishment it needs. Why should we not have an atomic-powered artificial whale, which could collect and compact the plankton and make it available for factory processing into palatable food for animals and men?

27 Fish Farming

ALTHOUGH SEA FISH have not been farmed, fresh-water fish have been domesticated for centuries by the Orientals and, indeed, by the medieval monks with their monastery carp ponds. This has been an invaluable supplement of high protein to the rice diet of the Eastern peasants and could well be extended for the benefit of many millions.

In Java the peasants have an ingenious method of farming their fish. They "plant" them with the rice. When the rice fields are flooded, they put in the fingerlings which forage and grow among the stems of the rice. When the fields are drained to allow the

THE WORLD BENEATH THE SEA *The U.S. Navy bathyscape* Trieste, *which descended 37,000 feet into the Pacific—8,000 feet deeper than Everest is high* [Wide World]

rice to ripen, the fish are about the size of pilchards, which is the size the Javanese like. In Thailand they have long had their carp ponds, but the experts of the Food and Agriculture Organization persuaded them to try growing tilapia fish with their rice. The Thais are accustomed to bigger fish, but they have compromised. They plant the fish with their rice, but in the center of the paddy field they put a pond into which the fish migrate when the draining of the paddy starts and where they remain until the next flooding. And this shuttle service goes on until they are the right size.

The tilapia introduced a minor revolution into fish farming. Thereby hangs a tale: one day in 1939 a peasant on the north coast of Java found in a lagoon five fish which he did not recognize. By pure accident, a Dutch fish biologist was in the district and recognized the find as specimens of *Tilapia mozambica*, which belonged, as the name suggests, to Mozambique, on the east coast of Africa. No one knows to this day how those fish got

419

to Java or whether they made a piscatorial *Kon-Tiki* expedition across the Indian Ocean. Anyway, the Javanese discovered what had not been fully appreciated in East Africa—the exceptional qualities of tilapia as a domesticated fish. It is highly accommodating. It can grow in sea water, brackish water, stagnant water, fresh water or paddy-field water. It has the useful quality of eating the larvae of mosquitoes and so reducing the amount of malaria. It multiplies fast. It is a mouth breeder, a fish which carries its spawn in its mouth, to keep the eggs safe from predators, and also carries its fingerlings in its mouth until they can look after themselves. In the rice fields they can grow to appetizing size.

When the Food and Agriculture Organization of the United Nations wanted to encourage fish farming in countries where people were undernourished, it discovered that the best practical teaching was to send fish experts from the various countries to study in the East. The "professors" were the illiterate Javanese farmers. The fish voted most likely to succeed was "Tilapia, Class '39." It was even reintroduced into East Africa with impressive results.

28 *The Sun We Eat*

ALL OUR FOOD derives from the physical rays from the sun. The plant is the mechanism which uses those rays to convert the physical elements in the atmosphere, in water or in the soil, into the palatable and digestible substances which we eat. Nature has spent hundreds of millions of years perfecting this process, so naturally it is complicated.

But in the past few years scientists have had available to them methods which have enabled them to study the living process in the plant. Those methods derive from atomic energy, which produces radioisotopes, chemicals which emit rays and are therefore detectable. But they are the "twins" of ordinary elements, and in any chemical process—test-tube or living—they will behave in exactly the same way as the non-radioactive variety. Thus, in effect, they can trace out the blueprint of the process of conversion of elements into food.

For a very long time it has been known that the green coloring of leaves, chlorophyll, is the trap for the sun's rays. The green cells absorb this energy and the plant uses it to convert, from the air, carbon dioxide, hydrogen and oxygen, nitrogen, phosphates, etc. Chlorophyll is being thoroughly investigated with radioisotopes. So is the "carbohydrate cycle" by which the plant turns carbon into sugar and starches. Indeed, it can be said that the carbohydrate cycle has been worked out to the complete detail of the flow-sheet of a chemical plant. This has been carried further into the study of the build-up of the amino acids, the chemical "building bricks" which form the proteins, and into the study of those complex proteins and how they, in turn, form, maintain and repair the cells and tissues of our bodies.

Theoretically it is possible to make such things as carbohydrates —sugars and starches—without the intervention of the soil or the plant, and radiochemists and the engineers could build factories to reproduce the processes of the living plant and create food directly from the elements—like a pharmacist dispensing a prescription.

But the age-old wheat or barley does it much more cheaply and more efficiently, so that there is no need to anticipate that ultimate crisis when the population will be so great or our soil so limited or exhausted that we shall have to have recourse to completely synthetic food.

One thing which research can show, however, is how, from a blueprint familiarity with nature's design, we can make growing plants more efficient.

Still using plants, we can also develop even further the practice of soilless farming—hydroponics. In this the plants are anchored by their roots in sand, or mulch or sawdust, and a flow of water, with all the necessary nutrients, is maintained. This is perfectly practical—it was used during the war on desert islands, such as Ascension, in the sub-Arctic in Labrador, and to supply the

American forces at Chofu in Japan. Its merits are in the production of fresh vegetables, but, in engineering and in supervision, it is expensive.

The other possibility is the cultivation of chlorella. This is the most direct way of "eating the sun," because this microscopic plant (one kind of green scum on duck ponds) is conversion at its simplest. It multiplies rapidly. About 50 per cent or more of its dry weight is protein, and it contains various kinds of vitamins. In Japan they have got 15 to 20 metric tons of chlorella per acre per year, compared with yields of half a ton of soya, or 1.8 tons a year. This microscopic plant can thus yield ten times more food per acre than rice!

The idea of eating the scum of a duck pond is not very appetizing, and chlorella is not very palatable, but it makes good cattle feed and it nourishes fishes (on fish farms) so that we can get it on the menu, at one remove, as a juicy steak or a fish fillet.

Another thing that has to be borne in mind is that much more could be extracted from plants than merely the seeds, roots or straw. The leaves are particularly rich in protein and sugar, and it is possible by modern methods to extract this leaf protein. Or, again, there are the parts of the plants which are not digestible by humans and have to be processed through the ruminants into milk or meat before we can "stomach" them. But there are yeasts and microorganisms which do this just as efficiently as stockyard animals.

29 Feeding the Machines

MODERN SOCIETY does not depend on food alone. We have moved a long way since the Sumerian peasant first bartered bread for a better tool. In Britain today only one out of every twenty workers is employed on the land (as compared with nine out of ten in Siam). Two hundred years ago the British farmer was almost self-sufficient. On his farm he could support himself, his wife, a hired man, five or six children and possibly a few other dependents. They were all fed and clothed from his farm. All that he had to buy was minimal—a few tools and a few home amenities. Today, from a similar farm, he would be feeding eighty people—mostly industrial workers. But it is even more complicated than that. If he wants a tractor (and there are in Britain as many tractors as there are farms) he contributes to the livelihood of a great many people as remote from his farm as the oil driller in Saudi Arabia, the iron miner in Labrador, the rubber tapper in Liberia, and the civil servant in Whitehall.

Industrialization has meant a rise in the material standards of life—what is called "prosperity," by which we usually mean that we can enjoy things we never knew we needed and that luxuries become necessities. Such industrialization in the 200 years of the "Steam Revolution" has meant recourse to metals and to fossil fuels (coal, oil and natural gas). In 1880 the production of steel in the world was about 5,000,000 tons. Today it is about 250,000,-000 tons. The consumption of coal throughout the world is about 1,500,000,000 tons a year nowadays. For our industrial purposes we need vast quantities of copper, tin, lead, aluminum, nickel, cobalt, wolfram, etc. All that has to come out of the crust of the earth. In the past fifty years more minerals have been taken out of the rocks of the fifty states of America than have been taken out of the entire crust of the earth throughout the entire history of Man. Mountains of iron have been literally smelted away.

Only a small portion of the world's 2,900,000,000 people are making use of those resources, but, as more and more countries industrialize and the world population increases, obviously more and more minerals will be extracted. This, almost as much as the food problem, alarms some authorities. They foresee the time when "indispensable" metals and minerals will be exhausted. We need not worry unduly; no minerals are "indispensable," since modern science and technology can be counted on to find substitutes; but even that will not be necessary. For instance, 5

423

per cent of the composition of our world is iron, so that we could armor-plate the whole planet with a layer a mile or so thick and still have a great deal left. Britain has been taking over 200,000,000 tons of coal a year out of the ground for well over a century, and the "known reserves" are sufficient for at least another 300 years. The coal, however, is more difficult to get; the accessible seams have been worked out, and it is necessary to go deeper and deeper and farther and farther (under the seas) to get it. That is true, in localities, of all minerals; when the rich ores give out it is necessary to work poorer ores, which means expensive extraction and refining. But in the rocks and in the sea are minerals sufficient for whatever Man's needs are likely to be.

30 *The Riddle of the Rocks*

FOR AS LONG as one can remember, the oil companies have been setting a time limit for the exhaustion of oil. In terms of "proven reserves," which means what they actually know of the capacity of the oil fields which they are working, such predictions at any moment may be justified. Then somebody discovers a vast new oil field and the predictions are falsified. The truth is that we know very little, still, about the crust of the earth.

For instance, the United Nations Economic and Social Council for the Far East tried to measure the natural resources of southeast Asia. They collected all the geological evidence available and found that 95 per cent of the area had not been surveyed on a scale of geological charting which would allow even a guess at the resources. Of the remaining 5 per cent which had been adequately surveyed, only 2 ½ per cent had been developed. This 2 ½ per cent represented what we had been calling "the wealth of the Indies."

The reason for this ignorance is that most prospecting and test

boring has been done by private concerns, which are always looking for something in particular, ignoring what they do not want
and keeping the information to themselves. Professor Dudley
Stamp tells how as a young geologist he went to prospect for oil
in the Chindwin River basin in Burma:

I was very much excited at finding a hill which seemed to be a
solid mass of iron ore. . . . I rode back two days' journey to the
nearest telegraph, sent cables to secure a prospecting monopoly, and
to advise my head office in Rangoon of my action. The reply from
headquarters came quickly. It read: What on earth do you think is
the good of iron ore in the Chindwin stop Get on with your work.

31 *New Materials*

THE VALUE of minerals changes. On the terrible trek across
Canada, by Lake Athabaska to the Klondike, hundreds of men
died and were buried on top of the gold which they had been
going another thousand miles to find or in soil which contained a
wealth, greater today than gold itself—uranium. Only a few years
ago the most precious substance on earth was radium. Today
radium is discarded with the "tailings" of uranium! In the Canadian northwest rich-yielding gold mines have been closed because
the price of gold, and the requirements of it, are fixed and the
miners might just as well be hewing coal or quarrying slate. But
in the hard rocks of the Pre-Cambrian Shield there is greater
wealth—the metals of the Atomic Age, lithium, beryllium, colum-
bium, titanium, zirconium, uranium, etc. Those a few years
ago were just laboratory curiosities. Today they are the materials
which the engineers need for reactors, for jet propulsion and for
space engineering.

This relative value of metals was sardonically illustrated during the "Manhattan Project" which produced the atom bomb. There was a shortage of copper for wire for electric coils which were needed in vast quantity. They took $70,000,000 worth of silver from the caves of the Federal Bank and used it instead!

Moreover, the materials of industry can drastically change in character. The development of ceramic materials and, above all, of plastics will offset or replace many of the most familiar uses of metals. And one of the most exciting developments in the age of transistors and automation is the use for innumerable purposes of the silicons. Silica is in unlimited abundance.

32   Can Machines Buy Cars?

WITH A FLICK of a switch a modern industrial worker can command the equivalent of the muscle effort of a hundred slaves. Not merely is he relieved of the strain on his own muscles, but he can magnify and make more precise his own skills. The ultimate logic of what has been called "automation" is that human effort will be dispensed with altogether. But, although a long way short of machines which will breed machines, the industrial worker can create abundant wealth and a rising standard of living which he must share.

Must? In an argument with Walter Reuther of the Automobile Workers' Union, an American employer said, portentously, that machines could replace his dues-paying members.

"But," said Reuther, "will the machines also buy your cars?"

This was a salutary reminder that prosperity depends not only on making things but in distributing them and providing the means to buy them. Reuther might also have added, "And will the machines go out and get their 'food'—the metals and raw materials—from the underdeveloped countries?"

There is also economic "cannibalism" by which nations devour their own prosperity. When everyone has a car, the roads will be unusable; when there is a television in every room, including the bathroom, life will be intolerable; and when we are glutted with gadgets, culture will die. Nations can, of course, vaingloriously throw their surplus wealth into space in the form of satellites and rockets—space pyramids, for, remember, other civilizations similarly boasted their material success and died from the neglect of their own "back yard."

The "back yard" of the industrial nations is that part of the planet which is called "underdeveloped"—those countries which are too poor to buy commercial surpluses or invest in the industrial plants which could create their own prosperity. Those are the countries which are getting poorer and poorer as the industrial nations get richer and richer. Their peasants scrape the soil for bare subsistence, and their workers, as primary producers, export the raw materials to make the goods which they cannot afford to buy.

33 *Power Is Wealth (and Vice Versa)*

THE DISPARITY BETWEEN wealth and poverty of countries can be measured in units of industrial energy as well as in units of currency. If we convert all energy (coal, oil, electricity, etc.) into "coal equivalent" and all currencies into dollars, we can see the correlation between the per capita consumption of energy and the per capita income.

Power costs money. The most expensive power in the world

MUSCLE POWER *Java-nese peasants digging a canal* [United Nations]

Country	Per capita income in dollars	Per capita energy consumption in metric tons of coal equivalent
U.S.A.	$2,094	8.00
Canada	1,498	6.00
Gt. Britain	983	4.75
Belgium & Lux.	896	3.80
W. Germany	770	3.45
Italy	431	1.10
Mexico	252	1.00
Brazil	168	0.85
Peru	109	0.60
India	67	0.40
Burma	45	0.30

Based on U.N. figures for 1958

is muscle power, and, paradoxically, that is all poor people can afford. The cheapest power is hydroelectric—once the heavy capital costs of dams, turbines and generators have been met. It is also a geographical truth that over 80 per cent of all the hydro-electric potential of the world is south of the latitude 20° north. North of this line lie 90 per cent of all coal reserves and 81 per cent of all oil reserves, the fossil fuels which gave Temperate-Zone Man the breakaway in the first Industrial Revolution. And south of the line lie most of the countries we call "underdeveloped." Thus a potential source of energy is abundantly available. But there are the snags: how are impoverished countries to provide the capital for the hydroelectric installation? And great "heads" of water are not necessarily convenient to centers to be developed, and transmission over long distances is costly and wasteful.

MACHINE POWER *Giant disemboweling dragline, 187½ horsepower* [Ruston-Bucyrus Ltd., England]

34 *Atomic Short Cuts*

THE ANSWER which most of the underdeveloped countries see as their "short cut" to the second Industrial Revolution (since they missed the first) is nuclear energy. This is a foot-loose energy which is not anchored, geologically, like coal and oil or, geographically, like hydroelectricity. They see it as energy which can be disposed where it is needed.

That was the expectation, but it is liable to be disappointed. There has been a noticeable reluctance on the part of the atomic powers, which have the nuclear materials and the know-how, to deploy nuclear reactors in underdeveloped countries.

One of the arguments is the risk of making available fissile fuels and reactors which may be used to produce bombs. With proper international safeguards this hazard could be avoided. If the power units were provided by an effective international agency —leased to the countries—the problems of supervision would not be insuperable. No ill-intentioned parties could divert or "sneak" fissile materials for mischievous purposes because the power produced is a factor of the fissile materials in a reactor and can be easily checked; in any event, it requires elaborate chemical technology and chemical plants to remove such material.

Another argument is that the only economical form of reactor is that based on natural uranium, like Calder Hall, the British station which was the first to make commercial electricity available from the atom at costs comparable to conventional fuels. Such stations, to "pay off," must be large (of the order of hundreds of thousands of kilowatts) and must be worked as "base-load" stations. That means that they must work twenty-four hours a day and therefore must be part of an electricity grid system for supplying a large industrial conurbation. They could therefore be supplied to countries like Germany, Italy or Japan, which are already industrialized and can afford to buy—a case of "unto every one that hath shall be given." But what most of the underdeveloped countries need are "package" reactors of lower rating, which means using enriched fuels, pepping up the natural uranium with fissile materials like uranium 235 or plutonium. This also means, if the reluctant atomic powers are frank, diverting such materials from their own military stock piles.

A further, and more valid, excuse is that power is useless unless it is used, that countries must develop industries to absorb the power, and that this means having literate and trained people for the industrial plants. This is the "chicken and the egg" argument —you cannot have power until you have industries and you cannot have industries until you have power; you cannot have industries until you have educated and trained people and you cannot afford to educate and train them until you have industries.

When, at the United Nations Second Conference on Peaceful Uses of Atomic Energy in 1958, the spokesman of the atomic powers produced these hope-deferring arguments, the reply of India was forthright. Professor Homi J. Bhabha, one of the world's great physicists, repudiated the suggestions. He proved the economics of natural uranium reactors for India. He showed that a conventional power station of 140,000 kilowatts needed for New Delhi would require 2,000 tons of coal a day. To secure this coal would mean enormous investment in mining and in railways to bring the fuel from the mines. It would mean 1,700 cars and 30 locomotives to transport it. He cost the financing of such a coal-fueled station and showed that the capital cost of a nuclear power station would be less than the capital investment required to get the coal and, moreover, nuclear fuel would involve no problems in transportation. Once a reactor is installed and "critical," the uranium replacements bulk very small indeed. India, as he reminded them, has its own abundant supplies of uranium and that other fissional element, thorium.

35 Power Unlimited

HOMI J. BHABHA, as President of the First Conference on Peaceful Uses of Atomic Energy in 1955, figuratively, and almost literally, set off a powder keg by suggesting the possibilities of fusion energy. Fusion energy is released in the conversion of hydrogen into helium. It had already happened in cataclysmic proportions in the explosion of the H-bomb. The general assumption, however, was that this fierce energy could never be controlled. To produce it, heat as great as that of the interior of the sun is necessary, and heat of that intensity had been produced on earth only by the explosion of fission bombs. Such bombs—similar to those which destroyed Hiroshima and Nagasaki—were therefore used as the detonators, or percussion caps, of the H-bombs. So it appeared that H-energy would always have to be accompanied by violent explosions. Bhabha, however, contended otherwise. He maintained that such energy could be controlled and that when this was achieved all the power problems of mankind would be solved because there would be as much power as there is heavy hydrogen (deuterium) in the Seven Seas. That is a lot of heavy hydrogen, because there is one atom of heavy hydrogen to every 6,000 atoms of ordinary hydrogen and, of course, the water which covers seven tenths of the earth's surface consists of hydrogen and oxygen (H_2O).

His calculated indiscretion caused consternation because at that time the Americans, the Russians and the British were carrying out, in secrecy, such experiments. Subsequent disclosures, including the British Zeta project, showed that controlled fusion was possible but that the difficulties were immense. To produce fusion and release energy on an industrial scale would mean temperatures of over 100,000,000° centigrade—nearly seven times the temperature of the interior of the sun. That may seem as though man is becoming bombastic, trying to excel the sun itself, but the difference is that the sun has millions of years in which to convert hydrogen atoms into helium atoms and Man has not. So he has to create higher temperatures. Eventually he will make the gases themselves produce such temperatures and create their own conditions of fusion, in a process which, once started, will be self-sustaining.

One thing which should be made clear is that such a fusion engine does not derive in any way from the experiments or experience with the H-bomb. It has a separate genealogy and, what is more, the fusion process does not produce any fission products, those dangerous radioactive substances, the disposal of which is such a problem (pp. 296–301).

Another exciting possibility is that it will be possible to get electricity direct from the fusion engine. With fission reactors the heat produced by the splitting atoms is removed and used to heat steam or gases to drive turbines and generate electricity. The heat involved in the fusion process is far too great to be transferred in this way, but there is every likelihood that the electricity will be obtained without the intervening turbines and generators.

This is one of the new advances in scientific thinking. It is not confined to the fusion process. In 1959 a uranium battery was announced in America. In this the fission of uranium atoms generated heat in liquid cesium and freed electrons, to be tapped and taken off as currents of electricity. In principle, conventional heating methods could similarly produce a flow of current, given a hot enough flame.

Thus the world will have access, eventually, to unlimited power which can transform the condition of all mankind and expand industry, plumb the depths, and tap the hidden waters for desert irrigation (or desalt the sea), open up the climatically forbidding areas and enable us to extract food and raw materials. But, with that teaming population of 4,000,000,000 only twenty years away, and most of it in the countries which we call "underdeveloped," power, and therefore prosperity, is still aggregating in those countries which had had the runaway successes in the first Industrial Revolution. Consequently the gulf between wealth and poverty, as between nations, is widening; the wealthy countries are building the pyramids of their prosperity and neglecting their own "back yards."

36 *The Count-Down*

SOMEWHERE, sometime, in unrecorded history, Man overcame his fear of lightning and snatched the burning brand which made him Master of Fire.

At 5:30 A.M. on Monday, July 26, 1945, at Alamogordo in New Mexico, energy was released from the atom. At 45 seconds from zero hour, switches were thrown and electronic gadgets took over for the "count-down." So we know to the exact second when the atomic epoch began.

In the first sixty years of the twentieth century Man, the toolmaking animal, made more and greater advances than he had done in the previous 60,000 years. He has conquered time and space and has shrunk his planet to the dimensions around which a machine of his own creation could circle once an hour. He has reached out for the moon and for the sun, with probes which are the inanimate pilots for the human explorers adventuring into space.

Time, in terms of communications, has almost reached the vanishing point. A radio voice from London or New York can reach Tokyo, or a base in Antarctica, faster than it could be

SIGNPOST TO THE STARS *Rocket leaving launching pad at Cape Canaveral*
[Wide World]

heard on the other side of the room, because radio waves travel at 183,000 miles per second and sound waves at less than 700 miles per hour. Signals disclosing cosmic events of 200,000,000 years ago can be picked up by radio-telescopes—yet they occurred so far away in the universe that they took all that time to reach the earth.

Jet-propelled planes can carry passengers in six and a half hours over the Atlantic, which the Pilgrim Fathers took 106 days to cross.

There is no place on earth which is inaccessible. Antarctica has been crossed and "occupied" by hundreds of scientists during the International Geophysical Year. Airliners use the Arctic and the North Pole in ordinary scheduled flights. The last "Shangri-La" on earth, a forgotten valley in New Guinea, has been discovered and its inhabitants exposed to our "civilizing influences." Aircraft and helicopters can seek out the interstices of the earth's surface.

Man can woo or bludgeon nature, according to his wisdom or his willfulness. He can trifle with his climate and produce artificial rain. He can explode H-bombs in the stratosphere and produce artificial auroras or he can disperse poison, in the form of radioactivity, in the atmosphere on which the survival of his own species depends. He can coax the soil to give him abundance or so ravage it as to destroy his means of subsistence. He can devise plants to grow where nature has been inhospitable or ravage the forest regions where nature has been indulgent. He can make war on the invisible enemies which cause his diseases, or he can destroy the invisible allies, the microorganisms which are indispensable to his means of living. By the surgery of his civil engineering he can cosmetically change the face of his world or disfigure it forever by his military engineering.

37 *And the Count-Up*

SINCE HOMO SAPIENS first covered his nakedness in furs and kindled fires in his cave, he has been striving to overcome the limits of his local environment. Since he ceased to be a hunter and a food gatherer, and became a tiller and a husbandman, he has been trying to order the ways of nature to meet the plenitude of his needs. Since he made the first club to outreach his natural enemies and tamed his first draft animal, he has been trying to overcome the limitations of his own physique and his own muscles. Since he first discovered that metals were more useful than flints, he has been mining and quarrying the rocks. But until recently such efforts and activities have been local or at least on a scale which had only local effects.

Civilizations grew in geographically confined areas. They had their successes and their failures. They reached the limits of their resources or their technology. Usually they developed delusions of grandeur which encouraged them in wars of conquest. Or their ostentatious wealth encouraged others to make war on them. They languished or they perished, and often, as in the man-made deserts of the Middle East, they left the havoc of their decline, not only in the ruins of their cities, but also in the ruins of the soil. But always there was another civilization to replace them, to inherit their culture and, too often, to repeat their mistakes.

Today our civilization is not bounded by the Tigris and the Euphrates; it is the whole world. It is such a close community, so interdependent, that distance has become just a back-yard fence. And just as we do not like the slums at the bottom of our garden, we cannot, or should not, tolerate Poverty next door to Plenty.

The land area of the world is 135,000,000 square miles. Of that only 10 per cent has been cultivated. We could add another

10 per cent merely by the spread and encouragement of existing methods. By capital expenditure, by flood control and irrigation schemes and by mechanization of farm work we could extend that by at least another 20 per cent. By the recovery of deserts, by the agricultural development of Arctic lands and by growing at altitudes, as the Incas did, we could extend the cultivatable areas still further. At the ‹lowest estimate, we could by such means support a population of at least 10,000,000,000. So, however much we may deplore them, we need not be terrified by figures like 4,000,000,000—except that they are only twenty years away. It is the time factor, not the numbers, that is the real cause for concern. That is why the development of under-developed countries, which includes industrialization to remove the pressure on the land, is a matter of urgency.

To raise the impoverished countries to the average European level of advance would mean, according to the U.N. experts, the investment of outside capital of about $14,000,000,000 a year. This sounds like a prohibitive figure unless we have a sense of proportion. *The Times* of London has pointed out that the launching of the Soviet Sputnik cost the American economy $13,000,-000,000 in one year. This was not the cost of the U.S. space program but included the secondary effects on the national budget and the national product of the sudden recognition that Russia was a technological, as well as a military, competitor. To achieve a sense of proportion we should also remember that the world is spending something like $110,000,000,000 a year on armaments for defense. For a fraction of that we could be changing living standards for all mankind. So the costs of development are not at all astronomical.

The facts of our situation should appear abundantly plain. No one can doubt that mankind could destroy itself in the suicide pact of a nuclear war. Yet those same powers of destruction can be turned to industrial uses and to the benefit of the human race. Almost as serious as the nuclear explosion is the population explosion. How are 4,000,000,000 people going to coexist twenty years from now? Unless we read aright the lessons of the past, apply the science and technology of the present, and plan, with wisdom, for the future, we shall not find the answer.

ROCKET'S-EYE VIEWS   1 *The top side of the earth as seen from a rocket 100 miles up. In the upper left-hand corner of this view of 1,250,000 square miles is a hurricane* [Wide World]   2 *The far side of the moon as seen from a Russian lunik* [Wide World]

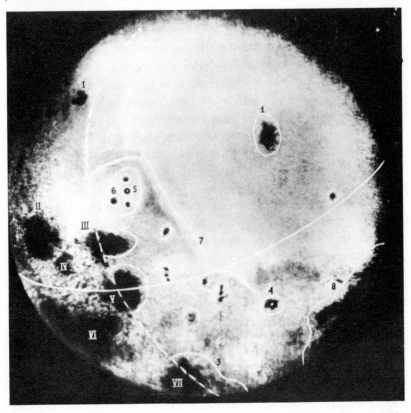

That answer cannot lie in space excursions. No one can, or would want to, curb the restless, outreaching curiosity of Man. It is true that, throughout all history, nations have diverted their material surpluses to military adventures, to destruction and killing. And if mankind could conceivably find a common purpose in space enterprises, it might be a rational alternative to wars but it ought to be a common purpose, not a competitive one—not "throwing pyramids into space" at the expense of our own back yard.

But the real answer must lie here, on our own planet. Our civilization is now global, patterned with diverse cultures, ideologies and ways of life, but, in terms of material survival and interdependence, inescapably one. We have seen, in this book, how a procession of civilizations perished and were succeeded by others, which salvaged the enduring values of the predecessors. Mistakes were made on a local or regional scale, but now they can be made on a global scale.

Ever since primeval Man made his first tools, clothed himself in pelts so that he could emerge from the tropics of his nakedness, harvested his first crops so that he was no longer dependent on an elusive food supply and stored his grains so that he was no longer constrained by the seasons, the generations of mankind have been struggling to master their environment. To mere survival have been added the opportunities for the fuller life, the material amenities and cultural enjoyments—still denied to the many and rejected by many.

With the resources of modern science and technology, tempered by wisdom, we can escape from the limitations of past civilizations and succeed where they failed.

But, remembering the 4,000,000,000 people who will share this planet in twenty years' time, science and statesmanship will have to work fast.

Index

441

Index

Index

48411

Index

INVENTORY '80